Date Due

QUANTUM PHYSICS OF ELECTRONICS

Quantum

The Macmillan Company, New York
Collier-Macmillan Limited, London

Physics
of Electronics

SUMNER N. LEVINE

State University of New York at
Stony Brook

First Printing

Library of Congress catalog card number: 65–11071

THE MACMILLAN COMPANY, NEW YORK

COLLIER-MACMILLAN CANADA, LTD., TORONTO, ONTARIO

Printed in the United States of America

Design: N. Sylvester

To
CAROLINE
and
JOANNE

Preface

This book is the outgrowth of a one semester course intended to equip engineering students with the physical background required to understand modern electronic devices. Accordingly, this book places emphasis on physical principles and leaves the discussion of electronic devices to more specialized works. The material presented here should be easily accessible to seniors and first year graduate students, who have had an introduction to vector calculus and elementary matrix algebra as well as a descriptive course in modern physics.

The first three chapters provide a modern introduction to quantum mechanics. An attempt has been made to steer an effective course between excessive mathematical formalisms and abstraction on the one hand, and a purely descriptive approach on the other hand. Subsequent chapters utilize the quantum mechanical background to develop such topics as statistical thermodynamics, electron emission, band theory of solids, transport theory, and electromagnetic interactions with a brief introduction to masers and lasers. Such topics as *pn*-junctions, transistor theory, and tunnel diodes have been omitted since they are now dealt with in conventional electronic texts. It is assumed, of course, that the student has had the usual introductory course in electronics.

The author wishes to express his gratitude to his wife Caroline and to Mrs. Elizabeth Gates for help in preparing the manuscript.

Sumner N. Levine

Contents

Brillouin Zone in Three Dimensions / *Density of Energy States* / *Effective Mass* / *Energy Bands* / *Band Theory of Conduction* / *Intrinsic Semiconductors* / *Thermal Ionization* / *Semiconductors with Impurities.*

QUANTUM PHYSICS OF ELECTRONICS

CHAPTER *1* / *Mathematical*

Preliminaries

The revolution in electronics marked by the development of such devices as transistors, tunnel diodes, masers, and lasers has placed a new emphasis on the education of engineers. In order to understand modern devices the engineer requires a good grasp of a large number of concepts comprising modern physics. Foremost among these theories is, of course, that of quantum mechanics.

Quantum mechanics is based on the premise that the observables (i.e., measurable quantities such as energy, linear and angular momentum, position, etc.) which are associated with elementary particles can be represented by linear operators. Consequently in this chapter we shall lay the groundwork for the development of quantum theory by discussing some of the more important properties of linear operators.

1.1 *LINEAR OPERATORS*

An operator, in the general sense, is a set of rules for changing a given set of objects into another set of objects. A simple example is the identity operator **E**, such as multiplication by unity, which transforms a function into itself. Some well known examples of operators, which may be regarded as acting on a function, $y(x)$ are shown below:

$$\text{a.} \quad \nabla^2 = \frac{\partial^2}{\partial x^2} + \frac{\partial^2}{\partial y^2} + \frac{\partial^2}{\partial z^2}$$

$$\text{b.} \quad \int (\quad) \, dx$$

1

c. $\left(\dfrac{d}{dx} + a\right)$

d. $\sin(\quad)$

e. $y\,\dfrac{d}{dx}$ •

A *linear operator* **L** is defined by the property that if $c_1 y_1 + c_2 y_2$ is employed as the dependent variable, where c_1 and c_2 are constants, then

$$\mathbf{L}(c_1 y_1 + c_2 y_2) = c_1 \mathbf{L} y_1 + c_2 \mathbf{L} y_2 \qquad (1.1)$$

It may be readily verified that (a), (b), and (c) are linear, while (e) and (d) are not.*

Another class of linear operators is the symmetry operators. These operators transform the coordinate system by rotation, translation, or reflection. If a function is unaltered by a transformation it is said to be invariant with respect to the transformation. An example is the inversion operator **I** which changes the sign of the independent variable

$$\mathbf{I}f(x) = f(-x)$$

Functions such as x^2 and $\cos x$ are unaltered by **I** and are said to be of *even parity* while functions such as x and $\sin x$ which undergo a change of sign are said to be of *odd parity*.

Some of the more important symmetry operators are listed below:

$$\begin{aligned}
\mathbf{E}f(x) &= f(x), \text{ i.e., the identity operator}\\
\mathbf{I}f(x) &= f(-x), \text{ i.e., inversion operator}\\
\mathbf{T}_a f(x) &= f(x + a), \text{ i.e., translation operator}\\
\mathbf{C}_n &= \text{rotation through an angle } 2\pi/n\\
\boldsymbol{\sigma}_p &= \text{reflection through a specified plane, } p
\end{aligned} \qquad (1.2)$$

As an example of how these operators are used to specify the symmetry characteristics of an object, we consider the triangle shown in figure 1.1 where the z axis projects out of the page. It is evident that the triangle is transformed into itself by six operations: c_{-3} (clockwise rotation through 120°), c_{+3} (counterclockwise rotation through 120°), σ_{yz} (reflection in the yz plane), σ_p (reflection in the plane p perpendicular to ab), $\sigma_{p'}$ (reflection in the plane p' perpendicular to cb), and E.

---

* In this book operators will be indicated by bold-faced characters, thus **L**.

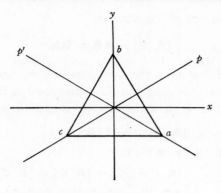

Figure 1.1

1.2 OPERATOR ALGEBRA

An algebra of linear operators may be defined in a manner analogous to ordinary algebra. Representing linear operators by **A**, **B**, **C**, we have

a. $(\mathbf{A} + \mathbf{B})y = \mathbf{A}y + \mathbf{B}y$ (distributive law)

b. $(\mathbf{A}\,\mathbf{B}\mathbf{C})y = (\mathbf{A}\,\mathbf{B})(\mathbf{C}y)$ (associative law)

(1.3)

We may define higher power of operators by expressions of the form

$$\mathbf{B}\,\mathbf{B}y = (\mathbf{B}\,\mathbf{B})y \equiv \mathbf{B}^2 y$$

and in general

$$\mathbf{B}\,\mathbf{B}^{n-1}y = \mathbf{B}^n y \tag{1.4}$$

However, operator algebra differs from ordinary algebra in that operators do not necessarily commute:

$$\mathbf{A}\,\mathbf{B} \quad \text{may not equal} \quad \mathbf{B}\,\mathbf{A} \tag{1.5}$$

An example of noncommuting operators is $\mathbf{A} = d/dx$ and $\mathbf{B} = x$:

$$\mathbf{A}\,\mathbf{B}y = \frac{d}{dx}(xy) = y + x\frac{dy}{dx}$$

$$\mathbf{B}\,\mathbf{A}y = x\frac{dy}{dx}$$

We see that in this case

$$(\mathbf{A}\,\mathbf{B} - \mathbf{B}\,\mathbf{A})y = y$$

It is convenient to introduce the notation

$$[\mathbf{A}, \mathbf{B}] = \mathbf{A}\mathbf{B} - \mathbf{B}\mathbf{A} \tag{1.6}$$

where $[\mathbf{A}, \mathbf{B}]$ is referred to as the *commutator* of the operators $\mathbf{A}$ and $\mathbf{B}$. In the above example it is clear that the commutator is $\mathbf{E}$ or unity.

From the definition of the commutator it is easy to verify the following:

a. $[\mathbf{A}, \mathbf{B}] = -[\mathbf{B}, \mathbf{A}]$

b. $[\mathbf{A}, \mathbf{A}] = 0$

c. $[(\mathbf{A} + \mathbf{B}), \mathbf{C}] = [\mathbf{A}, \mathbf{C}] + [\mathbf{B}, \mathbf{C}]$

d. $[\mathbf{A}\mathbf{B}, \mathbf{C}] = [\mathbf{A}, \mathbf{C}]\mathbf{B} + \mathbf{A}[\mathbf{B}, \mathbf{C}]$

$$\tag{1.7}$$

Operator algebra may be extended by introducing the concept of operator functions. We define an operator polynomial by

$$f(\mathbf{A}) = a_n\mathbf{A}^n + a_{n-1}\mathbf{A}^{n-1}\cdots + a_0 \tag{1.8}$$

and an exponential operator by

$$e^{\mathbf{A}} = 1 + \mathbf{A} + \frac{\mathbf{A}^2}{2!} + \frac{\mathbf{A}^3}{3!} + \cdots \tag{1.9}$$

An inverse operator, $\mathbf{A}^{-1}$, may be defined by

$$\mathbf{A}\mathbf{A}^{-1} = \mathbf{A}^{-1}\mathbf{A} = \mathbf{E} \tag{1.10}$$

thus

$$\left(\frac{d}{dx}\right)^{-1} = \int (\quad)\, dx$$

$$(x)^{-1} = \frac{1}{x}$$

$$(c_n)^{-1} = c_{-n}$$

We note that

$$(\mathbf{A}\mathbf{B})^{-1} = \mathbf{B}^{-1}\mathbf{A}^{-1} \tag{1.11}$$

since by the associative law

$$(\mathbf{B}^{-1}\mathbf{A}^{-1})(\mathbf{A}\mathbf{B}) = \mathbf{B}^{-1}(\mathbf{A}^{-1}\mathbf{A})\mathbf{B} = \mathbf{B}^{-1}\mathbf{B} = \mathbf{E}$$

Finally we note that linear operators may be factored but attention must be given to the commutator. Suppose that $[\mathbf{A}, \mathbf{B}] \neq 0$, then

$$(\mathbf{A} + \mathbf{B})(\mathbf{A} - \mathbf{B}) = \mathbf{A}^2 - \mathbf{A}\mathbf{B} + \mathbf{B}\mathbf{A} - \mathbf{B}^2$$

so that

$$(\mathbf{A}^2 - \mathbf{B}^2) = (\mathbf{A} + \mathbf{B})(\mathbf{A} - \mathbf{B}) - [\mathbf{A}, \mathbf{B}]$$

It follows that the ordinary rules for factoring do not apply unless the operators commute.

1.3 *LINEAR EQUATIONS AND EIGENFUNCTIONS*

Linear operators frequently occur in the context of differential equations of the general form $\mathbf{L}y = f(x)$ where x denotes the independent variable. In the special case where $f(x)$ is zero we have the homogeneous equation. A particularly important case arises when the differential operator is of the form $(\mathbf{L} - \lambda)$ where λ is a constant. We can then write the homogeneous equation as

$$\mathbf{L}y_n = \lambda_n y_n \tag{1.12}$$

A function y_n which satisfies (1.12) is said to be an *eigenfunction* of $\mathbf{L}$ and the constant λ_n the *eigenvalue* of y_n. Thus e^{ikx} is an eigenfunction of the differential operator d/dx since

$$\frac{d}{dx}(e^{ikx}) = ike^{ikx}$$

the eigenvalue ik, is imaginary assuming k is real. Similarly we find that

$$\frac{d^2}{dx^2}(e^{ikx}) = -k^2 e^{ikx}$$

and the eigenvalue $-k^2$ is real. In the first example we note that corresponding to each eigenfunction there is only one eigenvalue while in the second example we notice that both e^{ikx} and e^{-ikx} correspond to the same eigenvalue. When the latter is the case, when n linearly independent eigenfunctions correspond to the same eigenvalue, the eigenvalues are said to be *n*-fold *degenerate*.

The homogeneous linear equation has the important property that if $y_1, y_2, \ldots, y_k$ are solutions to the equation, then any linear combination of these functions is also a solution:

$$\mathbf{L}(\textstyle\sum a_n y_n) = \sum a_n \mathbf{L}y_n \equiv 0 \tag{1.13}$$

since for each y_n

$$\mathbf{L}y_n = 0$$

and a_n is constant.

Moreover, if a and y are dependent on a continuous parameter ξ, and $\mathbf{L}$ is independent of ξ, then according to (1.13) we have

$$\mathbf{L} \sum_i a(\xi_i) y(\xi_i) \, \Delta\xi = 0$$

and as $\Delta\xi \to 0$, we find in the limit

$$\mathbf{L} \int a(\xi) y(\xi) \, d\xi = 0 \tag{1.14}$$

Thus if $y(\xi)$ is a solution then the integral $a(\xi) y(\xi)$, with respect to the parameter, is also a solution. The results (1.13) and (1.14) are known as the *superposition principle*. It is clear from this result that the nonhomogeneous equation

$$\mathbf{L}y = f(x) \tag{1.15}$$

has a general solution of the form

$$y = \sum a_n y_n + \mathbf{L}^{-1} f(x) \tag{1.16}$$

where $\mathbf{L}^{-1} f(x)$ is a particular integral of (1.15) and y_n is the solution of the corresponding homogeneous equation. This conclusion is readily verified by substituting (1.16) into (1.15):

$$\mathbf{L}y = \mathbf{L}[\sum a_n y_n + \mathbf{L}^{-1} f(y)] = \mathbf{L}\mathbf{L}^{-1} f(y) = f(y)$$

since $\mathbf{L}y_n = 0$.

In forming a linear combination of solutions we are generally interested only in the linearly independent functions. A set of functions is said to be *linearly independent* if no relationship of the form

$$\sum a_n y_n = 0 \tag{1.17}$$

holds, except in the trivial case $a_1 = a_2 = \cdots = a_n = 0$. Thus the functions ay and by are not linearly independent, since for any choice of $a = -b$ the linear combination vanishes. If a linear combination contains linearly dependent functions it is always possible to eliminate these by successive application of (1.17).

1.4   ORTHOGONAL FUNCTIONS

A set of functions is said to be orthogonal in an interval (a, b) if for any members of the set

$$\int_a^b f_i^*(x) f_j(x) \, dx = a_j \delta_{ij} \tag{1.18}$$

where a is a nonzero positive constant, $f_i^*(x)$ is the complex conjugate of $f_i(x)$ and δ_{ij} is the Kronecker delta defined by

$$
\begin{aligned}
\delta_{ij} &= 0 \qquad i \neq j \\
&= 1 \qquad i = j
\end{aligned}
\tag{1.19}
$$

If a_j is unity, then the set is a normalized orthogonal or an orthonormal set. If a set is not orthonormal, it can always be normalized by dividing each function by $(a_j)^{1/2}$, then

$$
\frac{1}{(a_j)^{1/2}(a_j)^{1/2}} \int_a^b f_j^* f_j \, dx = \frac{a_j}{(a_j)^{1/2}(a_j)^{1/2}} = 1
\tag{1.20}
$$

If the set includes all of the mutually orthogonal functions it is said to be *complete*. It is not difficult to show that mutually orthogonal functions *are linearly independent*.

We now state an important result. If ϕ is a reasonably well behaved but arbitrary function, and f_n is a complete orthogonal set over an interval (a, b) then we may represent ϕ in the interval (a, b) by the linear combination

$$
\phi = \sum_n c_n f_n(x)
\tag{1.21}
$$

In order to determine the coefficient c_n in the series, we multiply both sides of (1.21) by f_n^* and then integrate over the interval (a, b). Since the functions are othogonal, all of the terms on the right vanish except that involving c_n and we find, assuming the functions are normalized,

$$
c_n = \int_a^b f_n^* \phi \, dx
\tag{1.22}
$$

Hence we can determine the coefficients provided the integrals exist and do not vanish for all c_n. If all of the above integrals were to vanish this would imply that ϕ is orthogonal to all f_n, and hence the set f_n was not complete, contrary to our assumption. Assuming the existence of the integrals (1.22) and the proper convergence of (1.21) we then see that an arbitrary function may be represented in the interval (a, b) by a complete orthogonal set. Such a set is also referred to as an *orthogonal basis* for the representation of a function.

An interesting analogy can be established between ordinary vector algebra and the above orthogonal expansion. In vector algebra an arbitrary vector function, $\bar{u}$, can be represented in terms of the unit orthogonal vectors $\bar{e}_n$ by

$$\bar{u} = (\bar{e}_1 \cdot \bar{u})\bar{e}_1 + (\bar{e}_2 \cdot \bar{u})\bar{e}_2 + (\bar{e}_3 \cdot \bar{u})\bar{e}_3$$

$$= \sum_{n=1}^{3} (\bar{e}_n \cdot \bar{u})\bar{e}_n \qquad (1.23)$$

where $(\bar{e}_n \cdot \bar{u})$ is the scalar product and

$$\bar{e}_i \cdot \bar{e}_j = \delta_{ij} \qquad (1.24)$$

The square of the absolute magnitude is given by

$$|\bar{u}|^2 = (\bar{u} \cdot \bar{u}) = (\bar{e}_1 \cdot \bar{u})^2 + (\bar{e}_2 \cdot \bar{u})^2 + (\bar{e}_3 \cdot \bar{u})^2 \qquad (1.25)$$

This quantity is also referred to as the *norm* of a vector; the *length* is just the square root of the norm.

The analogy between (1.23) and (1.21) can be emphasized by representing the *scalar product* (or inner product) of two functions by the notation

$$\int g^* h \, dx = (g, h) \qquad (1.26)$$

It will be noted that the operation of taking the complex conjugate is indicated by merely placing the function to the left of the comma. In terms of this notation we can represent an arbitrary function ϕ in terms of an orthonormal basis f_n by

$$\phi = \sum_n (f_n, \phi)f_n \qquad (1.27)$$

where $(f_i, f_j) = \delta_{ij}$.

The analogy between the orthogonal expansions is now apparent. We therefore regard the orthonormal basis f_n as defining a set of unit vectors in a generalized vector space. If the complete set contains n functions we refer to the vector space as n-dimensional. Very often the complete set contains an infinite number of functions (i.e., Fourier series) so that such vector spaces are infinite-dimensional. The function ϕ may be regarded as a vector in this space with components along the unit vectors given by the scalar products (f_n, ϕ). In analogy with (1.25) we define the *norm*, N, of the vector ϕ by

$$N = (\phi, \phi) = \sum_n |(f_n, \phi)|^2 \qquad (1.28)$$

In the infinite-dimensional case there will be an infinite number of terms in the sum. The last result follows directly on substituting (1.27) into the scalar product defining the norm. The *length* of a vector ϕ is just the square root of the norm. The set of all functions for which a finite norm exists is referred to as a *Hilbert space*. As we shall see in the next chapter in quantum mechanics, we are only interested in functions which are vectors in Hilbert space, i.e., functions ϕ, for which the integral $\int \phi^* \phi \, dx$ is always finite.

1.5 DIRAC NOTATION

A very convenient notation has been introduced by Dirac and we shall find it convenient to use this notation from time to time in subsequent sections of this book. In this notation the function ϕ_j is represented by the *ket* symbol $|j\rangle$, while the complex conjugate ϕ_j^* is represented by the *bra* symbol $\langle j|$. The scalar product is formed by taking the product of a bra and ket to form a bra(c)ket:

$$\langle i|j\rangle \equiv (\phi_i, \phi_j) \equiv \int_a^b \phi_i^* \phi_j \, dx \tag{1.29}$$

Using this notation we can also write

$$\langle i|\mathbf{L}|j\rangle \equiv (\phi_i, \mathbf{L}\phi_j)$$

while if $|j\rangle$ is an eigenfunction of $\mathbf{L}$ with an eigenvalue j then

$$\mathbf{L}|j\rangle = j|j\rangle$$

The utility of this notation may be extended by expressing ϕ_j as a vector in matrix notation. Thus using f_i as an orthonormal basis we write

$$\phi_j = \sum_i c_{ij} f_i$$

$$c_{ij} = (f_i, \phi_j)$$

Then we have, in matrix notation, for a ket

$$\phi_j = |j\rangle = \begin{pmatrix} c_{1j} \\ c_{2j} \\ \vdots \end{pmatrix}$$

The bra may be written as the complex conjugate of the transposed vector

$$\langle j| = (c_{j1}^*, c_{j2}^*, \ldots)$$

where $c_{ij} = c_{ji}$.

The scalar product then may be expressed

$$\langle j | j \rangle = \sum_i c_{ji}^* c_{ji} = \sum_i |c_{ij}|^2$$

which is one form of the well-known closure relationship.

PROBLEMS

1. Evaluate the matrix $|i\rangle\langle j|$.
2. Show that a set of mutually orthogonal functions f_n are linearly independent.

Hint: Consider

$$\sum c_n f_n = 0$$

Multiply by the complex conjugate of f_n, integrate over the orthogonal interval and hence show that the coefficients vanish.

3. Prove the following
(a) $(\phi, \phi) \geqslant 0$
(b) If

$$g = \sum c_n f_n$$

then

$$\int_a^b \left(g - \sum_{n=1}^m c_n f_n \right)^2 dx \geqslant 0$$

and hence obtain *Bessel's inequality*

$$\int_a^b |g|^2 dx \geqslant \sum_{i=1}^\infty |c_n|^2$$

assuming f_n is orthonormal.

If the series converges to g then the equality sign holds and we obtain the *closure relationship*.

4. A more general closure relationship (Parseval's equation) may also be obtained. Thus if f_n is orthonormal

$$g = \sum c_n f_n$$

and

$$h = \sum b_n f_n$$

then show by direct substitution

$$\int_a^b g^* h \, dx = (g, h) = \sum c_n^* b_n$$

5. Establish the *Schwartz inequality*

$$0 \leqslant (f,g)(g,f) \leqslant (f,f)(g,g)$$

Hint: Let a be a scalar then

$$(f + ag, f + ag) = (f,f) + |a|^2(g,g) + a(f,g) + a^*(g,f) \geqslant 0$$

Let $a = r + is$ and find the values of r and s which minimizes the above expression.

1.6 FOURIER SERIES AND INTEGRALS

An important example of orthogonal functions is provided by the complex exponentials

$$\psi_n = e^{i(n\pi/L)x} \qquad n = 0, \pm 1, \pm 2, \ldots$$

$$i = \sqrt{-1}$$

which can easily be shown to be orthogonal over the interval $(-L, L)$:

$$\int_{-L}^{+L} e^{i(n\pi/L)x} \cdot e^{-i(m\pi/L)x} \, dx = 0 \qquad n \neq m \tag{1.33}$$

$$= 2L \qquad n = m$$

The complete set clearly has an infinite number of members. If $\phi(x)$ is an arbitrary function (which is piecewise continuous over $(-L, L)$), then we can represent $\phi(x)$ as

$$\phi(x) = \sum_{-\infty}^{+\infty} c_n e^{i(n\pi/L)x} \tag{1.34}$$

Applying (1.22) and using the above integrals we find that

$$c_n = \frac{1}{2L} \int_{-L}^{L} \phi(x) e^{-i(n\pi/L)x} \, dx \tag{1.35}$$

This result can be put into the usual form for the Fourier series by introducing

$$e^{i(n\pi/L)x} = \cos \frac{n\pi}{L} x + i \sin \frac{n\pi}{L} x \tag{1.36}$$

and summing over the pairs corresponding to n and $-n$:

$$\phi(x) = c_0 + \sum_{n=1}^{\infty} (c_n e^{i(n\pi/L)x} + c_{-n} e^{-i(n\pi/L)x})$$

$$= \frac{1}{2L} \int_{-L}^{L} \phi(x)\, dx + \sum_{n=1}^{\infty} \left(A_n \cos \frac{n\pi}{L} x + B_n \sin \frac{n\pi}{L} x \right) \qquad (1.37)$$

where

$$A_n = (c_n + c_{-n}) = \frac{1}{L} \int_{-L}^{L} \phi(x) \cos \frac{n\pi}{L} x\, dx$$

$$B_n = i(c_n - c_{-n}) = \frac{1}{L} \int_{-L}^{L} \phi(x) \sin \frac{n\pi}{L}\, dx \qquad (1.38)$$

The Fourier series goes over to the Fourier integral in the limit as $L \to \infty$ since we may write

$$\phi(x) = \sum_{-\infty}^{+\infty} \left(\frac{1}{2L} \int_{-L}^{L} \phi(s) e^{-i(n\pi/L)s}\, ds \right) e^{i(n\pi/L)x} \qquad (1.39)$$

where we have made the substitution $x \equiv s$ in the expression for c_n. On introducing

$$k = \frac{n\pi}{L} \quad \text{and} \quad \Delta k = \frac{\pi}{L}$$

we have

$$\phi(x) = \sum_{-\infty}^{+\infty} \left(\frac{1}{2\pi} \int_{-L}^{L} \phi(s) e^{-iks}\, ds \right) e^{ikx}\, \Delta k \qquad (1.40)$$

Now as $L \to \infty$, Δk becomes an infinitesimal and the sum passes over to the integral. We have

$$\phi(x) = \frac{1}{\sqrt{2\pi}} \int_{-\infty}^{\infty} F(k) e^{ikx}\, dk \qquad (1.41a)$$

where, on reintroducing x,

$$F(k) = \frac{1}{\sqrt{2\pi}} \int_{-\infty}^{\infty} \phi(x) e^{-ikx}\, dx \qquad (1.41b)$$

The last two integrals constitute a *Fourier transform pair* for the functions $F(k)$ and $\phi(x)$.

The above considerations may be readily generalized to three dimensions. We introduce a triple Fourier series

$$\phi(F) = \sum_{l,m,n} c_{l,m,n} e^{i(\vec{r} \cdot \vec{k}_{lmn})} \tag{1.42}$$

where $\vec{r}$ is a position vector with components $(x\vec{i} + y\vec{j} + z\vec{k})$. The *wave number* vector k_{lmn} has components

$$\left(\frac{l\pi}{L_1} \vec{i} + \frac{m\pi}{L_2} \vec{j} + \frac{n\pi}{L_3} \vec{k} \right)$$

The basis can readily be shown to be orthogonal over the intervals $(-L_1, L_1)$, $(-L_2, L_2)$, and $(-L_3, L_3)$ in the x, y, and z directions respectively. The coefficients c_{lmn} may be determined as before by multiplying each side of the representation by $e^{-i(\vec{r} \cdot \vec{k}_{lmn})}$ and integrating over the orthogonal intervals. We find

$$c_{lmn} = \frac{1}{8L^3} \int_{-L_3}^{L_3} \int_{-L_2}^{L_2} \int_{-L_1}^{L_1} e^{-i(\vec{r} \cdot \vec{k}_{lmn})} \phi(\vec{r}) \, dx \, dy \, dz \tag{1.43}$$

On permitting the orthogonal interval to become infinite and repeating the same arguments as above, we obtain the three-dimensional Fourier transform pair:

$$d(\vec{r}) = \left(\frac{1}{2\pi} \right)^{3/2} \int_{-\infty}^{\infty} F(\vec{k}) e^{i\vec{r} \cdot \vec{k}} \, dv_k \tag{1.44a}$$

$$F(\vec{k}) = \left(\frac{1}{2\pi} \right)^{3/2} \int_{-\infty}^{\infty} \phi(\vec{r}) e^{-i\vec{r} \cdot \vec{k}} \, dx \tag{1.44b}$$

where

$$dv = dx \, dy \, dz$$
$$dv_k = dk_x \, dk_y \, dk_z$$

1.7 HERMITIAN OPERATORS

Linear operators of particular importance in quantum mechanics are the *Hermitian operators* defined by

$$\int \phi_1^* \mathbf{L} \phi_2 \, dx = \int \phi_2 \mathbf{L}^* \phi_1^* \, dx$$

or

$$(\phi_1, \mathbf{L}\phi_2) = (\mathbf{L}\phi_1, \phi_2) \tag{1.45}$$

where it is understood that the integrals are taken over the whole range of the variable. As an example, consider the operator

$$\mathbf{L} = ai\,\frac{d}{dx} \tag{1.46}$$

where a is a real constant, then

$$\int_{-\infty}^{+\infty} \phi_1^* \left(ai\,\frac{d}{dx}\right)\phi_2\,dx = ai\left[\phi_1^*\phi_2 \Big|_{-\infty}^{+\infty} - ai \int_{-\infty}^{\infty} \phi_2\,\frac{d\phi_1^*}{dx}\,dx\right]$$

$$= \int_{-\infty}^{+\infty} \phi_2 \left(ai\,\frac{d}{dx}\right)^* \phi_1^*\,dx$$

The operator is clearly Hermitian provided $\phi_1^*\phi_2$ vanishes at infinity which is true of functions in a Hilbert space.

If an operator is not Hermitian it may be possible to construct an operator $\mathbf{L}^\dagger$, the *adjoint operator* to $\mathbf{L}$, such that

$$(\phi_1,\ \mathbf{L}\phi_2) = (\mathbf{L}^\dagger\phi_1,\ \phi_2) \tag{1.47}$$

A Hermitian operator is clearly self-adjoint, $\mathbf{L} = \mathbf{L}^\dagger$. The following properties follow from the definition of the adjoint.

$$\text{a.} \qquad (\mathbf{L}^\dagger)^\dagger = \mathbf{L} \tag{1.48}$$

PROOF $\qquad (\phi_1,\ \mathbf{L}\phi_2) = (\mathbf{L}^\dagger\phi_1,\ \phi_2) = (\phi_1,\ (\mathbf{L}^\dagger)^\dagger\phi_2)$

$$\text{b.} \qquad (\mathbf{L}_1 \pm \mathbf{L}_2)^\dagger = \mathbf{L}_1^\dagger \pm \mathbf{L}_2^\dagger \tag{1.49}$$

PROOF $\qquad (\phi_1,\ (\mathbf{L}_1 + \mathbf{L}_2)\phi_2) = (\mathbf{L}_1^\dagger\phi_1,\ \phi_2) + (\mathbf{L}_2^\dagger\phi_1,\ \phi_2)$

$$= ((\mathbf{L}_1^\dagger + \mathbf{L}_2^\dagger)\phi_1,\ \phi_2)$$

but

$$[\phi_1,\ (\mathbf{L}_1 + \mathbf{L}_2)\phi_2] = [(\mathbf{L}_1 + \mathbf{L}_2)^\dagger\phi_1,\ \phi_2]$$

$$\text{c.} \qquad (a\mathbf{L})^\dagger = a^*\mathbf{L}^\dagger \tag{1.50}$$

PROOF $\qquad (\phi_1,\ a\mathbf{L}\phi_2) = (a^*\phi_1,\ \mathbf{L}\phi_2) = (a^*\mathbf{L}^\dagger\phi_1,\ \phi_2)$

$$\text{d.} \qquad (\mathbf{L}_1\mathbf{L}_2)^\dagger = \mathbf{L}_2^\dagger\mathbf{L}_1^\dagger \tag{1.51}$$

PROOF $\qquad (\phi_1,\ \mathbf{L}_1\mathbf{L}_2\phi_2) = (\mathbf{L}_1^\dagger\phi_1,\ \mathbf{L}_2\phi_2) = (\mathbf{L}_2^\dagger\mathbf{L}_1^\dagger\phi_1,\ \phi_2)$

We observe in the last result that the operators are reversed in order, as is the case with the inverse of two operators given by (1.11).

As an example we show that if L_1 and L_2 are Hermitian and c a real constant then $L_1 + ic L_2$ is not Hermitian, since from (1.49) and (1.50)

$$(L_1 + ic L_2)^\dagger = L_1^\dagger + (ic L_2)^\dagger = L_1^\dagger - ic L_2^\dagger = L_1 - ic L_2 \qquad (1.52)$$

hence the operator is not self-adjoint.

1.8 PROPERTIES OF HERMITIAN OPERATORS

Several important theorems will now be established concerning Hermitian operators.

THEOREM I   *The eigenvalues of Hermitian operators are real.*

PROOF   Let L be a Hermitian operator and ψ a normalized eigenfunction of L, then

$$L\psi = \lambda\psi \qquad (1.53)$$

and on taking the complex conjugate

$$\overset{\circ}{L}{}^*\psi^* = \lambda^*\psi^* \qquad (1.54)$$

Multiplying (1.53) by ψ^* and (1.54) by ψ and integrating we have

$$\begin{aligned}
\int \psi^* L\psi \, dv &= \lambda \int \psi^*\psi \, dv = \lambda \\
\int \psi L^*\psi^* \, dv &= \lambda^* \int \psi\psi^* \, dv = \lambda^*
\end{aligned} \qquad (1.55)$$

but since L is Hermitian the two integrals on the left are equal so that

$$\lambda = \lambda^*$$

and hence λ must be real.

We now establish an important theorem concerning the orthogonal properties of eigenfunctions.

THEOREM II   (a) *Let ψ_1 and ψ_2 be eigenfunctions of a Hermitian operator. If ψ_1 and ψ_2 have different eigenvalues they are orthogonal.*
(b) *If ψ_1 and ψ_2 have the same eigenvalue, that is ψ_1 and ψ_2 are degenerate, then they may not be orthogonal. However, it is then possible to construct linear combinations of ψ_1 and ψ_2 which are orthogonal.*

P R O O F   We first establish part (a). We have

$$\mathbf{L}\psi_1 = \lambda_1\psi_1$$
$$\mathbf{L}\psi_2 = \lambda_2\psi_2 \qquad \lambda_1 \neq \lambda_2 \tag{1.56}$$

and since the eigenvalues are real by theorem I

$$\int \psi_2^* \mathbf{L}\psi_1 \, dv = \lambda_1 \int \psi_1 \psi_2^* \, dv$$
$$\int \psi_1 \mathbf{L}^* \psi_2^* \, dv = \lambda_2 \int \psi_1 \psi_2^* \, dv \tag{1.57}$$

the two integrals on the left are equal since by hypothesis $\mathbf{L}$ is Hermitian. Subtracting we have

$$(\lambda_1 - \lambda_2) \int \psi_1 \psi_2^* \, dv = 0 \tag{1.58}$$

but since $\lambda_1 \neq \lambda_2$ it follows that

$$\int \psi_1 \psi_2^* \, dv = 0 \tag{1.59}$$

and hence ψ_1 and ψ_2 are orthogonal.

––––––––––

If $\lambda_1 = \lambda_2$ then the above argument fails and the functions may not be orthogonal. Suppose that the latter is the case, then it is possible to construct a linear combination of ψ_1 and ψ_2 which will be orthogonal to either ψ_1 or ψ_2. Suppose that

$$\int \psi_1^* \psi_2 \, dv = a \tag{1.60}$$

where a is a constant. Let us construct a function U given by

$$U = a\psi_1 - \psi_2 \tag{1.61}$$

then U is orthogonal to ψ_1 since

$$\int \psi_1^* U \, dv = a \int \psi_1 \psi_1^* \, dv - \int \psi_1^* \psi_2 \, dv = a - a = 0 \tag{1.62}$$

since ψ_1 is assumed to be normalized. It is also clear that U is an eigenfunction of $\mathbf{L}$ since $\lambda_1 = \lambda_2 = \lambda$

$$\mathbf{L}U = a_1\mathbf{L}\psi_1 - \mathbf{L}\psi_2 = \lambda(a_1\psi_1 - \psi_2) = \lambda U \tag{1.63}$$

The orthogonalization may be generalized to any number of linearly independent degenerate eigenfunctions. In fact it is always possible to construct an orthonormal set of eigenfunctions by the *Schmidt orthogonalization* procedure.

Let ψ_n designate a set of linearly independent degenerate eigenfunctions, and let ϕ_n designate an orthogonal set constructed from ψ_n. Since ϕ_n are not necessarily normalized we designate U_n as the set of normalized functions corresponding to ϕ_n. We now construct an orthonormal set U_n from ψ_n. The first member of the orthonormal set U_1, is simply

$$U_1 = \frac{\psi_1}{(\psi_1, \psi_1)^{1/2}} \tag{1.64}$$

We next construct a function ϕ_2 normal to U_1 from ψ_2 and U_1. Let

$$\phi_2 = \psi_2 - a_1 U_1 \tag{1.65}$$

then require that

$$(U_1, \phi_2) = (U_1, \psi_2) - a_1(U_1, U_1) = 0 \tag{1.66}$$

so that

$$a_1 = (U_1, \psi_2) \tag{1.67}$$

and we find that

$$\phi_2 = \psi_2 - (U_1, \psi_2)U_1 \tag{1.68}$$

If we now divide ϕ_2 by the product $(\phi_2, \phi_2)^{1/2}$ we find the corresponding orthonormal function:

$$U_2 = \frac{\phi_2}{(\phi_2, \phi_2)^{1/2}} \tag{1.69}$$

The third member of the set is found by similar procedures. We require that $\phi_3 = \psi_3 - a_2 U_1 - a_3 U_2$ be simultaneously orthogonal to U_1 and U_2 so that

$$(U_1, \phi_3) = (U_1, \psi_3) - a_2 = 0 \tag{1.70}$$

$$(U_2, \phi_3) = (U_2, \psi_3) - a_3 = 0 \tag{1.71}$$

and therefore

$$\begin{aligned} a_2 &= (U_1, \psi_3) \\ a_3 &= (U_2, \psi_3) \end{aligned} \tag{1.72}$$

and we have

$$\phi_3 = \psi_3 - (U_1, \psi_3)U_1 - (U_2, \psi_3)U_2 \tag{1.73}$$

The orthonormal function is

$$U_3 = \frac{\phi_3}{(\phi_3, \phi_3)^{1/2}} \tag{1.74}$$

In general it follows that

$$\phi_n = \psi_n - \sum_{k=1}^{n-1} (U_k, \psi_n)U_k \tag{1.75}$$

and

$$U_k = \frac{\phi_k}{(\phi_k, \phi_k)^{1/2}} \tag{1.76}$$

THEOREM III *If two operators have a common set of eigenfunctions they commute. Moreover if two Hermitian operators commute they have a common set of eigenfunctions.*

The first part of the theorem is easily proven. We have

$$\begin{aligned} \mathbf{L}_1\psi &= \lambda_1\psi \\ \mathbf{L}_2\psi &= \lambda_2\psi \end{aligned} \tag{1.77}$$

and therefore

$$\begin{aligned} \mathbf{L}_2\mathbf{L}_1\psi &= \lambda_1\lambda_2\psi \\ \mathbf{L}_1\mathbf{L}_2\psi &= \lambda_1\lambda_2\psi \end{aligned} \tag{1.78}$$

Hence on subtracting the above

$$(\mathbf{L}_1\mathbf{L}_2 - \mathbf{L}_2\mathbf{L}_1)\psi = 0 \tag{1.79}$$

or

$$[\mathbf{L}_1, \mathbf{L}_2] = 0 \tag{1.80}$$

which proves the first part of the theorem.

We next prove the converse theorem. Suppose that $\mathbf{L}_1$ has a nondegenerate set of eigenfunctions so that corresponding to say ψ_1 there is only one eigenvalue λ_1. Consider a second operator $\mathbf{L}_2$ which commutes with $\mathbf{L}_1$, then

$$\mathbf{L}_1(\mathbf{L}_2\psi_1) = \mathbf{L}_2\mathbf{L}_1\psi_1 = \lambda_1(\mathbf{L}_2\psi_1) \tag{1.81}$$

so that $L_2\psi_1$ is also an eigenfunction of L_1; but since λ_1 is nondegenerate it must uniquely correspond to ψ_1. We require that

$$L_2\psi_1 = \lambda_2\psi_1 \tag{1.82}$$

since then

$$L_1(\lambda_2\psi_1) = \lambda_2 L_1\psi_1 = \lambda_2(\lambda_1\psi_1) \tag{1.83}$$

or

$$L_1\psi_1 = \lambda_1\psi_1 \tag{1.84}$$

as required. Condition (1.82) means that ψ_1 is also an eigenfunction of L_2 which proves the theorem in the nondegenerate case. If λ_1 is degenerate then there may exist some other eigenfunction in addition to ψ_1 which satisfies (1.81), and (1.82) need no longer hold. Thus if ψ_2 also corresponds to λ_1 then

$$L_2\psi_1 = \psi_2 \tag{1.85}$$

will satisfy (1.81) since

$$L_1(L_2\psi_1) = L_1\psi_2 = \lambda_1\psi_2 \tag{1.86}$$

However, in degenerate cases we can always construct a linear combination of the degenerate eigenfunctions of L_1 which are eigenfunctions of L_2. We require that

$$L_2(c_1\psi_1 + c_2\psi_2) = \lambda(c_1\psi_1 + c_2\psi_2) \tag{1.87}$$

In order to determine c_1 and c_2 we suppose that ψ_1 and ψ_2 are orthonormal or can be made so according to theorem II. On multiplying (1.87) by ψ_1^* and ψ_2^* and integrating over the configuration space we have

$$\begin{aligned} c_1(\psi_1, L_2\psi_1) + c_2(\psi_1, L_2\psi_2) &= \lambda c_1 \\ c_1(\psi_2, L_2\psi_1) + c_2(\psi_2, L_2\psi_2) &= \lambda c_2 \end{aligned} \tag{1.88}$$

or

$$\begin{aligned} c_1(B_{11} - \lambda) + c_2 B_{12} &= 0 \\ c_1(B_{21}) + c_2(B_{22} - \lambda) &= 0 \end{aligned} \tag{1.89}$$

where $(\psi_n, L_2\psi_m) = B_{nm}$. A nontrivial solution exists only if

$$\begin{vmatrix} B_{11} - \lambda & B_{12} \\ B_{21} & B_{22} - \lambda \end{vmatrix} = 0 \tag{1.90}$$

This equation has two roots, λ_1 and λ_2. On substituting each root into (1.89) we can determine the ratio of c_2/c_1 corresponding to each root and application of the normalizing condition permits us to determine c_1 i.e., let $\phi = c_1(\psi_1 + c_2/c_1\psi_2)$, then $(\phi, \phi) = 1$. Clearly if the two roots of the secular equation are different we obtain two mutually orthogonal eigenfunctions of $\mathbf{L}_2$. If the roots are equal we can still obtain two mutually orthogonal functions by a somewhat more extended procedure.

THEOREM IV   *If $\mathbf{L}_2$ commutes with $\mathbf{L}_1$ and if ψ_1 and ψ_2 are eigenfunctions of $\mathbf{L}_1$ with different eigenvalues, λ_1 and λ_2, then the scalar product $\int \psi_1^* \mathbf{L}_2\psi_2 \, dv$ vanishes.*

Consider the scalar product

$$\int \psi_1^* \mathbf{L}_2(\mathbf{L}_1\psi_2) \, dV = \lambda_2 \int \psi_1^* \mathbf{L}_2\psi_2 \, dv \tag{1.91}$$

but since $\mathbf{L}_1$ and $\mathbf{L}_2$ commute and $\mathbf{L}_1$ is Hermitian we also have

$$\int \psi_1^* \mathbf{L}_2(\mathbf{L}_1\psi_2) \, dV = \int \psi_1^* \mathbf{L}_1(\mathbf{L}_2\psi_2) \, dv$$

$$= \int (L_2\psi_2)\mathbf{L}_1^*\psi_1^* \, dv$$

$$= \lambda_1 \int \psi_1^* \mathbf{L}_2\psi_2 \, dv \tag{1.92}$$

on subtracting (1.92) from (1.91) we have

$$(\lambda_2 - \lambda_1) \int \psi_1^* \mathbf{L}_2\psi_2 \, dv = 0 \tag{1.93}$$

but since $\lambda_1 \neq \lambda_2$ we must have

$$\int \psi_1^* \mathbf{L}_2\psi_2 \, dv = 0 \tag{1.94}$$

which proves the theorem.

1.9 *MATRIX REPRESENTATION OF OPERATORS*

A linear operator may also be represented by a matrix. Consider an operator $\mathbf{A}$ acting on a function ϕ, then

$$\mathbf{A}\phi_j = \mathbf{A}\left(\sum_n c_{nj}f_n\right) = \sum_n c_{nj}\mathbf{A}f_n \tag{1.95}$$

The functions $\mathbf{A}f_n$ may be expressed by an orthogonal series in the same basis:

$$\mathbf{A}f_n = \sum_k a_{kn} f_k \tag{1.96}$$

where by the usual arguments

$$a_{kn} = (f_k, \mathbf{A}f_n) \tag{1.97}$$

This scalar product is the *matrix element* of $\mathbf{A}$ which may be fully displayed as

$$A = \begin{pmatrix} a_{11} & a_{12} & \cdots & a_{1n} \\ a_{21} & a_{22} & \cdots & a_{2n} \\ \vdots & & & \vdots \\ a_{m1} & \cdot & \cdot & \cdot & a_{mn} \end{pmatrix} \tag{1.98}$$

where A designates the matrix representation of $\mathbf{A}$. If the basis chosen for the representation is a set of orthonormal eigenfunctions of $\mathbf{A}$ with eigenvalues λ_k, then the representation is a diagonal matrix, $a_{kn} = \lambda_k \delta_{kn}$.

As an example of the matrix representation of an operator we consider $[(d/dx) + a]$. Using the eigenfunctions $(1/\sqrt{2L})e^{-(n\pi/L)ix}$, of the operator as a basis, application of (1.97) over the interval $(-L, L)$ gives the result

$$a_{kn} = \left(\frac{n\pi}{L}i + a\right)\delta_{kn} \qquad n = 0, \pm 1, \pm 2, \pm 3, \ldots$$

and the matrix is diagonal. However, if we represent $x(d/dx)$ in the same basis, we obtain

$$a_{kn} = \frac{n}{n-k}\cos \pi(k-n) \qquad k \neq n$$

$$= 0 \qquad\qquad\qquad k = n$$

where k and n are integers. The matrix is not diagonal since of course the basis is not an eigenfunction of the operator nor does $x(d/dx)$ commute with $[(d/dx) + a]$ (see theorem IV above). Sometimes, however, it is more convenient to determine the matrix representation directly from

$$\mathbf{A}f_j = \sum_i d_{ij} f_i \qquad j = 1, 2, \ldots, n$$

Thus, suppose we are interested in representing the effect of the operator d/dx on a specified set of functions $\cos nx$ and $\sin nx$. Choosing as the basis $f_1 = \cos nx$ and $f_2 = \sin nx$, we have

$$-n \sin nx = a_{11} \cos nx + a_{21} \sin nx$$
$$n \cos nx = a_{12} \cos nx + a_{22} \sin nx$$

By inspection it is clear that $a_{11} = 0$, $a_{12} = n$, $a_{21} = -n$, and $a_{22} = 0$. Noting that the first subscript represents the row and the second subscript the column of the matrix, we have for the representation

$$\begin{pmatrix} 0 & -n \\ -n & 0 \end{pmatrix}$$

1.10   UNITARY OPERATORS

A unitary operator $\mathbf{U}$ has the property that

$$\mathbf{U}^\dagger \mathbf{U} = \mathbf{E}$$

or   (1.99)

$$\mathbf{U}^\dagger = \mathbf{U}^{-1}$$

where $\mathbf{E}$ is the identity operator and $\mathbf{U}^\dagger$ the adjoint operator of $\mathbf{U}$. The importance of unitary operators in quantum mechanics lies in the fact, which we now demonstrate, that the transformation from one orthonormal basis to another such basis is a unitary transformation. Let f_n and g_n be two orthonormal bases, then the transformation is given by

$$f_n = \sum_i a_{ni} g_i \tag{1.100}$$

where the matrix element is

$$a_{ni} = (g_i, f_n)$$

the transformation matrix is said to be unitary if

$$(a_{mi})(t_{in}) = \delta_{mn} \tag{1.101}$$

where (t_{in}) is the adjoint matrix given by

$$(t_{in}) = (a_{ni}^*) \tag{1.102}$$

i.e., the adjoint matrix is the complex conjugate of the transposed matrix. Now consider the scalar product

$$(f_n, f_m) = \delta_{nm} = \sum_{i,j} \int_a^b a_{mi} a_{nj} g_i g_j^* \, dx$$

$$= \sum_i a_{mi} a_{ni}^*$$

In matrix notation the above may be written as°

$$(f_n, f_m) = (\delta_{nm}) = (a_{mi})(t_{in})$$

where t_{in} is given by (1.102). We conclude that the *transformation matrix* (a_{ij}) *relating two orthonormal bases is unitary.*

It is also easy to show that a unitary operator is represented by a unitary matrix. We first show that the *scalar product of two functions is unaltered by a unitary operation*:

$$(\mathbf{U}\phi, \mathbf{U}\phi) = (\mathbf{U}^\dagger\mathbf{U}\phi, \phi) = (\phi, \phi) \tag{1.103}$$

Now let

$$\mathbf{U}f_n = \sum b_{ni} f_i \tag{1.104}$$

where the matrix element of $\mathbf{U}$ in the basis f_n is

$$b_{in} = (f_n, \mathbf{U}f_i)$$

The desired result now follows since

$$(\mathbf{U}f_m, \mathbf{U}f_n) = (f_m, f_n) = \delta_{nm} = \sum_i b_{ni} t_{im}$$

where, as before

$$t_{im} = b_{mi}^*$$

so that (b_{in}) is a unitary matrix.

PROBLEMS

1. An operator is defined as anti-Hermitian if

$$\mathbf{L}^\dagger = -\mathbf{L}$$

Show that for any linear A the operator $(\mathbf{A} + \mathbf{A}^\dagger)/2$ is Hermitian and $(\mathbf{A} - \mathbf{A}^\dagger)/2$ is anti-Hermitian. Hence an operator may always be represented as the sum of a Hermitian and anti-Hermitian operator.

2. Use the definition of the matrix element of an operator $[a_{12} = (f_1, \mathbf{L}f_2)]$ to show that a Hermitian operator is represented by a Hermitian matrix, i.e., $a_{12} = a_{21}^*$.

3. (a) Show that if

$$\mathbf{A}f = af$$

then

$$\mathbf{A}^n f = a^n f$$

(b) Show that if $F(\mathbf{A})$ is a polynomial function of $\mathbf{A}$, then

$$F(\mathbf{A})f = F(a)f$$

Use this result to evaluate

$$(2\mathbf{A}^5 + 3\mathbf{A}^2 + 1)f$$

1.11 *EXPONENTIAL OPERATORS*

The exponential operator is defined by (1.9). In this section we shall show that a unitary operator may be represented as an exponential operator. We first examine the eigenvalues of $\mathbf{U}$. From the identity

$$\mathbf{U} = \frac{\mathbf{U} + \mathbf{U}^\dagger}{2} + i\frac{\mathbf{U} - \mathbf{U}^\dagger}{2i} \equiv \mathbf{A} + i\mathbf{B}$$

it is easy to show, using the results of section 1.7, that $\mathbf{A}$ and $\mathbf{B}$ are Hermitian. Since $\mathbf{U}\mathbf{U}^\dagger = \mathbf{U}^\dagger\mathbf{U}$ it also follows that $\mathbf{A}$ and $\mathbf{B}$ commute and hence, by theorem III above, they have a common set of eigenfunctions ϕ with real eigenvalues which we represent by a and b:

$$\mathbf{U}\phi = (\mathbf{A} + i\mathbf{B})\phi = (a + ib)\phi$$

It follows that the *eigenvalues of* $\mathbf{U}$ *are complex*. Moreover

$$\mathbf{U}^\dagger\mathbf{U} = (\mathbf{A} + i\mathbf{B})^\dagger(\mathbf{A} + i\mathbf{B}) = (\mathbf{A} - i\mathbf{B})(\mathbf{A} + i\mathbf{B})$$
$$= \mathbf{A}^2 + \mathbf{B}^2 = \mathbf{E} \tag{1.105}$$

where we have used (1.49) and (1.50). From the last result it is easily seen

$$\mathbf{E}\phi = (\mathbf{A}^2 + \mathbf{B}^2)\phi = (a^2 + b^2)\phi = \phi$$

so that

$$a^2 + b^2 = 1$$

and we see that the *eigenvalues of* **U** *have an absolute value of unity.* As a consequence we write the eigenvalues u of a unitary operator as

$$u = e^{i\lambda}$$

where λ is a real quantity and hence

$$\mathbf{U}\phi = e^{i\lambda}\phi$$

From the results of problem (3) above and the exponential expansion (1.9) we see that

$$\mathbf{U} = e^{i\mathbf{A}} \tag{1.106}$$

where **A** is a linear operator. Now

$$\mathbf{U}^\dagger = \mathbf{U}^{-1}$$

and therefore on introducing (1.106) and expanding the result it is easy to show that **A** must be Hermitian. A unitary operator may therefore be represented as indicated (1.106), where **A** is Hermitian.

Finally we establish an interesting and useful general result, namely

$$e^{\mathbf{A}}\mathbf{B}e^{-\mathbf{A}} = \mathbf{B} + [\mathbf{A}, \mathbf{B}] + \frac{1}{2!}[\mathbf{A}[\mathbf{A}, \mathbf{B}]]$$

$$+ \frac{1}{3!}[\mathbf{A}[\mathbf{A}[\mathbf{A}, \mathbf{B}]]]$$

$$+ \cdots \tag{1.107}$$

In order to prove this formula we write

$$\mathbf{H}(\theta) = e^{\theta\mathbf{A}}\mathbf{B}e^{-\theta\mathbf{A}} \tag{1.108}$$

and expand (1.108) by means of a Taylor series about $\theta = 0$:

$$\mathbf{H}(\theta) = \mathbf{H}(0) + \left(\frac{\partial\mathbf{H}(\theta)}{\partial\theta}\right)_{\theta=0}\theta + \frac{1}{2!}\left(\frac{\partial^2\mathbf{H}(\theta)}{\partial\theta^2}\right)_{\theta=0}\theta^2 + \cdots \tag{1.109}$$

We find

$$\mathbf{H}(0) = \mathbf{B}$$

$$\left.\frac{\partial H(\theta)}{\partial\theta}\right)_{\theta=0} = \mathbf{A}\mathbf{H}(0) - \mathbf{H}(0)\mathbf{A} = [\mathbf{A}, \mathbf{B}]$$

$$\left.\frac{\partial^2\mathbf{H}(\theta)}{\partial\theta^2}\right)_{\theta=0} = [\mathbf{A}[\mathbf{A}, \mathbf{B}]]$$

The desired result then follows on setting $\theta = 1$ in (1.109).

PROBLEMS FOR CHAPTER I

1. (a) Expand

$$[A[A, B]]$$

(b) Prove equations (1.7a) through (1.7c).

2. (a) Evaluate

$$(\sigma_p C_n)^{-1}$$

(b) Show that for the triangle in figure 1.1 $C_3^2 = \sigma_{yz}$.

3. Expand

$$(e^{d/dx})x^2$$

4. Factor the operator $A^2 + i B^2$.

5. (a) Show that if **A** and **B** are Hermitian and $[A, B] = 0$, then **A B** is Hermitian.

(b) If the operators **A** and **B** do not commute, it is often convenient to define a *symmetrized operator* $C = (AB + BA)/2$. Show that **C** is Hermitian. What is **C** if $[A, B] = 0$?

6. Normalize $\sin \pi x/L$, $\cos \pi x/L$, and $e^{i(\pi x/L)}$ over the interval $-L$ to L.

7. Find the matrix of the operator d^2/dx^2 acting on Ae^{inx} and Ae^{-inx} using these functions as the basis.

8. Show that if

$$[M_y, M_z] = i\hbar M_x$$
$$[M_z, M_x] = i\hbar M_y$$

$\hbar$ is a constant and $i = \sqrt{-1}$
then

$$M_z(M_x + iM_y) = (M_x + iM_y)(M_z + h)$$
$$M_z(M_x - iM_y) = (M_x - iM_y)(M_z - h)$$

9. Use the above results to show that if Y_m is an eigenfunction of M_z and

$$M_z Y_m = k_m Y_m$$

then $(M_x \pm iM_y) Y_m$ is also an eigenfunction of M_z with the eigenvalue $(k_m \pm \hbar)$.

10. Show that if M_x, M_y, and **H** together with their complex conjugates are Hermitian and $[M_x, H] = 0$ and $[M_y, H] = 0$ that

$$\int [(M_x + iM_y)f_1]^* H(M_x + iM_y)f_2 \, d\tau = \int f_1^* H(M_x - iM_y)(M_x + iM_y)f_2 \, d\tau$$

CHAPTER 2 / *Principles of*

Quantum Theory

2.1 *QUANTUM MECHANICS*

Quantum mechanics, in the form that we shall use it, is built up from the several postulates given below. These are not derivable from classical physics. However, the results of quantum mechanics tend to approach those of classical physics when one passes from the atomic scale to the macroscopic scale of everyday experience. In this sense, the laws of classical physics may be regarded as approximations to the more exact results of quantum mechanics.

The calculations of quantum mechanics are performed in terms of a state function ϕ, which depends on the position and time coordinates of the system. This function may be regarded essentially as a mathematical device for calculating dynamical quantities such as the position, energy, or the momentum of a system. The state function never enters into the final results nor is it an observable quantity. It is, in short, a mathematical fiction which permits useful and experimentally verifiable results to be obtained. Our postulates provide rules for obtaining the state function and of relating this function to observable quantities.

POSTULATE I   Corresponding to every system there is a state function ϕ of position and time coordinates which is, together with its first derivatives, *finite, continuous* and *single valued* over the *configuration space* of the system.

By *configuration space* is meant the space defined by the complete range of all of the position variables entering into the description of the system. Thus the configuration space of a free particle is the complete range of the

(x, y, z) coordinates. In the instance of two such particles, the configuration space is defined by the position coordinates of both particles and thus consists of the six variables $(x_1, y_1, z_1, x_2, y_2, z_2)$. The range of a coordinate in configuration space need not be infinite, since for example, in the instance of a particle moving in a plane around a central field, the position is defined by an angular displacement which varies only from 0 to 2π and a radical coordinate which, of course, may be infinite.

POSTULATE 2   The probability of observing a system in an element of volume $d\tau$ in configuration space is $\phi\phi^* \, d\tau$, where ϕ^* is the complex conjugate of ϕ.

Since the probability must by definition be a positive quantity, and since ϕ is in general a complex quantity, it is clearly necessary to multiply the state function by its complex conjugate in order to insure a positive result. It also follows from the definition of probability that if we integrate over the entire configuration space then

$$\int \phi^* \phi \, d\tau = \int |\phi|^2 \, d\tau = 1 \tag{2.1}$$

since the probability of finding the system somewhere in space is certainty. The quantity $|\phi|^2$ is the probability density, i.e., the probability of finding the particle in the region $d\tau$ per unit volume of configuration space. Equation (2.1) places a further condition on the acceptable class of state function, namely, the *state function must be square integrable*. It is clear, therefore, that $|\phi|^2 \to 0$ on passing to infinity. The set of all such functions is said to constitute a Hilbert space, as was indicated in the previous chapter, with a unit norm.

The following postulate informs us as to how we may obtain the state functions of a system.

POSTULATE 3   To every dynamical quantity, L, there corresponds a linear operator, **L**, and that when measurements are made on a system the *only observable results of L are the eigenvalues*, λ, of **L**:

$$\mathbf{L}\psi = \lambda\psi \tag{2.2}$$

where ψ designates a state function, ϕ, which is an eigenfunction of **L**. Equation (2.2) is the Schrödinger time independent equation. When the state function is an eigenfunction of **L** the system is said to be in an *eigenstate* with respect to the observable L. When the system is in an eigenstate and a series of measurements is carried out on L we can, ideally, obtain the value λ precisely. As we shall see, if the system is not in an eigenstate with respect to L, then a distribution of results will be obtained for L on repeating the measurements.

We now consider the rules for obtaining the operators corresponding to the energy and angular momentum of a system. It is convenient to start with the classical expressions in Cartesian coordinates and expressed in terms of the linear momentum $\bar{p}$, position $\bar{r}$, and time t. The following substitutions are then introduced:

$$\text{a.} \quad \bar{p} \rightarrow -i\hbar\nabla \tag{2.3}$$

where $i = \sqrt{-1}$ and $\hbar$ is Planck's constant divided by 2π, i.e., $\hbar = h/2\pi$.

$$\text{b.} \quad \bar{p}^2 = \bar{p}\bar{p} \rightarrow (-i\hbar\nabla)(-i\hbar\nabla) = -\hbar^2\nabla^2$$

$$\text{c.} \quad \bar{r} \rightarrow \bar{r} \quad *$$

where $\bar{r} = x\bar{i} + y\bar{j} + z\bar{k}$

$$\text{d.} \quad t \rightarrow t$$

Some important examples will make the application of these rules clear:
a. *Hamiltonian operator for the total energy of a single particle*
The classical expression for total energy in Cartesian coordinates is

$$E = \tfrac{1}{2}m(\bar{v}_x^2 + \bar{v}_y^2 + \bar{v}_z^2) + V(x, y, z, t) \tag{2.4}$$

where m is the mass of the particle
$\bar{v}_x, \bar{v}_y, \bar{v}_z$ are the velocity components
V is the potential energy

We convert to the Hamiltonian form by introducing the linear momentum ($\bar{p}_x = m\bar{v}_x$, etc.) so that

$$\tfrac{1}{2}m\bar{v}^2 = \frac{\bar{p}^2}{2m} \tag{2.5}$$

and there results

$$H = \frac{1}{2m}(\bar{p}_x^2 + \bar{p}_y^2 + \bar{p}_z^2) + V(x, y, z, t) \tag{2.6}$$

* It should be noted that $\bar{r}$ is replaced by a position operator which strictly should be represented as **r**. However, for the present purpose no great confusion will result if we represent the position operator by $\bar{r}$.

where H is the energy, in Hamiltonian form. Applying the postulate we obtain the operator for H:

$$\mathbf{H} = -\frac{\hbar^2}{2m}\nabla^2 + V(x, y, z, t) \tag{2.7}$$

b. *Angular momentum operator*

The classical definition of angular momentum of a particle is

$$\bar{L} = \bar{r} \times \bar{p} \tag{2.8}$$

where $\bar{r}$ is the position vector and $\bar{p}$ the linear momentum. Expanding this product we find

$$\bar{L} = \begin{vmatrix} i & j & k \\ x & y & z \\ p_x & p_y & p_z \end{vmatrix} \tag{2.9}$$

so that the classical components are

$$\begin{aligned} L_x &= (yp_z - zp_y) \\ L_y &= (zp_x - xp_z) \\ L_z &= (xp_y - yp_x) \end{aligned} \tag{2.10}$$

and the corresponding operators are, from (2.3),

$$\begin{aligned} \mathbf{L}_x &= -i\hbar\left(y\frac{\partial}{\partial z} - z\frac{\partial}{\partial y}\right) \\ \mathbf{L}_y &= -i\hbar\left(z\frac{\partial}{\partial x} - x\frac{\partial}{\partial z}\right) \\ \mathbf{L}_z &= -i\hbar\left(x\frac{\partial}{\partial y} - y\frac{\partial}{\partial x}\right) \end{aligned} \tag{2.11}$$

The total angular momentum operator $\mathbf{L}$ is defined as a *vector operator* whose components are (2.11), i.e.,

$$\begin{aligned} \mathbf{L} &= \mathbf{L}_x \bar{i} + \mathbf{L}_y \bar{j} + \mathbf{L}_z \bar{k} \\ &= -i\hbar\bar{r} \times \nabla \end{aligned} \tag{2.12}$$

where here $\bar{i}, \bar{j}, \bar{k}$ are the unit vectors; we have also

$$\mathbf{L}\mathbf{L} = \mathbf{L}^2 = \mathbf{L}_x^2 + \mathbf{L}_y^2 + \mathbf{L}_z^2 \tag{2.13}$$

according to the usual rule for the scalar product of two vectors.

In future work we shall find the commutator relationship of the angular momentum of importance. From the definition of the commutator, and (2.11), it follows that

$$[\mathbf{L}_x, \mathbf{L}_y] = i\hbar\mathbf{L}_z$$
$$[\mathbf{L}_y, \mathbf{L}_z] = i\hbar\mathbf{L}_x \qquad (2.14)$$
$$[\mathbf{L}_z, \mathbf{L}_x] = i\hbar\mathbf{L}_y$$

These results may be written more compactly as

$$\mathbf{L} \times \mathbf{L} = i\hbar\mathbf{L} \qquad (2.15)$$

Hence it is clear that the components of the angular momentum operator do not commute among themselves. However, it can be similarly shown that the components commute with $\mathbf{L}^2$ i.e.,

$$[\mathbf{L}^2, \mathbf{L}_x] = [\mathbf{L}^2, \mathbf{L}_y] = [\mathbf{L}^2, \mathbf{L}_z] = 0 \qquad (2.16)$$

c. *The Hamiltonian of a many particle system*

In the case of a system consisting of n particles, the extension of the method is straightforward. The total energy is

$$E = \sum_{i=1}^{n} \frac{1}{2m_i} (\bar{p}_{x_i}^2 + \bar{p}_{y_i}^2 + \bar{p}_{z_i}^2) + V(\bar{r}_1, \bar{r}_2, \ldots, \bar{r}_n) \qquad (2.17)$$

where $V(\bar{r}_1, \bar{r}_2, \ldots, \bar{r}_n)$ is the potential energy, and the Hamiltonian operator is

$$\mathbf{H} = -\hbar^2 \sum_{i=1}^{n} \frac{1}{2m_i} \nabla_i^2 + V(\bar{r}_1, \bar{r}_2, \ldots, \bar{r}_n) \qquad (2.18)$$

POSTULATE 4   The state function ϕ satisfies the wave equation

$$\mathbf{H}\phi = i\hbar \frac{\partial \phi}{\partial t} \qquad (2.19)$$

Because of the form of (2.19) the state function is also referred to as the wave function of the system. Equation (2.19) is the celebrated *Schrödinger time-dependent equation*. If the system is in an energy eigenstate then from (2.2) we also have, on setting $\phi = \psi$,

$$\mathbf{H}\psi = E\psi \qquad (2.20)$$

where E is the eigenvalue or observed energy. Equating (2.19) and (2.20), we have

$$E\psi = i\hbar \frac{\partial \psi}{\partial t} \qquad (2.21)$$

or

$$\psi(x, y, z, t) = \psi(x, y, z)e^{-(Eit/\hbar)} \qquad (2.22)$$

where $\psi(x, y, z)$ is the spatial part of the wave function. Thus for a system in an eigenstate the time is separable and we need only solve the time-independent equation (2.20) for the spatially dependent function.

POSTULATE 5 The average or expected value of an observable A corresponding to an operator **A** when a system is in the state ϕ is

$$\langle \mathbf{A} \rangle = \int \phi^* \mathbf{A}\phi \, d\tau = (\phi, \mathbf{A}\phi) \qquad (2.23)$$

where the integral is taken over the entire configuration space. Since the average value of a physical quantity must be real we require that

$$\langle \mathbf{A} \rangle = \langle \mathbf{A} \rangle^* \qquad (2.24)$$

therefore

$$\int \phi^* \mathbf{A}\phi \, d\tau = \int \phi \mathbf{A}^* \phi^* \, d\tau \qquad (2.25)$$

This result means that **A** *must be a Hermitian operator*, according to the definition (1.45). Hence observables must be represented by Hermitian operators. It may be shown by the arguments employed in Chapter 1 that **H** and **L** are Hermitian in Hilbert space.

The probability density $|\phi|^2$ defined in postulate 2 can be shown to obey an equation which is analogous to the classical continuity equation. From postulate 4, we have

$$-\frac{\hbar^2}{2m} \nabla^2 \phi + V\phi = i\hbar \frac{\partial \phi}{\partial t} \qquad (2.26)$$

and on taking the complex conjugate we find

$$-\frac{\hbar^2}{2m} \nabla^2 \phi^* + V\phi^* = -i\hbar \frac{\partial \phi^*}{\partial t} \qquad (2.27)$$

Eliminating V we have

$$\frac{\hbar^2}{2m}(\phi\nabla^2\phi^* - \phi^*\nabla^2\phi) = i\hbar\left(\phi^*\frac{\partial\phi}{\partial t} + \phi\frac{\partial\phi^*}{\partial t}\right) \tag{2.28}$$

or

$$\frac{\hbar^2}{2m}\nabla\cdot(\phi\nabla\phi^* - \phi^*\nabla\phi) = i\hbar\frac{\partial|\phi|^2}{\partial t} \tag{2.29}$$

On rearranging

$$\frac{\partial|\phi|^2}{\partial t} + \frac{\hbar}{2mi}\nabla\cdot(\phi^*\nabla\phi - \phi\nabla\phi^*) = 0 \tag{2.30}$$

this result is clearly in the form of the continuity equation

$$\frac{\partial\rho}{\partial t} + \nabla\cdot\bar{J} = 0$$

where ρ is a density and $\bar{J}$ a current density. In the present case we have

$$\rho = |\phi|^2 \tag{2.31}$$

$$\bar{J} = \frac{\hbar}{2mi}(\phi^*\nabla\phi - \phi\nabla\phi^*) \tag{2.32}$$

Several interesting consequences follow from these results. Thus if we identify $-e|\phi|^2$·with the charge density ρ due to an electron, where $-e$ is the electronic charge, then the current density $\bar{J}$ is given by

$$\bar{J} = \frac{-e\hbar}{2mi}(\phi^*\nabla\phi - \phi\nabla\phi^*) \tag{2.33}$$

It also follows from (2.30) that the integral of the probability density over configuration space is constant in time, since the Laplacian (and hence the Hamiltonian operator) is Hermitian. Application of the divergence theorem gives

$$\frac{\partial}{\partial t}\int|\phi|^2\,d\tau = \frac{\hbar^2}{2mi}\int(\phi\nabla^2\phi^* - \phi^*\nabla^2\phi)\,d\tau = 0 \tag{2.34}$$

Thus we see that the normalization of ϕ does not change with time.

2.2 *CONTINUITY OF THE DERIVATIVE*

We can easily show that if the potential V is discontinuous, but not infinite, at a point x_0, then the first derivative of ψ is continuous at x_0. Consider a potential (figure 2.1a) defined by

$$
\begin{array}{lll}
V = V_1 & & x < x_0 - \varepsilon \\
V \text{ is continuous} & & x_0 - \varepsilon < x < x_0 + \varepsilon \\
V = V_2 & & x > x_0 + \varepsilon
\end{array}
\tag{2.35}
$$

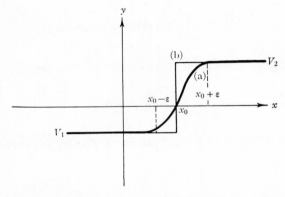

Figure 2.1: Continuous (a) and discontinuous (b) potential at x_0.

The first integral of the time-independent equation in the continuous region is given by

$$
\int_{x_0 - \varepsilon}^{x_0 + \varepsilon} \frac{d^2 \psi}{dx^2}\, dx = -\frac{2m}{\hbar^2} \int_{x_0 - \varepsilon}^{x_0 + \varepsilon} (E - V)\psi\, dx
\tag{2.36}
$$

hence

$$
\left. \frac{d\psi}{dx} \right|_{x_0 + \varepsilon} - \left. \frac{d\psi}{dx} \right|_{x_0 - \varepsilon} = -\frac{2m}{\hbar^2} \int_{x_0 - \varepsilon}^{x_0 + \varepsilon} (E - V)\psi\, dx
\tag{2.37}
$$

As $\varepsilon \to 0$, the integral approaches zero and V becomes discontinuous, so that

$$
\lim_{\varepsilon \to 0} \left[\left(\frac{d\psi}{dx} \right)_{x_0 + \varepsilon} - \left(\frac{d\psi}{dx} \right)_{x_0 - \varepsilon} \right] = 0
\tag{2.38}
$$

This condition will be used in our discussion of potential barriers.

2.3 APPLICATIONS

In order to illustrate the application of the above postulates, the solution of the Schrödinger time-independent equation (2.20) will be obtained for a variety of situations. The solutions discussed below apply to a system in an eigenstate, i.e., a system with a precisely determinable energy. The time factor $e^{i\omega t}(\omega = E/\hbar)$ will not be explicitly exhibited since it does not influence our considerations. The factor may be introduced by multiplying by $e^{i\omega t}$, as was discussed above (2.22).

1. Particle in a Well

We consider a particle with energy E moving in a potential field V given by (figure 2.2)

$$V_1 = 0 \qquad 0 < x < a$$
$$V_2 = V_0 \qquad x > a$$
$$V_3 = V_0 \qquad x < 0$$

where $E < V_0$.

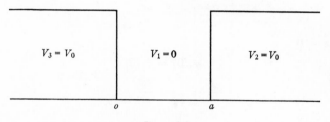

Figure 2.2

On introducing the single particle Hamiltonian (2.7) into the wave equation (2.20) we have for each region

$$\frac{\hbar^2}{2m}\frac{d^2\psi_1}{dx^2} + E\psi_1 = 0 \qquad 0 < x \leqslant a$$

$$\frac{\hbar^2}{2m}\frac{d^2\psi_2}{dx^2} + (E - V_0)\psi_2 = 0 \qquad x \geqslant a \qquad (2.39)$$

$$\frac{\hbar^2}{2m}\frac{d^2\psi_3}{dx^2} + (E - V_0)\psi_3 = 0 \qquad x < 0$$

The solutions are readily found to be

$$\psi_1 = A_1 \cos \alpha x + A_2 \sin \alpha x$$
$$\psi_2 = B_1 e^{\beta x} + B_2 e^{-\beta x} \qquad (2.40)$$
$$\psi_3 = C_1 e^{\beta x} + C_2 e^{-\beta x}$$

where

$$\alpha = \sqrt{\frac{2mE}{\hbar^2}}$$

and   (2.41)

$$\beta = \sqrt{\frac{2m(V_0 - E)}{\hbar^2}}$$

since $V_0 > E$ and β is always real. In order that these solutions be acceptable they must satisfy postulates 1 and 2, i.e., ψ must be finite, continuous, single valued, and quadratically integrable over the configuration space. In order that ψ remain finite as $x \to \infty$, B_1 and C_2 must be set equal to zero. The wave functions would now satisfy postulates 1 and 2 provided that the functions and their first derivatives are equal at the points (o) and (a). These continuity conditions are

AT $x = a$

$$\psi_1(a) = \psi_2(a)$$
$$\left.\frac{d\psi_1}{dx}\right|_{x=a} = \left.\frac{d\psi_2}{dx}\right|_{x=a}$$ (2.42)

AT $x = 0$

$$\psi_1(0) = \psi_3(0)$$
$$\left.\frac{d\psi_1}{dx}\right|_{x=0} = \left.\frac{d\psi_3}{dx}\right|_{x=0}$$ (2.43)

Introducing the eigenfunctions into the continuity conditions gives the result:

AT $x = a$

$$A_1 \cos \alpha a + A_2 \sin \alpha a = B_2 e^{-\beta a}$$ (2.44)

$$-\alpha A_1 \sin \alpha a + \alpha A_2 \cos \alpha a = -\beta B_2 e^{-\beta a}$$ (2.45)

AT $x = 0$

$$A_1 = C_1$$ (2.46)

$$\alpha A_2 = \beta C_1$$ (2.47)

It is easy to see that in order to satisfy these equations a condition must be imposed on α and β, that is, on the permissible energy states. From (2.46) and (2.47) we obtain

$$\frac{A_1}{A_2} = \frac{\alpha}{\beta}$$ (2.48)

Dividing (2.45) by (2.44) and using (2.48) we obtain

$$\tan \alpha a = \frac{2\beta\alpha}{\alpha^2 - \beta^2} \tag{2.49}$$

or

$$\tan a\sqrt{\frac{2mE}{\hbar^2}} = \frac{2\sqrt{E(V_0 - E)}}{2E - V_0} \tag{2.50}$$

Only those values of E which satisfy (2.50) are allowed energy states. Generally, graphical techniques must be employed to evaluate (2.50). However, the essential feature of the problem can be understood by considering the case $V_0 \to \infty$. Then

$$\tan a\sqrt{\frac{2mE}{\hbar^2}} = 0 \tag{2.51}$$

which requires that

$$\sin a\sqrt{\frac{2mE}{\hbar^2}} = 0 \tag{2.52}$$

This last result implies that the only allowed energies are those for which

$$a\alpha = a\sqrt{\frac{2mE}{\hbar^2}} = n\pi \qquad n = 1, 2, 3, \ldots$$

or $\hspace{11cm}$ (2.53)

$$E_n = \frac{\pi^2 \hbar^2}{2ma^2} n^2$$

The value $n = 0$ is eliminated since this implies that $\psi = 0$.

It is clear that the particle can assume only discrete energy states given by (2.53) and all other energy states are forbidden. The energy is now said to be quantized. It should be noted that the quantization in this case is a consequence of imposing the continuity conditions prescribed in postulate 1.

It is also interesting to note that the interval between allowed energy states decreases as the mass of the particle and the dimensions of the potential box increase relative to $\hbar$ (1.054×10^{-27} erg sec). For particles of large mass and systems of large dimensions, the allowed energy states form, for all practical purposes, a continuum and we no longer observe the quantization effect. This conclusion is in accordance with ordinary experience and provides an illustration of the *Bohr correspondence principle* which requires that on passing from the atomic realm to that of everyday dimensions (with action parameters which are large relative to $\hbar$) the results of quantum mechanics must approach those of classical physics.

PROBLEMS

1. Calculate E_n for $n = 1, 2, 3$ [when $a = 1$Å, $(10^{-8}$ cm) in the case of an electron, using $m = 9.10 \times 10^{-28}$ g and $\hbar = 1.05 \times 10^{-27}$ erg-sec]. Repeat the calculation for the case $a = 1$ cm and $m = 1$ gram.

2. Solve the above problem for the infinite potential case starting with the wave equation.

Turning our attention to the eigenfunctions, we see that in the infinite potential case ψ_2 and ψ_3 vanish, and in order to satisfy the continuity condition we must have

$$\psi_n = A_2 \sin \frac{n\pi}{a} x \qquad 0 < x < a \qquad (2.54)$$

$$\psi_n = 0 \qquad\qquad \text{all other } x \qquad (2.54a)$$

It is clear that (2.54) vanishes at the points $x = 0$ and where it joins continuously with (2.54a).

The constant A_2 is determined from the normalization condition:

$$\int_{-\infty}^{\infty} \psi\psi^* \, dx = 1 \qquad (2.55)$$

since the functions vanish outside of $x = 0$ and a, this becomes

$$A_2^2 \int_{-\infty}^{\infty} \sin^2 \frac{n\pi x}{a} \, dx = A^2 \int_{0}^{a} \sin^2 \frac{n\pi x}{a} \, dx \qquad (2.56)$$

which on integration gives

$$A_2 = \sqrt{\frac{2}{a}} \qquad (2.57)$$

PROBLEM

1. Sketch ψ_n, for $n = 1, 2, 3$, for the infinite potential case.

Finally, returning to the finite potential solutions (2.40) we observe that these consist of a sinusoidally varying wave function joined to exponentially

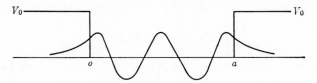

Figure 2.3: Representative wave function in the finite potential case showing penetration into the $V_0 > E$ regions.

decaying functions as indicated in figure 2.3. It is clear that the particle can penetrate into the regions V_0 even though $E < V_0$. This behavior is forbidden in classical physics but is allowed in quantum theory.

2. A Particle in a Three-Dimensional Box

The above problem may be generalized to a particle confined, by an infinite potential barrier, to a three-dimensional potential box, shown in figure 2.4. The potential in the interior is taken at zero. We assume that the box is a cube with sides of length a. The wave equation for the interior, where $V = 0$, is

$$\frac{\hbar^2}{2m} \nabla^2 \psi + E\psi = 0 \tag{2.58}$$

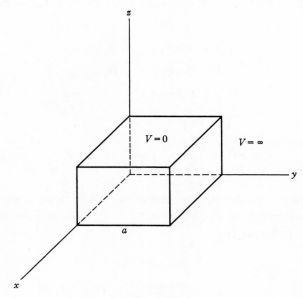

Figure 2.4

This equation is readily integrated by assuming separability of ψ so that

$$\psi(x, y, z) = \psi(x)\psi(y)\psi(z) \tag{2.59}$$

Substituting the separated form of ψ into the wave equation we find

$$\frac{\hbar^2}{2m}\left[\frac{1}{\psi(x)}\frac{\partial^2\psi(x)}{\partial x^2} + \frac{1}{\psi(y)}\frac{\partial^2\psi(y)}{\partial y^2} + \frac{1}{\psi(z)}\frac{\partial^2\psi(z)}{\partial z^2}\right] = -E \tag{2.60}$$

This implies that each term may be set equal to a constant, i.e.,

$$\frac{\hbar^2}{2m}\frac{1}{\psi(x)}\frac{\partial^2\psi(x)}{\partial x^2} = -E_1$$

$$\frac{\hbar^2}{2m}\frac{1}{\psi(y)}\frac{\partial^2\psi(y)}{\partial x^2} = -E_2 \tag{2.61}$$

$$\frac{\hbar^2}{2m}\frac{1}{\psi(z)}\frac{\partial^2\psi(z)}{\partial x^2} = -E_3$$

where

$$E_1 + E_2 + E_3 = E \tag{2.62}$$

The solution to the separated equations can now be obtained by the usual means

$$\psi(x) = A_1 \cos \alpha_1 x + A_2 \sin \alpha_1 x$$
$$\psi(y) = B_1 \cos \alpha_2 y + B_2 \sin \alpha_2 y \tag{2.63}$$
$$\psi(z) = C_1 \cos \alpha_3 z + C_2 \sin \alpha_2 z$$

where

$$\alpha_1 = \sqrt{\frac{2mE_1}{\hbar^2}}, \qquad \alpha_2 = \sqrt{\frac{2mE_2}{\hbar^2}}, \qquad \alpha_3 = \sqrt{\frac{2mE_3}{\hbar^2}} \tag{2.64}$$

Since ψ vanishes outside the box, continuity of the wave function requires that the cosine terms vanish (i.e., $A_1 = B_1 = C_1 = 0$), and also at the boundaries of the potential box

$$\sin \alpha_1 a = 0$$
$$\sin \alpha_2 a = 0 \tag{2.65}$$
$$\sin \alpha_3 a = 0$$

and hence the arguments of the sine functions must be an integral multiple of π. As before, this condition results in quantization of the energy:

$$E_1 = \frac{\hbar^2 \pi^2 l^2}{2ma^2} \qquad l = 1, 2, 3, \ldots$$

$$E_2 = \frac{\hbar^2 \pi^2 q^2}{2ma^2} \qquad q = 1, 2, 3, \ldots \qquad (2.66)$$

$$E_3 = \frac{\hbar^2 \pi^2 n^2}{2ma^2} \qquad n = 1, 2, 3, \ldots$$

The sum of these terms must be equal to E so that

$$E_{lqn} = \frac{\hbar^2 \pi^2}{2ma^2} [l^2 + q^2 + n^2] \qquad (2.67)$$

Thus the total energy of the system is quantized and characterized by three numbers, l, q, n, the *quantum numbers* of the system. The solution of this problem, as with the previous one-dimensional case, gives rise to an infinite number of eigenfunctions each of the form

$$\psi_{lqn} = A_{lqn} \sin \frac{l\pi x}{a} \sin \frac{q\pi}{a} y \sin \frac{n\pi}{a} z \qquad (2.68)$$

The constant can be found by normalizing the function and we find

$$A_{lqn} = \sqrt{\frac{8}{a^3}} \qquad (2.69)$$

PROBLEM

1. Normalize the above wave function (2.68).

———————

Though our results are analogous to the one-dimensional case we note an important difference, namely, corresponding to a given energy or eigenvalue, there is more than one eigenfunction. Such eigenvalues are said to be *degenerate*. Thus, if $l = 2$, $q = 2$, and $n = 3$ then

$$E_{322} = E_{232} = E_{223} = \frac{\hbar^2}{2ma} [(2)^2 + (2)^2 + (3)^2] \qquad (2.70)$$

while the three corresponding eigenfunctions are different

$$\psi_{322} = \sqrt{\frac{8}{a^3}} \sin \frac{3\pi}{a} x \sin \frac{2\pi}{a} y \sin \frac{2\pi}{a} z$$

$$\psi_{232} = \sqrt{\frac{8}{a^3}} \sin \frac{2\pi}{a} x \sin \frac{3\pi}{a} y \sin \frac{2\pi}{a} z \qquad (2.71)$$

$$\psi_{223} = \sqrt{\frac{8}{a^3}} \sin \frac{2\pi}{a} x \sin \frac{2\pi}{a} y \sin \frac{3\pi}{a} z$$

The eigenvalue is said in this case to be threefold degenerate.

3. *The Harmonic Oscillator—Power Series Solutions*

We next consider a problem whose solution requires the transformation of the wave equation into a modification of a standard differential equation known as the *Hermite* equation:

$$\frac{d^2y}{dx^2} - 2x \frac{dy}{dx} + 2\alpha y = 0 \qquad (2.72)$$

where α is a constant.

Hermite's equation can be solved by the usual power-series method of substituting

$$y = \sum_{n=0}^{\infty} C_n x^{n+k} \qquad (2.73)$$

We then obtain the result

$$\sum_{n=0}^{\infty} (n+k)(n+k-1)C_n x^{n+k-2} - 2x \left(\sum_{n=0}^{\infty} (n+k)C_n x^{n+k-1} \right)$$

$$+ 2\alpha \sum_{n=0}^{\infty} C_n x^{n+k} = 0 \qquad (2.74)$$

If this relationship is to hold, then the coefficients of each power of x must vanish. Arranging the terms in powers of x we have

$$k(k-1)C_0 x^{k-2} + (k+1)kC_1 x^{k-1}$$

$$+ \sum_{n=0}^{\infty} [C_{n+2}(n+k+2)(n+k+1) - 2C_n(n+k-\alpha)]x^{n+k} = 0$$

$$(2.75)$$

Therefore the following relationships must be satisfied:

$$k(k - 1)C_0 = 0 \qquad \text{(indicial equation)}$$

$$k(k + 1)C_1 = 0$$

$$C_{n+2} = \frac{2(n + k) - 2\alpha}{(n + k + 2)(n + k + 1)} C_n \qquad \text{(recurrence equation)}$$

(2.76)

We notice from this that if α is an integer equal to $(k + n)$, then the series terminates at the C_n term and the solution reduces to a polynomial. If α is not an integer, then the series is infinite. On choosing $C_1 = 0$ and $k = 0, 1$, the above relationships (2.76) are satisfied and the explicit form of the solutions can now be written as, for $k = 0$,

$$y_1 = C_0 \left[1 + \sum_{n=1}^{\infty} \frac{(-2)^n \alpha(\alpha - 2)\cdots(\alpha - 2n + 2)}{(2n)!} x^{2n} \right] \qquad (2.77)$$

and for $k = 1$,

$$y_2 = C_0 x \left[1 + \sum_{n=1}^{\infty} (-2)^n \frac{(\alpha - 1)(\alpha - 3)\cdots(\alpha - 2n + 1) x^{2n}}{(2n + 1)!} \right] \qquad (2.78)$$

The general solution is then the sum $y_1 + y_2$. We observe that if α is an even positive integer then y_1 becomes a polynomial in x, while if α is an odd positive integer, y_2 becomes a polynomial in x. The infinite series can be shown, by the ratio test, to converge for all finite values of x. Thus we have

$$\frac{C_{n+2} x^{n+2}}{C_n x^n} \bigg|_{n \to \infty} = \frac{2(k + n) - 2\alpha}{(k + n + 2)(k + n + 1)} x^2 \bigg|_{n \to \infty} \xrightarrow[\text{}]{\lim} 0 \qquad (2.79)$$

We observe that for the higher terms of the series the ratio (2.79) behaves like $2x^2/n$. These higher terms will of course dominate the series when x becomes large. Now consider the expansion

$$e^{x^2} = \sum_{\substack{n=0 \\ (n \text{ even})}}^{\infty} \frac{x^n}{\left(\frac{n}{2}\right)!} \qquad (2.80)$$

The ratio of two successive terms for large n is $2x^2/n$. Hence we conclude that if the solutions to the Hermite equation do not terminate, then the resulting infinite series for large x behaves like e^{x^2}.

If the solution does terminate, that is, *if α is a positive integer*, then the *Hermite polynomial, $H_\alpha(x)$* (as the solution is then called) is given by

$$H_\alpha(x) = (2x)^\alpha - \frac{\alpha(\alpha - 1)}{1!}(2x)^{\alpha - 2} + \frac{\alpha(\alpha - 1)(\alpha - 2)(\alpha - 3)}{2!}(2x)^{\alpha - 4}\cdots$$

(2.81)

for α either even or odd on choosing

$$C_0 = (-1)^{(\alpha - 1)/2}\frac{2\alpha!}{\left(\dfrac{\alpha - 1}{2}\right)!}$$

(2.82)

The Hermite equation may be transformed into a modified equation by substituting

$$y = e^{x^2/2}\psi$$

(2.83)

We then obtain

$$\frac{d^2\psi}{dx^2} + (1 - x^2 + 2\alpha)\psi = 0$$

(2.84)

The solution to the latter is clearly

$$\psi = ye^{-(x^2/2)}$$

(2.85)

or if α is a positive integer

$$\psi = H_\alpha(x)e^{-(x^2/2)}$$

(2.86)

Consider a particle subject to a restoring force given by kx, where k is a constant and x is a displacement. This situation is that of the classical harmonic oscillator. The potential energy of the particle is then $(k/2)x^2$ and the wave equation is

$$\frac{\hbar^2}{2m}\frac{d^2\psi}{dx^2} + \left(E - \frac{k}{2}x^2\right)\psi = 0$$

(2.87)

We shall show that this equation can be reduced to the modified Hermite equation. Let

$$\varepsilon = 2m\frac{E}{\hbar^2}$$

$$\beta^2 = \frac{mk}{\hbar^2}$$

(2.88)

then we find

$$\frac{d^2\psi}{dx^2} + (\varepsilon - \beta^2 x^2)\psi = 0 \qquad (2.89)$$

If we now substitute

$$Z = \sqrt{\beta}\, x \qquad (2.90)$$

the wave equation can easily be transformed into the modified Hermite equation of the form given by (2.84):

$$\frac{d^2\psi}{dZ} + \left[1 - Z^2 + 2 \cdot \frac{1}{2}\left(\frac{\varepsilon}{\beta} - 1\right)\right]\psi = 0 \qquad (2.91)$$

which has the solution

$$\psi = e^{-(Z^2/2)} y(Z) \qquad (2.92)$$

As we have seen for large values of Z, the infinite series $y(Z)$ behaves as e^{Z^2} and hence the wave function ψ is not square-integrable over the entire configuration space as demanded by Postulate 2. In order to obtain an acceptable wave function it is necessary that $\frac{1}{2}[(\varepsilon/\beta) - 1]$ be a positive integer n and hence $y(Z)$ becomes a Hermite polynomial. The acceptable solution to the harmonic oscillator is then

$$\psi_n = A_n e^{-(Z^2/2)} H_n(Z) = A_n e^{-(\beta x^2/2)} H_n(\sqrt{\beta}\, x) \qquad (2.93)$$

where A_n is chosen so as to normalize the wave function.

The energy is quantized through the relationship

$$\frac{1}{2}\left(\frac{\varepsilon}{\beta} - 1\right) = n \qquad n = 0, 1, 2, \ldots \qquad (2.94)$$

or

$$E_n = \frac{h}{2\pi}\sqrt{\frac{k}{m}}\left(n + \frac{1}{2}\right) \qquad (2.95)$$

If we recall that the classical frequency of an oscillator is

$$\nu = \frac{1}{2\pi}\sqrt{\frac{k}{m}} \qquad (2.96)$$

then the energy may be written

$$E_n = h\nu(n + \tfrac{1}{2}) \qquad n = 0, 1, 2, \ldots \qquad (2.97)$$

We observe that even when the oscillator is in its lowest energy state with $n = 0$, there is still a vibrational energy of $h\nu/2$, the so called zero-point energy.

PROBLEM

The wave equation for the harmonic oscillator in three-dimensional space is readily soluble. Representing the displacement from equilibrium by the vector $\bar{r}$ the wave equation is

$$\frac{\hbar^2}{2m} \nabla^2\psi + \left(E - \frac{1}{2} kr^2\right)\psi = 0 \qquad (2.98)$$

where

$$r^2 = x^2 + y^2 + z^2 \qquad (2.99)$$

This equation may be readily separated into three one-dimensional equations by the substitutions

$$\psi = \psi(x)\psi(y)\psi(z) \qquad (2.100)$$

and

$$E = E_x + E_y + E_z \qquad (2.101)$$

Carry through the details and show

$$\psi = A_{nx}A_{ny}A_{nz}e^{-(\bar{r}'^2/2)}H_{nx}(x')H_{ny}(y')H_{nz}(z') \qquad (2.102)$$

where $x' = \sqrt{\beta}\, x$ and similarly for the other primed expression and

$$E_n = (n_x + n_y + n_z + \tfrac{3}{2})h\nu$$

Note that ψ is now degenerate.

2.4 *PARTICLES IN A CENTRAL FIELD*

As a final example of a bound particle we consider the behavior of a charged particle moving about a central field. An electron moving about a nucleus provides a simple but important instance of this situation. We begin with the wave equation of a two-particle system with total energy E_s:

$$\frac{\hbar^2}{2m_1} \nabla^2_1\psi + \frac{\hbar^2}{2m_2} \nabla^2_2\psi + (E_s - V)\psi = 0 \qquad (2.103)$$

Here the Laplacians refer to particles of mass m_1 and coordinates (x_1, y_1, z_1), and mass m_2 with coordinates (x_2, y_2, z_2). The potential energy is in general a function of all six coordinates. If one particle has a positive charge Ze, where Z is a positive integer, and the other a negative charge $-e$ then the potential energy of the system may be written as

$$V = -\frac{Ze^2}{\sqrt{(x_1 - x_2)^2 + (y_1 - y_2)^2 + (z_1 - z_2)^2}} = -\frac{Ze^2}{|\vec{r}_1 - \vec{r}_2|}$$
$$= -\frac{Ze^2}{r} \qquad (2.104)$$

where we have introduced vector $\vec{r}$ giving the relative position of the two particles, i.e.,

$$\vec{r} = \vec{r}_1 - \vec{r}_2$$

We also find it convenient to introduce the center-of-mass vector,

$$\vec{r}_c = \frac{m_1}{m_1 + m_2}\,\vec{r}_1 + \frac{m_2}{m_1 + m_2}\,\vec{r}_2 = \mu\left(\frac{\vec{r}_1}{m_2} + \frac{\vec{r}_2}{m_1}\right) \qquad (2.105)$$

where μ *is the reduced mass*,

$$\frac{m_1 m_2}{m_1 + m_2} = \frac{m_1 m_2}{M}$$

and where $M = m_1 + m_2$.

On introducing the above new coordinates into the wave equation there results

$$\frac{\hbar^2}{2M}\,\nabla_c^2\psi + \frac{\hbar^2}{2\mu}\,\nabla^2\psi + \left(E_s + \frac{Ze^2}{r}\right)\psi = 0 \qquad (2.106)$$

where ∇_c^2 is the Laplacian with respect to the center of mass coordinates (x_c, y_c, z_c), and ∇^2 with respect to the relative position coordinates (x, y, z).

PROBLEM

Obtain (2.106) by using transformation

$$\frac{\partial}{\partial x_1} = \frac{\partial x_c}{\partial x_1}\frac{\partial}{\partial x_c} + \frac{\partial x}{\partial x_1}\frac{\partial}{\partial x} = \frac{m_1}{m_1 + m_2}\frac{\partial}{\partial x_c} + \frac{\partial}{\partial x} \qquad (2.107)$$

and hence show that

$$\nabla_1 = \frac{m_1}{m_1 + m_2}\,\nabla_c + \nabla$$
$$\nabla_2 = \frac{m_2}{m_1 + m_2}\,\nabla_c - \nabla \qquad (2.108)$$

Introduction of these operators into (2.103) gives the desired expression.

Equation (2.106) may be separated into two equations, one of which represents the translational motion of the center of mass, and the other the relative motion of the two particles about each other:

$$\psi(x_c, y_c, z_c, x, y, z) = \psi_c(x_c, y_c, z_c)\psi(x, y, z) \qquad (2.109)$$

If we let E_t be the translational energy, then the translational equation is

$$\frac{\hbar^2}{2M}\nabla_c^2\psi_c + E_t\psi_c = 0 \qquad (2.110)$$

An equation describing the relative motion of the two particles is

$$\frac{\hbar^2}{2\mu}\nabla^2\psi + [E - V(r)]\psi = 0 \qquad (2.111)$$

where

$$E = E_s - E_t$$

We now solve the latter equation by first transforming into polar coordinates (figure 2.5)

$$\frac{\hbar^2}{2\mu}\left\{\left[\frac{1}{r^2}\frac{\partial}{\partial r}\left(r^2\frac{\partial}{\partial r}\right) + \frac{1}{r^2\sin\theta}\frac{\partial}{\partial\theta}\left(\sin\theta\frac{\partial}{\partial\theta}\right) + \frac{1}{r^2\sin^2\theta}\frac{\partial^2}{\partial\phi^2}\right]\psi\right\}$$
$$+ [E - V(r)]\psi = 0 \quad (2.112)$$

or

$$\left[\frac{\partial}{\partial r}\left(r^2\frac{\partial\psi}{\partial r}\right) + \frac{2\mu r^2}{\hbar^2}(E - V)\psi\right] + \frac{1}{\sin\theta}\frac{\partial}{\partial\theta}\left(\sin\theta\frac{\partial\psi}{\partial\theta}\right) + \frac{1}{\sin^2\theta}\frac{\partial^2\psi}{\partial\phi^2} = 0$$
$$(2.113)$$

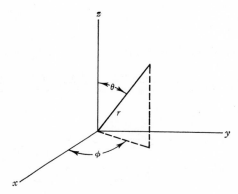

Figure 2.5

We can separate the radial coordinate from the angular functions by introducing

$$\psi = R(r)Y(\theta, \phi) \tag{2.114}$$

where the function $Y(\theta, \phi)$ is referred to as a *spherical harmonic*. The resulting equation can easily be shown to be

$$\left[\frac{1}{R(r)} \frac{\partial}{\partial r} \left(r^2 \frac{\partial R}{\partial r} \right) + \frac{2\mu r^2}{\hbar^2} (E - V(r)) \right]$$

$$+ \frac{1}{Y(\theta, \phi)} \left\{ \frac{1}{\sin \theta} \frac{\partial}{\partial \theta} \left[\sin \theta \frac{\partial Y(\theta, \phi)}{\partial \theta} \right] + \frac{1}{\sin^2 \theta} \frac{\partial Y(\theta, \phi)}{\partial \phi^2} \right\} = 0 \quad (2.115)$$

so that on setting the radial part equal to λ_1, we have

$$\frac{1}{R} \frac{\partial}{\partial r} \left(r^2 \frac{\partial R}{\partial r} \right) + \frac{2\mu r^2}{\hbar^2} [E - V(r)] = \lambda_1 \tag{2.115a}$$

and

$$\frac{1}{\sin \theta} \frac{\partial}{\partial \theta} \left[\sin \theta \frac{\partial Y(\theta, \phi)}{\partial \theta} \right] + \frac{1}{\sin^2 \theta} \frac{\partial^2}{\partial \phi^2} Y(\theta, \phi) = -\lambda_1 Y(\theta, \phi) \tag{2.115b}$$

The last equation may be further separated on setting

$$Y(\theta, \phi) = S(\phi)T(\theta)$$

so that

$$\frac{1}{T \sin \theta} \frac{\partial}{\partial \theta} \left(\sin \theta \frac{\partial T}{\partial \theta} \right) + \frac{1}{S \sin^2 \theta} \frac{\partial^2 S}{\partial \phi^2} = -\lambda_1 \tag{2.116}$$

hence

$$\frac{\sin \theta}{T} \frac{\partial}{\partial \theta} \left(\sin \theta \frac{\partial T}{\partial \theta} \right) + \lambda_1 \sin^2 \theta = \lambda_2$$

$$\frac{1}{S} \frac{\partial^2 S}{\partial \phi^2} = -\lambda_2 \tag{2.117}$$

The equation in $S(\phi)$ is easily solved to give

$$S = Ae^{\pm(\lambda_2)^{1/2}\phi i} \qquad \lambda_2 \neq 0$$

$$S = A + B\phi \qquad \lambda_2 = 0 \tag{2.118}$$

Since S must be single valued over $0 \leqslant \phi \leqslant 2\pi$ [i.e., $S(\phi + 2\pi) = S(\phi)$]

B must vanish and $(\lambda_2)^{1/2}$ must be a positive or negative integer m. We have therefore

$$S(\phi) = Ae^{m\phi i}$$

$$\lambda^{1/2} = m$$

(2.119)

The equation for $T(\theta)$ may now be expressed as

$$\frac{1}{T \sin \theta} \frac{\partial}{\partial \theta} \left(\sin \theta \frac{\partial T}{\partial \theta} \right) + \left(\lambda_1 - \frac{m^2}{\sin \theta} \right) = 0$$

(2.120)

This equation may be transformed into a standard form by substituting

$$\omega = \cos \theta$$

(2.121)

so that

$$\frac{\partial}{\partial \omega} \left[(1 - \omega^2) \frac{\partial T}{\partial \omega} \right] + \left(\lambda_1 - \frac{m^2}{1 - \omega^2} \right) T = 0$$

(2.122)

or

$$(1 - \omega^2) \frac{\partial^2 T}{\partial \omega^2} - 2\omega \frac{\partial T}{\partial \omega} + \left(\lambda_1 - \frac{m^2}{1 - \omega^2} \right) T = 0$$

(2.123)

On setting $\lambda_1 = l(l + 1)$ the last result is precisely in the form of the *associated Legendre* equation:

$$(1 - \omega^2) \frac{\partial^2 T}{\partial \omega^2} - 2\omega \frac{\partial T}{\partial \omega} + \left[l(l + 1) - \frac{m^2}{1 - \omega^2} \right] T = 0$$

(2.124)

This equation has singularities at $\omega = \pm 1$ corresponding to $\theta = 0$ and $\theta = \pi$. However, it can be shown by the usual power-series treatment that a finite solution still exists provided that *l is a positive integer or zero*, and also that the solution is zero for all ω unless $|m| \leqslant l$. Hence we must have

$$|m| \leqslant l \qquad l = 0, 1, 2, 3, \ldots$$

(2.125)

The solution to (2.124) is given by the *associated Legendre polynomial*, $P_l^{|m|}(\omega)$ of degree l and order m which we can write in the convenient form

$$P_l^{|m|}(\omega) = \frac{(1 - \omega^2)^{|m|/2}}{2^l l!} \frac{d^{l + |m|}}{d\omega^{l + |m|}} (\omega^2 - 1)^l$$

(2.126)

If $m = 0$, we obtain the *Legendre polynomial* of degree l

$$P_l(\omega) = \frac{1}{2^l l!} \frac{d^l}{d\omega^l} (\omega^2 - 1)^l$$

(2.127)

Finally we consider the radial equation for $R(r)$. Introducing

$$\lambda_1 = l(l + 1) \tag{2.128}$$

and

$$V = -\frac{Ze^2}{r} \tag{2.129}$$

we find that

$$\frac{d^2R}{dr^2} + \frac{2}{R}\frac{dR}{dr} + \frac{2\mu}{\hbar^2}\left[E + \frac{Ze^2}{r} - \frac{l(l + 1)}{r^2}\right]R = 0 \tag{2.130}$$

This may be reduced to a standard form by substituting a new parameter n and a new variable χ defined by

$$E = -\frac{Z^2\mu e^4}{2n^2\hbar^2} \tag{2.131}$$

$$r = \frac{n\hbar^2\chi}{2\mu Ze^2} = \frac{na_0\chi}{2Z} = \frac{\chi}{2\alpha} \tag{2.132}$$

where

$$a_0 = \frac{\hbar^2}{\mu e^2} \tag{2.133}$$

we obtain

$$\frac{d^2R}{d\chi^2} + \frac{2}{\chi}\frac{dR}{d\chi} - \left(\frac{1}{4} - \frac{n}{\chi} + \frac{l(l + 1)}{\chi^2}\right)R = 0 \tag{2.134}$$

This equation is known to have a finite solution at $\chi = 0$, if n is a positive integer, given by

$$R_{nl}(\chi) = e^{-(\chi/2)}\chi^l L_{l+n}^{2l+1}(\chi) \tag{2.135}$$

where

$$L_{l+n}^{2l+1}(\chi) = \frac{d^{2l+1}}{d\chi^{2l+1}}\left\{e^\chi \frac{d^{l+n}}{d\chi^{l+n}}(\chi^{l+n}e^{-\chi})\right\} \tag{2.136}$$

which is not identically zero if $n \geqslant l + 1$. The function $R_{nl}(\chi)$ is referred to as the *Laguerre function* while $L_{l+n}^{2l+1}(\chi)$ is the associated Laguerre polynomial.

In summary, we see that the solution to the problem of a particle moving in a central field is given by the wave function:

$$\psi_{nlm} = C_{nlm} P_l^{|m|}(\cos \theta) e^{-\alpha r} (2\alpha r)^l L_{l+n}^{2l+1}(2\alpha r) e^{im\phi} \qquad (2.137)$$

and the energy by

$$E_n = -\frac{Z^2 \mu e^4}{2n^2 \hbar^2} \qquad n = 1, 2, 3, \ldots \qquad (2.137a)$$

The constant C_{nlm} is determined by the normalization condition. Three quantum numbers, n, l, m appear in the solution to the problem and these integers are related by the conditions

$$
\begin{aligned}
n \geqslant l + 1 \qquad & n = 1, 2, \ldots \\
|m| \leqslant l \qquad & l = 0, 1, 2, \ldots \\
m = 0, \pm 1, & \pm 2, \ldots
\end{aligned}
\qquad (2.138)
$$

Thus if $n = 2$, then l may have the values 0 and 1. Corresponding to $l = 0$ we have $m = 0$, and to $l = 1$ we have $m = 0, +1, -1$. The quantum numbers associated with l are frequently referred to by the spectroscopic designation, i.e., $l = 0$ is designated by s, $l = 1$ by p, $l = 2$ by d, and $l = 3$ by f.

The energy E_n given by (2.137a) of the system is quantized since n must be an integer. Since E_n depends only on n it follows that for $n > 1$ the energy levels are degenerate. It is not difficult to see that for each value of n there are n^2 degenerate eigenfunctions.

Some normalized eigenfunctions are listed below:

$$
\begin{aligned}
\psi_{100} &= \frac{1}{\sqrt{\pi}} \left(\frac{Z}{a_0}\right)^{3/2} e^{-Zr/a_0} \\
\psi_{200} &= \frac{1}{4\sqrt{2\pi}} \left(\frac{Z}{a_0}\right)^{3/2} \left(2 - \frac{Zr}{a_0}\right) e^{-Zr/2a_0} \\
\psi_{210} &= \frac{1}{4\sqrt{2\pi}} \left(\frac{Z}{a_0}\right)^{3/2} \left(\frac{Zr}{a_0}\right) e^{-Zr/2a_0} \cos \theta \\
\psi_{21\pm1} &= \frac{1}{8\sqrt{2\pi}} \left(\frac{Z}{a_0}\right)^{3/2} \left(\frac{Zr}{a_0}\right) e^{-Zr/2a_0} \sin \theta e^{\pm i\phi}
\end{aligned}
\qquad (2.139)
$$

where

$$a_0 = \frac{\hbar}{\mu e^2} = 0.529 \times 10^{-8} \text{ cm} \qquad (2.140)$$

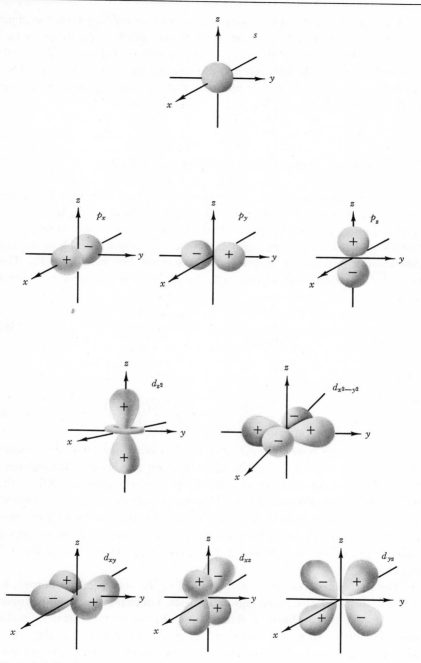

Figure 2.6: First s, p, and d orbitals [After H. B. Callen, *J. Chem. Phys.*, **22**, 518 (1954)].

The spatial distribution of some wave-function types is shown in figure 2.6. The wave functions for which $l = 0$, the so-called s orbitals, are spherically symmetrical about the origin. The functions for which $l = 1$, the p-orbitals, are dumbbell-shaped and are directed along the x, y, z axis. These are designated as p_x, p_y, p_z. We note also that the sign of p-orbitals reverses. The five orbitals corresponding to $l = 2$ are also shown.

2.5 THE FREE PARTICLE AND WAVE PACKETS

In the previous problems the potential fields were such that the particle was bound or confined to move in a restricted region of space. We now consider a second kind of situation in which the particle is not bound but is free to move over extended regions of space. A simple example is the one-dimensional potential well previously discussed but with $E > V_0$. Then $(E - V_0)$ is positive and we can write the solutions to the wave equation as

$$\psi_1 = A_1 e^{i\alpha x} + A_2 e^{-i\alpha x} \qquad 0 < x < a$$
$$\psi_2 = B_1 e^{i\beta x} + B_2 e^{-i\beta x} \qquad x > a \qquad (2.141)$$
$$\psi_3 = C_1 e^{i\beta x} + C_2 e^{-i\beta x} \qquad x < 0$$

where

$$\alpha = \sqrt{\frac{2mE}{h^2}}; \qquad \beta = \sqrt{\frac{2m(E - V_0)}{h^2}} \qquad (2.142)$$

In this case we have six constants related by only four conditions, namely, the continuity conditions of the wave function and its first derivatives at 0 and a. If for the moment we include the normalization condition, then we still have only five conditions. This means, of course, that the problem is underdetermined and that any finite values of α and β will satisfy the equations. We conclude, therefore, that there is no quantization of particle energy. The energy is now said to be a *continuous eigenvalue* of the wave equation.

The particle is now no longer confined to the region of the barrier, but is free to move over extended regions of space. Let us now pursue the problem and consider the problem of normalizing the above functions. It is clear that difficulties are now encountered since these functions, as they stand, are not square-integrable over the entire configuration space, and we must now consider means for constructing acceptable wave functions.

We begin by recalling the result discussed in Chapter 1, that if we have a number of functions, each of which is a solution of the differential equation

$$\mathbf{L}\psi_n = 0 \tag{2.143}$$

then any linear combination of these functions is also a solution

$$\mathbf{L}\sum_n c_n\psi_n = 0 \tag{2.144}$$

where, of course, c_n is not a function of the variable entering into $\mathbf{L}$. This result is the well-known superposition principle. If c_n and ψ_n depend continuously on some parameter k then the superposition principle becomes

$$\mathbf{L}\left[\int c_n(k)\psi_n(k)\ dk\right] = 0 \tag{2.145}$$

so that the integral is also a solution. In general, if a set of functions satisfies postulates 1 and 2 given above, then a linear combination will also satisfy the postulates. We may conclude that if we have a set of functions which are acceptable wave functions, then a linear superposition of these is also an acceptable solution.

We return now to the problem of a particle moving in a constant potential field such that $E > V_0$ and consider the eigenfunctions of the form e^{ikx} where

$$k = \pm\sqrt{\frac{2m(E - V_0)}{\hbar^2}} \tag{2.146}$$

We note that since E is the total energy and V_0 the potential energy, the difference is the kinetic energy so that

$$k = \sqrt{\frac{2m}{\hbar^2}\frac{p^2}{2m}} = \frac{p}{\hbar} \tag{2.147}$$

Hence k is proportional to the momentum p. Moreover, if we regard e^{ikx} as the expression for a wave, we must have on purely formal grounds

$$k = \frac{2\pi}{\lambda} \tag{2.148}$$

so that on equating the above expressions we find that the wavelength λ associated with ψ is just

$$\lambda = \frac{h}{p} \tag{2.149}$$

This last expression gives the *famous De Broglie wavelength* associated with ψ. More generally, $e^{i\bar{k}\cdot\bar{r}}$ can readily be shown to be an eigenfunction of the three-dimensional Hamiltonian operator where

$$\bar{k} = k_x\bar{i} + k_y\bar{j} + k_z\bar{k} \tag{2.150}$$

and

$$\bar{r} = x\bar{i} + y\bar{j} + z\bar{k} \tag{2.151}$$

so that according to postulate **4**, the eigenfunction, including time, is

$$\psi(\bar{r}, t) = a(k)e^{i[\bar{k}\cdot\bar{r} - (E/\hbar)t]} \tag{2.152}$$

Since in the case of a free particle, $\bar{k}$ may vary continuously, the integral form of the superposition principle permits us to state that another eigenfunction of the time-dependent equation is

$$\psi(\bar{r}, t) = \int_{-\infty}^{\infty} a(k)e^{i[\bar{k}\cdot\bar{r} - (E/\hbar)t]}\, dk \tag{2.153}$$

where

$$dk = dk_x\, dk_y\, dk_z \tag{2.154}$$

This can be put into the form of the three-dimensional Fourier integral discussed in Chapter 1 by choosing

$$a(k) = \frac{\psi(k)}{(2\pi)^{3/2}} \tag{2.155}$$

so that

$$\psi(\bar{r}, t) = \frac{1}{(2\pi)^{3/2}} \int_{-\infty}^{\infty} \psi(k)e^{i[\bar{k}\cdot\bar{r} - (Et/\hbar)]}\, dk \tag{2.156}$$

This is the Fourier integral representation of a free particle. Employing the Fourier transform pair we have also

$$\psi(k) = \frac{1}{(2\pi)^{3/2}} \int_{-\infty}^{\infty} \psi(\bar{r}, t)e^{-i[\bar{k}\cdot\bar{r} - (E/\hbar)t]}\, dv \tag{2.157}$$

where

$$dv = dx\, dy\, dz \tag{2.158}$$

Since k, according to (2.148) and (2.149), is proportional to the momentum of the particle, expression (2.157) is the momentum representation of the wave function $\psi\,(\bar{r},\,t)$.

Another way of stating our result is that if we are given a wave function $\psi(\bar{r},\,t)$ representing a distribution of the particle in space and time, then there generally corresponds another distribution representing the momentum of the particle, and visa versa. Suppose, however, that $\psi(\bar{r},\,t)$ is a fixed constant value, that is, that we have at any instant precise knowledge of the position of the particle, then according to (2.157) we can say nothing about the distribution of momentum associated with the particle since the integral now diverges. In other words, precise knowledge of position implies total ignorance of momentum. The converse also holds, as is implied by (2.156). This is an example of the *Heisenberg uncertainty principle* which we will discuss in detail in a later section.

Let us assume that $\psi(k)$ can be represented by the normal or Gaussian distribution given by

$$\psi(k) = \frac{1}{(\sigma\sqrt{\pi})^{3/2}}\, e^{-[(k - \langle k \rangle)^2/2\sigma^2]} \tag{2.159}$$

where $\langle k \rangle$ is the average or expected value of k, and σ is the dispersion of k. If the Gaussian distribution is substituted into (2.156) and the integration carried out there is obtained in the one-dimensional case, a Gaussian wave packet shown in figure 2.7. We observe that the probability-density function, $|\psi(x, t)|^2$, changes in such a way with time, that as the center of the packet moves along the x-axis, the dispersion of the packet in space increases with time.

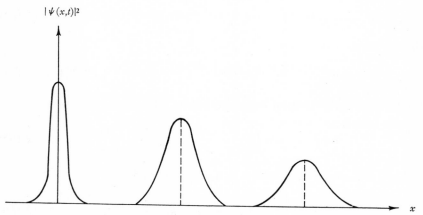

Figure 2.7: Spread of a Gaussian wave packet.

2.6 GROUP VELOCITY

In order to obtain an expression for the velocity of a wave packet, we first consider a simple wave formed by the superposition of two sinusoidal waves, characterized by k_0 and k and frequencies ω_0 and ω, where the frequency is a function of k:

$$\phi = e^{i(k_0 x - \omega_0 t)} + e^{i(kx - \omega t)} \qquad (2.160)$$

We now introduce

$$
\begin{aligned}
k - k_0 &= \Delta k \\
k + k_0 &= k_1 \\
\omega - \omega_0 &= \Delta \omega_1 \\
\omega + \omega_0 &= \omega_1
\end{aligned}
\qquad (2.161)
$$

so that

$$
\begin{aligned}
k_0 &= \frac{k_1 - \Delta k}{2} \\[6pt]
k &= \frac{k_1 + \Delta k}{2} \\[6pt]
\omega_0 &= \frac{\omega_1 - \Delta \omega}{2} \\[6pt]
\omega &= \frac{\omega_1 + \Delta \omega}{2}
\end{aligned}
\qquad (2.162)
$$

and

$$\phi = e^{i[(k_1 - \Delta k/2)x - (\omega_1 - \Delta\omega/2)t]} + e^{i[(k_1 + \Delta k/2)x - (\omega_1 + \Delta\omega/2)t]} \qquad (2.163)$$

The last result may be written

$$\phi = e^{i[(k_1 x/2) - (\omega_1 t/2)]}\{e^{-i[(\Delta k/2)x - (\Delta\omega/2)t]} + e^{i[(\Delta k x/2) - (\Delta\omega/2)t]}\} \qquad (2.164)$$

or on taking the real part of this last result we find

$$\operatorname{Re}\phi = 2\cos\left(\frac{k_1 x}{2} - \frac{\omega_1 t}{2}\right)\cos\left(\frac{\Delta k x}{2} - \frac{\Delta\omega t}{2}\right) \qquad (2.165)$$

If Δk and $\Delta\omega$ are small then $k \approx k_0$, $\omega \approx \omega_0$, and

$$\Delta\omega = \frac{d\omega}{dk}\bigg|_{k_0} \Delta k \qquad (2.166)$$

and we have finally

$$\text{Re } \phi = 2 \cos (k_0 x - \omega_0 t) \cos \frac{\Delta k}{2} \left[x - \left(\frac{d\omega}{dk} \right)_{k_0} t \right] \qquad (2.167)$$

The composite wave form is shown in figure 2.8 and consists of a relatively rapidly varying component of frequency ω_0, and phase velocity ω_0/k_0, modulated by slowly varying component of frequency $\Delta\omega/2$, and velocity $(d\omega/dk)_{k_0}$. The composite form thus moves from left to right as a sequence of "beats" with the velocity of the modulating envelope $(d\omega/dk)_{k_0}$. This latter velocity is referred to as the *group velocity* of a wave packet.

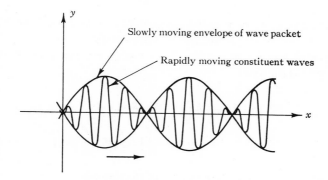

Figure 2.8: Motion of a sequence of wave packets.

These considerations apply directly to a quantum mechanical wave packet. Suppose that $\bar{k}$ is distributed over a narrow region $\Delta\bar{k}$ about $\bar{k}_0$, then to a first approximation

$$E(\bar{k}) = E(\bar{k}_0) + \nabla_k E(\bar{k}_0) \cdot \Delta\bar{k}$$
$$\Delta\bar{k} = (\bar{k} - \bar{k}_0) \qquad (2.168)$$

where ∇_k is the gradient of E with respect to $\bar{k}$, since the latter now consists of the components k_x, k_y, k_z. We also can write

$$\bar{k} \cdot \bar{r} = (\bar{k} - \bar{k}_0) \cdot \bar{r} + \bar{k}_0 \cdot \bar{r} \qquad (2.169)$$

substituting the above into the expression for a wave packet (2.156) consisting of components in the narrow region Δk we find

$$\psi(x, y, z, t) = \frac{e^{i[\bar{k}_0 \cdot \bar{r} - (E(\bar{k}_0)/\hbar)t]}}{(2\pi)^{3/2}} \int\limits_{\Delta k} \{ a(k) e^{i[\bar{r} - (t/\hbar)\nabla_k E][\bar{k} - \bar{k}_0]} \} \, dk \qquad (2.170)$$

The term outside the integral represents a wave moving from left to right with $\bar{k} = \bar{k}_0$. This wave is modulated by the integral which moves with a group velocity V_g given by

$$V_g = \frac{1}{\hbar} \nabla_k E(k) \tag{2.171}$$

Hence the group velocity of a packet is proportional to the gradient of $E(\bar{k})$ in $\bar{k}$ space.

2.7 *CHANGE IN EXPECTED VALUE—EFFECTIVE MASS*

In order to develop further the concept of a wave packet we must now establish a simple but important result. We consider the time rate of change of the expected value defined by (2.23) where the operator **A** does not explicitly depend on time:

$$i\hbar \frac{d}{dt} \langle A \rangle = i\hbar \frac{d}{dt} \int \phi^*(t) \mathbf{A}\phi(t) \, d\tau$$

$$= \left(\phi, \mathbf{A}i\hbar \frac{\partial \phi}{\partial t} \right) - \left(i\hbar \frac{\partial \phi}{\partial t}, \mathbf{A}\phi \right) \tag{2.178}$$

Introducing (2.19) and recalling that H is Hermitian

$$i\hbar \frac{d\langle A \rangle}{dt} = (\phi, \mathbf{A}\mathbf{H}\phi) - (\phi, \mathbf{H}\mathbf{A}\phi) \tag{2.179}$$

so that

$$i\hbar \frac{d\langle \mathbf{A} \rangle}{dt} = \langle \mathbf{A}\mathbf{H} - \mathbf{H}\mathbf{A} \rangle = \langle [\mathbf{A}, \mathbf{H}] \rangle \tag{2.180}$$

If **A** involves time explicitly, we then have the more general result

$$i\hbar \frac{d\langle \mathbf{A} \rangle}{dt} = \langle [\mathbf{A}, \mathbf{H}] \rangle + i\hbar \left\langle \frac{\partial \mathbf{A}}{\partial t} \right\rangle \tag{2.181}$$

If $\langle \mathbf{A} \rangle$ does not change with time A is said to be a *constant of motion*. We now consider operators which do not involve time explicitly. It is clear that the energy is a constant of motion since **H** commutes with itself. Moreover if the operator **A** commutes with **H**, then the observable A is also a constant of motion. However, not all operators have this property. Thus it is easily verified that the linear momentum operator **p** does not commute with **H** if the potential V is not uniform, nor does the position operator **x**. Since the observables p and x are not constants of motion, the best we can do is to relate their expected or average values. Substituting **p** and x into (2.180) we find

$$\frac{d}{dt} \langle x \rangle = \langle \bar{v} \rangle = \frac{\langle \bar{p}_x \rangle}{m} \tag{2.182}$$

and

$$\frac{d \langle \bar{p}_x \rangle}{dt} = -\langle \nabla V \rangle = \bar{F} \tag{2.183}$$

where $\bar{F}$ is the force due to the gradient in the potential energy. We observe that the above results for the expected values are exactly the same form as the classical expressions.

Another important relationship between classical and quantum mechanics is apparent on comparing 2.180 with the equation of motion in Poisson bracket notation (see 25.1A in Appendix I). We see that on passing from classical to quantum mechanics we replace the Poisson's bracket involving the observables by the commutator of the corresponding operators according to the prescription

$$\{A, H\} \rightarrow \frac{i}{i\hbar} \langle [\textbf{A, H}] \rangle \tag{2.183a}$$

and also

$$\frac{dA}{dt} \rightarrow \frac{d\langle \textbf{A} \rangle}{dt}$$

These results may be applied to wave packets by identifying $\langle v \rangle$ with V_g given by (2.171). In particular we may regard the wave packet as an electron moving in a metal or semiconductor and subject to internal potential fields, due to the constituent atoms, as well as to an applied field. Setting $\hbar \bar{k} = \langle P \rangle$ in analogy to (2.147) for the constant field case, we have for the velocity and acceleration of the electron

$$\langle v \rangle = \frac{1}{\hbar} \nabla_k E(k)$$

$$a = \frac{d\langle v \rangle}{dt} = \frac{1}{\hbar} \nabla_k \nabla_k E(k) \cdot \frac{d\bar{k}}{dt}$$

$$= \frac{1}{\hbar^2} \nabla_k \nabla_k E(k) \cdot \frac{d\langle P \rangle}{dt} \tag{2.184}$$

$$= \frac{1}{\hbar^2} \nabla_k \nabla_k E(k) \bar{F}$$

It is clear from this important result that the form of Newton's laws of motion is preserved by the wave packet moving in a nonuniform potential field, provided an effective mass m^* is used in place of the electron mass m. This effective mass is given by the second order tensor:

$$\frac{1}{m^*} = \frac{1}{\hbar^2} \nabla_k \nabla_k E(k) \tag{2.185}$$

The components of the tensor may be exhibited by introducing the expression for the gradient in k space:

$$\nabla_k \nabla_k = \left(\frac{\partial}{\partial k_x} i + \frac{\partial}{\partial k_y} j + \frac{\partial}{\partial k_z} k \right) \left(\frac{\partial}{\partial k_x} i + \frac{\partial}{\partial k_y} j + \frac{\partial}{\partial k_z} k \right)$$

$$= \frac{\partial^2}{\partial k_x^2} ii + \frac{\partial^2}{\partial k_x \, \partial k_y} ij + \quad \text{etc.}$$

The effective mass may also be expressed in matrix notation as

$$\frac{1}{m_{ij}} = \frac{1}{\hbar^2} \frac{\partial^2 E(k)}{\partial k_i \, \partial k_j} \tag{2.185a}$$

PROBLEM

Show that for a free particle

$$E = \frac{k_x^2 \hbar^2}{2m}$$

and that

$$m^* = m \tag{2.186}$$

2.8 SYSTEMS NOT IN EIGENSTATES AND THE UNCERTAINTY PRINCIPLE

Suppose that a system in an eigenstate ψ_{Ak} corresponding to the observable quantity A i.e.,

$$\mathbf{A}\psi_{Ak} = A_k \psi_{Ak} \tag{2.187}$$

According to the above postulate this means that every measurement of the property yields the same result, namely A_k, so that in principle we can have precise knowledge of **A**. This is consistent with the postulate (5) concerning the expected value of A, for

$$\langle A \rangle = \int \psi_{Ak}^* \mathbf{A} \psi_{Ak} \, d\tau = A_k \qquad (2.188)$$

since the eigenfunctions form an orthonormal set. Now let us retain the system in the state ψ_{Ak} and conduct a series of measurements on some property B. We assume that ψ_{Ak} is not an eigenfunction of **B**, that is insofar as a property B is concerned the system is not in an eigenstate. According to postulate (3), the only values of B we observe, for any particular measurement, are the eigenvalues of **B**, namely B_i, given by

$$\mathbf{B}\psi_{Bi} = B_i \psi_{Bi} \qquad (2.189)$$

where ψ_{Bi} is an eigenfunction of **B**. However, we have assumed that the system is not in an eigenstate with reference to the physical observable B and we ask what values of B are observed on making successive measurements. According to postulate 5 the expected value of the property B when the system is in a state ψ_{A_k} is just

$$\langle B \rangle = \int \psi_{Ak}^* \mathbf{B} \psi_{Ak} \, d\tau \qquad (2.190)$$

Since ψ_{Bi} are the eigenfunctions of **B**, they constitute an orthogonal set which we assume to be complete so that we can expand ψ_{Ak} in terms of ψ_{Bi}:

$$\psi_{Ak} = \sum_i C_{ki} \psi_{Bi} \qquad (2.191)$$

On substituting (2.191) into (2.190) we have

$$\begin{aligned}
\langle B \rangle &= \int \left(\sum_i C_{kj}^* \psi_{Bj}^* \right) \mathbf{B} \left(\sum_i C_{ki} \psi_{Bi} \right) dV \\
&= \sum_i B_i |C_{ki}|^2 \qquad (2.192)
\end{aligned}$$

It is natural to interpret $|C_{ki}|^2$ as the probability that the value B_i is observed where the system is in an eigenstate ψ_{Ak} so that (2.192) is just the expression for the average value of B_i. We see that the observable B will be distributed over all values of B_i, each value occurring in a series of measurements with probability $|C_{ki}|^2$. Thus precise knowledge of B in principle is not possible and we can only know B in the statistical sense. In order for properties A and B to be simultaneous constants, the eigenfunctions of **A** must be those of **B** or, in view of Theorem III in Chapter 1, **A** and **B** must commute:

$$[\mathbf{A}, \mathbf{B}] = 0 \tag{2.193}$$

If this is not the case then precise knowledge of A rules out precise knowledge of B. We have already encountered one such case with the position and momentum of a wave packet, which is consistent with the fact that x and $\mathbf{p}_x$ do not commute.

The above considerations concerning the indeterminancy of noncommuting variables can be put on a more quantitative basis. We define the indeterminancy of the observables A and B as the square root of the variances. The latter are given by

$$(\Delta A)^2 = \sum_i (A_i - \langle A \rangle)^2 |a_i|^2 = \langle A^2 \rangle - \langle A \rangle^2 \tag{2.194}$$

$$(\Delta B)^2 = \sum_k (B_k - \langle B \rangle)^2 |b_k|^2 = \langle B^2 \rangle - \langle B \rangle^2 \tag{2.195}$$

where $|a_i|^2$ and $|b_k|^2$ are the probabilities of observing A_i and B_k. We assume that **A** and **B** do not commute so that

$$[\mathbf{A}, \mathbf{B}] = i\mathbf{C} \qquad \mathbf{C} \neq 0 \tag{2.196}$$

Commutators of this form have already been encountered in the instances of momentum and position coordinates as well as the angular momentum components.

It is convenient to introduce the operators

$$\begin{aligned} \mathbf{A}' &= \mathbf{A} - \langle A \rangle \\ \mathbf{B}' &= \mathbf{B} - \langle B \rangle \end{aligned} \tag{2.197}$$

so that

$$\begin{aligned} \langle A' \rangle &= 0 \\ \langle B' \rangle &= 0 \end{aligned} \tag{2.198}$$

and therefore

$$\begin{aligned} (\Delta A')^2 &= (\Delta A)^2 = \langle A'^2 \rangle \\ (\Delta B')^2 &= (\Delta B)^2 = \langle B'^2 \rangle \end{aligned} \tag{2.199}$$

Moreover it is easily shown

$$[\mathbf{A}', \mathbf{B}'] = i\mathbf{C} \tag{2.200}$$

We define a new operator G:

$$\mathbf{G} = \mathbf{A'} + \alpha \mathbf{B'} + i\beta \mathbf{B'} \qquad (2.201)$$

where α and β are real numbers which may be arbitrarily assigned. Now on making use of the Hermitian properties of $\mathbf{A'}$ and $\mathbf{B'}$ and the commutator relationships (2.200) we find that

$$(G\psi, G\psi) = \langle A'\rangle^2 + (\alpha^2 + \beta^2)\langle B'^2\rangle + \alpha\langle E\rangle + \beta\langle C\rangle \geqslant 0 \qquad (2.202)$$

where

$$\langle E\rangle = \langle A'B' + B'A'\rangle \qquad (2.203)$$

The expression (2.202) may be put into the form

$$\langle A'^2\rangle + \langle B'^2\rangle\left(\alpha + \frac{1}{2}\frac{\langle E\rangle}{\langle B'^2\rangle}\right)^2 + \langle B'^2\rangle\left(\beta + \frac{1}{2}\frac{\langle C\rangle}{\langle B'^2\rangle}\right)^2$$
$$- \frac{1}{4}\frac{\langle E\rangle^2}{\langle B'^2\rangle} - \frac{1}{4}\frac{\langle C\rangle^2}{\langle B'^2\rangle} \geqslant 0 \qquad (2.204)$$

If we now choose α and β so that the terms in the squared brackets vanish then we have

$$\langle A'^2\rangle\langle B'^2\rangle \geqslant \left(\frac{\langle C\rangle}{2}\right)^2 + \left(\frac{\langle E'\rangle}{2}\right)^2 \geqslant \left(\frac{\langle C\rangle}{2}\right)^2 \qquad (2.205)$$

or on introducing (2.199)

$$|\Delta A|\,|\Delta B| \geqslant \left|\frac{\langle C\rangle}{2}\right| \qquad (2.206)$$

The last result is the well-known Heisenberg indeterminancy principle. In the instance, for example, of position and momentum we have seen that $c = \hbar$ so that

$$|\Delta x|\,|\Delta p| \geqslant \left|\frac{\hbar}{2}\right| \qquad (2.207)$$

PROBLEM

The energy operator is $i\hbar(\partial/\partial t)$. Show that

$$|\Delta t|\,|\Delta E| \geqslant \frac{\hbar}{2} \qquad (2.208)$$

This problem establishes a relationship between the time in a state E and the indeterminancy in E.

We conclude therefore that the observables associated with noncommuting variables cannot be determined with arbitrary precision. The more carefully the system is prepared to determine one such observable the greater will be the indeterminancy in the other, as indicated by (2.206).

2.9 *SPIN AND ANGULAR MOMENTUM*

We have had occasion to mention the orbital angular momentum operator **L** in a previous section. However, in addition to **L** there is a great deal of experimental and theoretical evidence that an electron is also characterized by an intrinsic *spin angular momentum, S*. Hence, a complete description of a system must include the electron spin. Experimental evidence indicates that the projection of S onto an axis, say in the z direction, can have only one of two values, namely, $\hbar/2$ or $-\hbar/2$. It follows from postulate (3), corresponding to the spin S, there must be a spin operator **S** given by

$$\mathbf{S} = \mathbf{S}_x \bar{i} + \mathbf{S}_y \bar{j} + \mathbf{S}_z \bar{k} \tag{2.209}$$

Since the projection of the spin onto an axis has a constant value, the state function including the spin must be an eigenfunction of $\mathbf{S}_z$ so that

$$\mathbf{S}_z \psi(x, y, z, m_s) = m_s \psi(x, y, z, m_s) \qquad m_s = \pm\frac{\hbar}{2} \tag{2.210}$$

Moreover, from the fact that S_z is a constant of motion it follows from (2.180) that $\mathbf{S}_z$ and **H** commute and, since the direction associated with $\mathbf{S}_z$ is arbitrary, that **S** and **H** commute. This last result suggests that the state function can be separated into the product of two other functions, $\psi(x, y, z)$ and $\chi(m_s)$, so that **H** acts only on the spatial function and **S** on the spin function $\chi(m_s)$:

$$\psi(x, y, z, m_s) = \psi(x, y, z)\chi^{\pm}(m_s) \tag{2.211}$$

We denote by χ^+ the spin state corresponding $s = \hbar/2$ along the positive z direction, and χ^- for the oppositely directed state:

$$\mathbf{S}_z \chi^+ = \frac{\hbar}{2}\chi^+$$

$$\mathbf{S}_z \chi^- = -\frac{\hbar}{2}\chi^- \tag{2.212}$$

These spin functions must, from theorem II, be orthogonal. It is easily seen that an orthonormal matrix representation is given by

$$\chi^+ = \begin{pmatrix} 1 \\ 0 \end{pmatrix}, \qquad \chi^- = \begin{pmatrix} 0 \\ 1 \end{pmatrix} \tag{2.213}$$

Since χ^+ and χ^- can assume only discrete values, the scalar product corresponds to a bra-ket product (section 1.5) of the above matrices:

$$(\chi^+, \chi^-) = \langle \chi^+ \mid \chi^- \rangle = (1, 0)\begin{pmatrix} 0 \\ 1 \end{pmatrix} = 0 \tag{2.214}$$

The functions χ^+ and χ^- form a complete set, and a spin function χ corresponding to an arbitrarily oriented spin state may be expressed as

$$\chi = C_1 \chi^+ + C_2 \chi^- = \begin{pmatrix} C_1 \\ C_2 \end{pmatrix} \tag{2.215}$$

PROBLEM

Show that

$$\mathbf{S}_z = \begin{pmatrix} \tfrac{1}{2} & 0 \\ 0 & \tfrac{1}{2} \end{pmatrix} \hbar$$

and evaluate $\langle \chi | S_z | \chi \rangle$.

Show that $|C_1|^2$ is the probability of measuring $\hbar/2$ and $|C_2|^2$ and that of measuring $-\hbar/2$:

Rather than pursue spin as an isolated topic we shall now sketch a more general theory of angular momentum. We designate a general angular momentum operator by $\mathbf{J}$; thus $\mathbf{J}$ may correspond to $\mathbf{L}_x$, $\mathbf{L}$, $\mathbf{S}$ or $\mathbf{L} + \mathbf{S}$, and so forth. Of the various possibilities, we are particularly interested in a J which is a constant of motion, since a system is often characterized by the values assumed by its constants of motion. According to (2.180) this means that $\mathbf{J}$ and $\mathbf{H}$ will commute and, hence according to theorem III, $\mathbf{H}$ and $\mathbf{J}$ must have a common set of eigenfunctions. If we find the matrix representation of the commuting operators in terms of this set of common eigenfunctions, then the resulting matrices will be diagonal, according to (1.97), with elements which are the various possible constants of motion.

We next inquire into the factors which influence the commutivity of **J** with **H**. One criteria for commutivity is immediately evident, namely that **H** must be invariant under a similarity transformation with **J**:

$$\mathbf{JH} = \mathbf{HJ}$$

i.e.

$$\mathbf{JHJ}^{-1} = \mathbf{J}^{-1}\mathbf{HJ} = \mathbf{H} \tag{2.216}$$

However, there is a more basic implication to commutivity for we have shown (section 1.11) that corresponding to any Hermitian operator **J** there is a unitary operator $e^{i\bar{a}\cdot\mathbf{J}}$, and if the Hermitian operator commutes with a second operator, say **H**, then **H** is invariant under the unitary transformation, i.e.,

$$[\mathbf{J}, \mathbf{H}] = 0 \tag{2.217}$$

then from (1.107) we have

$$\bar{e}^{i\bar{a}\cdot\mathbf{J}}\mathbf{H}e^{i\bar{a}\cdot\mathbf{J}} = \mathbf{H} \tag{2.218}$$

or

$$e^{i\bar{a}\cdot\mathbf{J}}\mathbf{H} = \mathbf{H}e^{i\bar{a}\cdot\mathbf{J}} \tag{2.219}$$

In order to appreciate the significance of (2.218), we consider the effect of rotating a set of coordinates about an arbitrarily oriented axis passing through the origin. Let the unit vector along the axis of rotation be denoted by $\bar{e}$, and the positive direction of rotation given by the usual right-handed screw convention. Consider a small rotation $d\theta$, then for an arbitrary function $f(r)$

$$f(r_0 + dr) = f(r_0) + d\bar{r}\cdot\nabla f(r) \tag{2.220}$$

where the change in the position vector $\bar{r}$ is

$$d\bar{r} = d\theta\cdot\bar{e} \times \bar{r} \tag{2.221}$$

or

$$df(r) = (d\theta\bar{e} \times \bar{r})\cdot\nabla f(r) = d\bar{\theta}\cdot\bar{r} \times \nabla f(r) \tag{2.222}$$

PROBLEM

ow by integrating (2.221) that for a finite rotation θ

$$\vec{r}' = (e^{\bar{\theta} \times})\vec{r} \tag{2.222a}$$

where $\bar{\theta} = \theta\bar{e}$.

Introducing from (2.12)

$$\mathbf{L} = -i\hbar\vec{r} \times \nabla \tag{2.223}$$

and taking the integral of the above we have the rotation operator:

$$f(r') = e^{-(i/\hbar)\bar{\theta}\cdot\mathbf{L}}f(r) = \mathbf{U}_L f(r) \tag{2.224}$$

If we identify $\bar{a} = \bar{\theta}/\hbar$ we see that the unitary operator in (2.218) represents a rotation in space, and we conclude that if L is a constant of motion then $\mathbf{H}$ is invariant under $\mathbf{U}_L^{-1}\mathbf{H}\mathbf{U}_L$, i.e., the similarity transformation with U. The converse may also be readily established. We may similarly introduce a rotation in spin space defined by the unitary operator

$$\mathbf{U}_s = e^{-(i/\hbar)\bar{\theta}\cdot\mathbf{S}} \tag{2.225}$$

where $\mathbf{S}$ is a *spin operator*. Consequently if

$$\mathbf{J} = \mathbf{L} + \mathbf{S} \tag{2.226}$$

we have the more general rotation operator

$$\mathbf{U}_J = e^{-(i/\hbar)\theta\cdot(\mathbf{L}+\mathbf{S})} = e^{-(i/\hbar)\bar{\theta}\cdot\mathbf{J}} \tag{2.227}$$

and if

$$[\mathbf{H}, \mathbf{J}] = 0$$

then

$$\mathbf{U}_J^{-1}\mathbf{H}\mathbf{U}_J = \mathbf{H} \tag{2.228}$$

We now consider the effect of the rotation operator $\mathbf{U}_J$ on an arbitrary vector operator $\mathbf{A}$ given by

$$\mathbf{A} = A_x\vec{\imath} + A_y\vec{\jmath} + A_z\vec{k} \tag{2.229}$$

The requirement is placed on **A** that the effect of $\mathbf{U}_J^{-1}\mathbf{A}\mathbf{U}_J$ is to rotate **A** through an angle $\bar{\theta} = \theta\bar{e}$. Introducing the expression for the rotation of a vector (2.222a) we have

$$\mathbf{U}_J\mathbf{A}\mathbf{U}_J^{-1} = (e^{\bar{\theta}\times})\mathbf{A} \tag{2.230}$$

This key relationship together with (2.218) provides much of the foundation for angular momentum theory. Equation (2.218) states that if **J** is a constant of motion then **H** is invariant under a similarity transformation with $\mathbf{U}_J$, while (2.230) states that a vector operator **A** is merely rotated in space under the same similarity transformation. This last statement is in effect a definition of a vector operator.

The implications of (2.230) are most readily seen by considering an infinitesimally small rotation $d\bar{\theta}$. On expanding the exponential operators according to (1.9), and neglecting the higher order infinitesimals we find

$$(1 + i\,d\bar{\theta}\cdot\mathbf{J})\mathbf{A}(1 - i\,d\bar{\theta}\mathbf{J}) = \mathbf{A} + d\bar{\theta}\times\mathbf{A} \tag{2.231}$$

or on simplifying and neglecting the second order infinitesimal

$$i\,d\bar{\theta}\cdot\mathbf{J}\mathbf{A} - i\mathbf{A}\,d\bar{\theta}\cdot\mathbf{J} = d\bar{\theta}\times\mathbf{A} \tag{2.232}$$

This last result clearly establishes the commutivity relationships between **J** and **A**. If we require that **J** itself be a vector operator, then (2.232) must also hold when **A** is replaced by **J**. This replacement is assumed in what follows. On expressing the vectors in terms of their components, expanding, and equating terms with the same components of $d\theta$ and unit vectors, for a typical term

$$\frac{i}{\hbar}[\mathbf{J}_x\mathbf{J}_y - \mathbf{J}_y\mathbf{J}_x]\,d\theta_x\bar{j} = -\mathbf{J}_z\,d\theta\bar{j} \tag{2.233}$$

we obtain the nine relationships

$$
\begin{array}{lll}
[\mathbf{J}_x, \mathbf{J}_x] = 0 & [\mathbf{J}_y, \mathbf{J}_x] = -i\hbar\mathbf{J}_z & [\mathbf{J}_z, \mathbf{J}_x] = i\hbar\mathbf{J}_y \\
[\mathbf{J}_x, \mathbf{J}_y] = i\hbar\mathbf{J}_z & [\mathbf{J}_y, \mathbf{J}_y] = 0 & [\mathbf{J}_z, \mathbf{J}_y] = -i\hbar\mathbf{J}_x \\
[\mathbf{J}_y, \mathbf{J}_z] = -i\hbar\mathbf{J}_y & [\mathbf{J}_y, \mathbf{J}_z] = i\hbar\mathbf{J}_x & [\mathbf{J}_z, \mathbf{J}_z] = 0
\end{array} \tag{2.234}
$$

These commutator relationships may be conveniently summarized by

$$\mathbf{J}\times\mathbf{J} = i\hbar\mathbf{J} \tag{2.235}$$

Since **J** may be specialized to **S** or **L**, these vector operators also obey the same commutator relationships:

$$\mathbf{L} \times \mathbf{L} = i\hbar\mathbf{L}$$
$$\mathbf{S} \times \mathbf{S} = i\hbar\mathbf{S}$$

(2.236)

If **J** is a constant of motion we also may add to our list the relationships

$$[\mathbf{H}, \mathbf{J}] = 0 \qquad [\mathbf{H}, \mathbf{J}^2] = 0$$

(2.237)

In discussing the properties of **J** it is convenient to introduce the operators

$$\mathbf{J}_+ = \mathbf{J}_x + i\mathbf{J}_y \qquad \mathbf{J}_- = \mathbf{J}_x - i\mathbf{J}_y$$

(2.238)

We note that these operators are not Hermitian. Using (2.234) we can easily establish the following results

$$[\mathbf{J}_+, \mathbf{J}_-] = 2\hbar\mathbf{J}_z$$
$$[\mathbf{J}_-, \mathbf{J}_z] = \hbar\mathbf{J}_-$$
$$[\mathbf{J}_+, \mathbf{J}_z] = -\hbar\mathbf{J}_+$$
$$\mathbf{J}_\pm \mathbf{J}_\mp = \mathbf{J}^2 - \mathbf{J}_z^2 \pm \hbar\mathbf{J}_z$$
$$[\mathbf{J}^2, \mathbf{J}_\pm] = 0$$

(2.239)

2.10 EIGENVALUES OF COMMUTING OPERATORS

In the theory of atomic spectra the properties of the commuting set of operators **H**, $\mathbf{J}^2$, and $\mathbf{J}_z$ play an important role. In this section we shall establish some important results concerning the eigenvalues of these operators.

In preparation for our work it is helpful to recall some of the results obtained for the single electron in the central field neglecting spin effects. We remark that the eigenvalues of **J**, **L**, and $\mathbf{L}_z$ for a single electron are usually designated by j, l, m. The eigenvalues for **H** have been shown to be given by (2.137a). It is also clear that $[\mathbf{H}, \mathbf{L}] = 0$, since **H** is spherically symmetrical and therefore invariant under a rotation of coordinates. We have not as yet determined the eigenvalues of the orbital angular-momentum operators. These, however, are easily derived by writing the operators $\mathbf{L}^2$ and $\mathbf{L}_z$ in spherical coordinates:

$$\mathbf{L}^2 = -\hbar^2\left[\frac{1}{\sin\theta}\frac{\partial}{\partial\theta}\left(\sin\theta\frac{\partial}{\partial\theta}\right) + \frac{1}{\sin^2\theta}\frac{\partial^2}{\partial\phi^2}\right]$$
$$\mathbf{L}_z = -\hbar i\frac{\partial}{\partial\phi}$$

(2.240)

We have already seen that the spherical harmonics given by (2.114) satisfy equation (2.115b) so that in terms of $\mathbf{L}^2$

$$\mathbf{L}^2 Y_{l,m} = \lambda \hbar^2 Y_{l,m} \tag{2.241}$$

It will also be recalled that $Y_{l,m}$ will be an acceptable wave function provided that $\lambda = l(l + 1)$ where l may take on the values $0, 1, 2, \ldots, n - 1$. We conclude, therefore, that the orbital angular momentum of an electron is a constant of motion which may assume values given by

$$L = \sqrt{l(l + 1)}\,\hbar \tag{2.242}$$

The eigenvalues corresponding to $\mathbf{L}_z$ may be obtained by noting that

$$Y_{l,m}(\theta, \phi) = Ne^{im\phi} P_l^{|m|}(\cos\theta) \tag{2.243}$$

(where N is a normalizing constant) is also an eigenfunction of $\mathbf{L}_z$ since on operating on the spherical harmonic with $\mathbf{L}_z$ we find that

$$\mathbf{L}_z Y_{l,m} = m\hbar Y_{l,m} \tag{2.244}$$

so that L_z has the value $m\hbar$, where according to (2.138) $|m| \leqslant l$.

These special results will now be shown to hold quite generally. Suppose that $\phi(\lambda m)$ is a set of normalized eigenfunctions of both $\mathbf{J}^2$ and $\mathbf{J}_z$ with eigenvalues $\lambda \hbar^2$ and $m\hbar$:

$$\begin{aligned} \mathbf{J}^2 \phi(\lambda m) &= \lambda \hbar^2 \phi(\lambda m) \\ \mathbf{J}_z \phi(\lambda m) &= m\hbar \phi(\lambda m) \end{aligned} \tag{2.245}$$

We next establish the key inequality $\lambda \geqslant m^2$ for we have from the Hermitian properties of the operators

$$\begin{aligned} (\phi, \mathbf{J}^2 \phi) &= (\phi, \mathbf{J}_x^2 \phi) + (\phi, \mathbf{J}_y^2 \phi) + (\phi, J_z^2 \phi) \\ &= (\mathbf{J}_x \phi, \mathbf{J}_x \phi) + (\mathbf{J}_x \phi, \mathbf{J}_y \phi) + (\mathbf{J}_z \phi, \mathbf{J}_z \phi) \\ &\geqslant (\mathbf{J}_z \phi, \mathbf{J}_z \phi) \end{aligned} \tag{2.246}$$

On introducing (2.245) we have

$$\lambda \geqslant m^2 \tag{2.247}$$

We can now determine the eigenvalues using the commutator relationships (2.234). On applying $\mathbf{J}_+$ there results, in Dirac notation,

$$\mathbf{J}_z \mathbf{J}_+ |\lambda m\rangle = \mathbf{J}_+ \mathbf{J}_z + \hbar \mathbf{J}_+ |\lambda m\rangle = \hbar(m + 1) \mathbf{J}_+ |\lambda m\rangle$$

and
$$\tag{2.248}$$

$$\mathbf{J}^2 \mathbf{J}_+ |\lambda m\rangle = \mathbf{J}_+ \mathbf{J}^2 |\lambda m\rangle = \mathbf{J}_+ \lambda \hbar^2 |\lambda m\rangle$$

We conclude that $\mathbf{J}_+|\lambda_1 m\rangle$ is an eigenfunction of $\mathbf{J}_z$ with an eigenvalue increased by one, and that this function is also an eigenvalue of $\mathbf{J}^2$ but with the same eigenvalue λ. If $\mathbf{J}_+$ is applied successively we can generate a set of eigenfunctions with successively greater eigenvalues m. But m is bounded by λ, which is the same for all members of the set, so that eventually we must come to an eigenfunction with the greatest $m = j$ and the series must then terminate, i.e.,

$$\mathbf{J}_+|\lambda j\rangle = 0 \qquad (2.249)$$

If we now successively apply $\mathbf{J}_-$ to $|\lambda j\rangle$ we can generate a series of eigenfunctions with decreasing m:

$$\mathbf{J}_z\mathbf{J}_-|\lambda j\rangle = \mathbf{J}_-\mathbf{J}_z - \hbar\mathbf{J}_-|\lambda j\rangle = \hbar(j-1)\mathbf{J}_-|\lambda m\rangle \qquad (2.250)$$

In this way we generate eigenfunctions with eigenvalues $j, j-1, j-z, \ldots$ but with the same eigenvalue λ. Since m is also bounded from below we must come to an eigenfunction with at least $m = j'$ such that

$$\mathbf{J}_-|\lambda j'\rangle = 0 \qquad (2.251)$$

From (2.239) we also find that

$$\begin{aligned}
\mathbf{J}_-\mathbf{J}_+|\lambda j\rangle &= 0 = (\lambda - j^2 - j)\hbar^2|\lambda j\rangle \\
\mathbf{J}_+\mathbf{J}_-|\lambda j'\rangle &= 0 = (\lambda - j'^2 + j')\hbar^2|\lambda j'\rangle
\end{aligned} \qquad (2.252)$$

and therefore

$$\lambda = j(j+1) = j'(j'-1) \qquad (2.253)$$

which requires that $j' = -j$. Since $j - j'$ must equal an integer n, it follows that j must be of the form $n/2$.

Our task of determining the eigenvalues of $\mathbf{J}^2$ and $\mathbf{J}_z$ is complete. We have in summary

$$\begin{aligned}
j &= 0, \tfrac{1}{2}, 1, \tfrac{3}{2} \\
\lambda &= j(j+1)
\end{aligned} \qquad (2.254)$$

and corresponding to each j there are $2j + 1$ values of m

$$m = -j, -j+1, \ldots, j-1, j \qquad (2.255)$$

We observe that both integral and half integral values of m are allowed, while the solution to the wave equation (2.112), neglecting spin, permitted only integral values in order that the wave function be single-valued.

The significance of half integral j may be seen by rotating the coordinate system through an angle of 2π about the z axis. According to (2.227) the eigenfunction then becomes

$$e^{-(2\pi i/\hbar)\cdot J_z}|jm\rangle$$

If the exponential operator is expanded and the relationship $J_z|jm\rangle = m\hbar|jm\rangle$ is introduced, we find that the eigenfunction is now $e^{-2\pi mi}|jm\rangle$. Clearly if m is an integer then the eigenfunction is unaltered by the rotation and hence is single-valued. Such functions are acceptable state functions if they satisfy the wave equations. However, if m is a half integral the rotation reverses the sign of the eigenfunction. This implies that corresponding to each point of space the function has two values which differ only in sign. However, such functions need not be discarded since they can be made single-valued by introducing an additional coordinate ξ to specify the eigenfunction which may now be written in coordinate notation as $\psi(x, y, z, \xi)$. We require that this additional coordinate can assume only two values one of which, say ξ_+, corresponds to the positive value of ψ, while the other point ξ_- corresponds to the negative value of ψ. The physical basis of this mathematical device is apparent from our discussion of spins; the function $\psi(x, y, z, \xi_+)$ corresponds to a system with the spin directed along the positive z-direction while $\psi(x, y, z, \xi_-)$ designates a state with the oppositely directed spin. Thus half integral values of m are a consequence of electron spin. Since the spin coordinates do not appear in the Hamiltonian operator we can represent the complete state function as $\psi(x, y, z)\chi(\xi)$, where $\chi(\xi)$ is the spin dependent part already discussed, and $\psi(x, y, z)$ is a function satisfying the wave equation. The quantum number m associated with $\psi(x, y, z)$ will be designated by m_l, and is an integer, while m associated with $\chi(\xi)$ is designated by m_s and has, as we have seen, the values $\pm\frac{1}{2}$.

We have in summary:

$$\mathbf{J}_z\psi(x, y, z) = m_l\hbar\psi(x, y, z) \qquad m_l = 0, \pm 1, \pm 2, \ldots$$

$$\mathbf{S}_z\chi^+ = \frac{\hbar}{2}\chi^+ \qquad \text{where } \chi^+ = \chi(\tfrac{1}{2})$$

$$\mathbf{S}_z\chi^- = -\frac{\hbar}{2}\chi^- \qquad \text{where } \chi^- = \chi(-\tfrac{1}{2})$$

$$\mathbf{J}_z\psi\chi^\pm = (\mathbf{L}_z + \mathbf{S}_z)\psi\chi^\pm = (m_l \pm \tfrac{1}{2})\hbar\psi\chi^\pm$$

$$= m\hbar\psi\chi^\pm$$

(2.256)

2.11 *EVALUATION OF MOMENTUM OPERATORS*

The effect of $\mathbf{J}_+$ and $\mathbf{J}_-$ on the orthonormal set $\phi(jm)$ may be determined from the previously established results (2.248):

$$\mathbf{J}_+ = \mathbf{J}_-^\dagger \quad \text{(adjoint relationship)}$$
$$\mathbf{J}_+\phi(jm) = l_m\phi(j, m + 1) \qquad (2.257)$$
$$\mathbf{J}_-\phi(jm) = k_m\phi(j, m - 1)$$

The coefficients l_m and k_m may be related since on taking the scalar product we have

$$(\phi(j, m + 1), \mathbf{J}_+\phi(j, m)) = l_m$$
$$= (\mathbf{J}_-\phi(j, m + 1), \phi(j, m)) = k_{m+1}^* \quad (2.258)$$

We also have

$$\mathbf{J}_-\mathbf{J}_+\phi(j, m) = k_{m+1}l_m\phi(j, m) = |l_m|^2\phi(j, m) \qquad (2.259)$$

but from (2.239)

$$= [j(j + 1) - m^2 - m]\hbar^2\phi(j, m)$$
$$= [(j - m)(j + m + 1)]\hbar^2\phi(j, m)$$

$$\therefore \ l_m = \sqrt{(j - m)(j + m + 1)}\,\hbar$$
$$k_m = \sqrt{(j + m)(j - m + 1)}\,\hbar \qquad (2.260)$$

so that

$$\mathbf{J}_+\phi(j, m) = \sqrt{(j - m)(j + m + 1)}\,\hbar\phi(j, m + 1)$$
$$\mathbf{J}_-\phi(j, m) = \sqrt{(j + m)(j - m + 1)}\,\hbar\phi(j, m - 1) \qquad (2.261)$$

We note also that

$$\mathbf{J}_x = \tfrac{1}{2}(\mathbf{J}_- + \mathbf{J}_+)$$
$$\mathbf{J}_y = \frac{i}{2}(\mathbf{J}_- - \mathbf{J}_+) \qquad (2.262)$$

In the special case $j = \frac{1}{2}$, then $\mathbf{J} = \mathbf{S}$, and we find from (2.245), (2.262), and (2.261)

$$\mathbf{S}_x \chi^\pm = \frac{\hbar}{2} \chi^\mp$$

$$\mathbf{S}_y \chi^\pm = \pm \frac{i\hbar}{2} \chi^\mp$$

$$\mathbf{S}_z \chi^\pm = \pm \frac{\hbar}{2} \chi^\pm$$

$$\mathbf{S}^2 \chi^\pm = \frac{1}{2}(\frac{1}{2} + 1)\hbar^2 \chi^\pm = \frac{3}{4}\hbar^2 \chi^\pm$$

(2.263)

If we regard χ^+ and χ^- as orthonormal functions, then the matrix representation of $\mathbf{S}$ is easily shown to be

$$\mathbf{S}_x = \begin{pmatrix} 0 & \frac{\hbar}{2} \\ \frac{\hbar}{2} & 0 \end{pmatrix} \qquad \mathbf{S}_y = \begin{pmatrix} 0 & \frac{-i\hbar}{2} \\ \frac{i\hbar}{2} & 0 \end{pmatrix} \qquad \mathbf{S}_z = \begin{pmatrix} \frac{1}{2} & 0 \\ 0 & -\frac{1}{2} \end{pmatrix} \hbar \quad (2.264)$$

The Pauli spin matrices are often used and are defined by $\boldsymbol{\sigma} = (2/\hbar)\mathbf{S}$:

$$\sigma_x = \begin{pmatrix} 0 & 1 \\ 1 & 0 \end{pmatrix} \qquad \sigma_y = \begin{pmatrix} 0 & -i \\ i & 0 \end{pmatrix} \qquad \sigma_z = \begin{pmatrix} 1 & 0 \\ 0 & -1 \end{pmatrix} \quad (2.265)$$

We note that the spin operator is Hermitian.

2.12 FURTHER ASPECTS OF THE HARMONIC OSCILLATOR

The Hamiltonian operator of the harmonic oscillator in generalized coordinates (Appendix 1) is given by

$$\mathbf{H} = \frac{1}{2} \left(\frac{\mathbf{p}^2}{m} + kq^2 \right) \quad (2.266)$$

On setting

$$k = \omega^2$$

and choosing our units such that

$$\hbar = m = 1$$

then we can write, on factoring the Hamiltonian,

$$\mathbf{H} = \frac{1}{2}(\mathbf{p}^2 + \omega^2 q^2) = \left(\frac{\mathbf{p} + i\omega q}{\sqrt{2}}\right)\left(\frac{\mathbf{p} - i\omega q}{\sqrt{2}}\right) - \frac{\omega}{2} \qquad (2.267)$$

since $[q, \mathbf{p}] = i$.

These last expressions may be put into a more convenient form by means of the *annihilation* and *creation operators* $\mathbf{a}$ and $\mathbf{a}^\dagger$ defined by

$$\mathbf{a} = \frac{\omega q + i\mathbf{p}}{(2\omega)^{1/2}} \qquad (2.268)$$

$$\mathbf{a}^\dagger = \frac{\omega q - i\mathbf{p}}{(2\omega)^{1/2}} \qquad (2.269)$$

We note that $\mathbf{a}^\dagger$ is the adjoint of $\mathbf{a}$.

On introducing (2.268) and (2.269) into (2.267) we have

$$\mathbf{H} = \omega(\mathbf{a}^\dagger\mathbf{a} + \tfrac{1}{2}) \qquad (2.270)$$

It is easy to show that

$$[\mathbf{a}, \mathbf{a}] = [\mathbf{a}^\dagger, \mathbf{a}^\dagger] = 0 \qquad (2.271)$$

and

$$[\mathbf{a}, \mathbf{a}^\dagger] = 1 \qquad (2.272)$$

so that

$$[\mathbf{H}, \mathbf{a}^\dagger] = \omega\mathbf{a}^\dagger \qquad (2.273)$$

$$[\mathbf{H}, \mathbf{a}] = -\omega\mathbf{a} \qquad (2.274)$$

We can now show that the eigenvalues E, of $\mathbf{H}$ cannot be less than $\omega/2$, since if ψ is the corresponding eigenfunction

$$(\psi, \mathbf{a}^\dagger\mathbf{a}\psi) = (\mathbf{a}\psi, \mathbf{a}\psi) \geqslant 0$$

but we also have

$$(\psi, \mathbf{a}^\dagger\mathbf{a}\psi) = \left(\psi, \left(\frac{E}{\omega} - \frac{1}{2}\right)\psi\right) = \frac{E}{\omega} - \frac{1}{2} \geqslant 0$$

or

$$\qquad (2.275)$$

$$E \geqslant \frac{\omega}{2}$$

Now it is easy to show that

$$\mathbf{H}\mathbf{a}\psi = (E - \omega)\mathbf{a}\psi \qquad (2.276)$$

$$\mathbf{H}\mathbf{a}^{\dagger}\psi = (E + \omega)\mathbf{a}^{\dagger}\psi \qquad (2.277)$$

Hence $\mathbf{a}\psi$ and $\mathbf{a}^{\dagger}\psi$ are eigenfunctions of $\mathbf{H}$. The latter operator "creates" a unit of energy of magnitude ω, while the former annihilates a similar unit of energy. The eigenvalues must have the values

$$E = n\omega + \frac{\omega}{2} \qquad n = 0, 1, 2, \ldots$$

The annihilation and creation operators play an important part in the quantum theory of fields. Applications of quantum field theory to electrical and magnetic properties of solids is discussed by Kittel (2b).

PROBLEMS FOR CHAPTER 2

1. Which of the following dynamic properties are associated with a Hermitian operator?
   a. total energy
   b. position
   c. potential energy
   d. $\vec{r} \cdot \vec{p}$, where $\vec{p}$ is the linear momentum, and $\vec{r}$ a position vector
   e. electron spin

2. Calculate $\langle L^2 \rangle$ and $\langle L_z \rangle$ for the hydrogen wave function ψ_{100} and ψ_{200}. Repeat the calculation for ψ_{210}.

3. Normalize the three-dimensional $\psi(k)$ given by equation (2.159).

4. Verify equations (2.182) and (2.183).

5. What is the effect on the wave functions and energy levels if the potential is increased by the same amount everywhere?

6. Show that the unitary operator

$$\mathbf{U} = \exp\frac{i}{\hbar}\,\bar{a}\cdot\mathbf{p}$$

where

$$\mathbf{p} = -i\hbar\nabla$$

represents translation in space by an amount $\bar{a}$.

   Hint: Consider the transformation

$$\mathbf{U}^{-1}\vec{r}\mathbf{U}$$

7. Two formulations of the wave mechanics are said to be equivalent if the operators **A** in one formulation have the same eigenvalues as **B** in the other and if the scalar products are equal, i.e.,

$$(\phi_A, \mathbf{A}\phi_A) = (\phi_B, \mathbf{B}\phi_B)$$

Show that if **U** is a unitary operator and **A** is an operator in the Schrödinger formulation, that an equivalent formulation is given by

$$\mathbf{B} = \mathbf{U}\mathbf{A}\mathbf{U}^{-1}$$
$$\phi_B = \mathbf{U}\phi_A$$

If we choose

$$\mathbf{U} = e^{i(\mathbf{H}t/\hbar)}$$

then the equivalent representation is referred to as the Heisenberg representation. Show that for a simple harmonic oscillator the Heisenberg operators corresponding to **x** and $\mathbf{p}_x$ are

$$\mathbf{x}_B = x \cos \omega t - \frac{1}{\sqrt{km}} i\hbar \sin \omega t \frac{\partial}{\partial x}$$

$$\mathbf{p}_B = -i\hbar \cos \omega t \frac{\partial}{\partial x} - \sqrt{km}\, x \sin \omega t$$

CHAPTER 3 / *Approximation Methods and*
Many-Particle Systems

In the previous chapter we have discussed several problems which can be solved exactly. However, aside from these, very few problems are amenable to an exact solution. In the present chapter we shall, therefore, consider some of the more important approximation techniques for solving the wave equation.

3.1 *PERTURBATION THEORY WITHOUT DEGENERACY*

Perturbation theory permits us to approximate the solution to the wave equation when a term of relatively small magnitude is added to a wave equation whose solution is already known. The added term is referred to as a perturbation. Mathematically speaking we may say that perturbation theory permits us to approximate the eigenfunctions and eigenvalues of

$$(\mathbf{L}^{(0)} + \mathbf{L}^{(1)})\psi = l\psi \qquad (3.1)$$

if the effect of the perturbation $\mathbf{L}^{(1)}$ is small and we know the solution of

$$\mathbf{L}^{(0)}\psi^{(0)} = l^0\psi^{(0)} \qquad (3.2)$$

An example of this situation is the Hamiltonian of the two electron atoms (for example, the helium atom) which may be written (neglecting nuclear, spin-orbital, and other interactions) as

$$\left[-\frac{h^2}{2m}(\nabla_1^2 + \nabla_2) - \frac{Ze^2}{r_1} - \frac{Ze^2}{r_2} + \frac{e^2}{r_{12}}\right]\psi = E\psi \qquad (3.3)$$

where ∇_1^2 and ∇_2^2 are the Laplacians of electrons 1 and 2; r_1 and r_2 are the distances of these electrons from the nucleus; and r_{12} is the distance between the two electrons. The term in r_{12} represents the perturbation since the equation without this term is satisfied by the product of two hydrogen-like functions.

We shall first develop the perturbation technique in the case when the eigenvalues are nondegenerate. Let us suppose that we have a set of known eigenfunctions $\psi_1^0, \psi_2^0, \ldots, \psi_n^0$ which satisfy the wave equation

$$H^{(0)}\psi_n^{(0)} = E_n^{(0)}\psi_n^{(0)} \tag{3.4}$$

The perturbed equation corresponding to (3.4) may in general be written as

$$(\mathbf{H}^{(0)} + \lambda\mathbf{H}^{(1)})\psi_n = E_n\psi_n \tag{3.5}$$

where λ is a parameter which may be regarded as varying from 0 to 1, and thereby determining the effect of the perturbation. Thus when $\lambda = 0$ the perturbation vanishes; while $\lambda = 1$ we have the fully perturbed equation. Since we will usually set $\lambda = 1$, this parameter is essentially a device for facilitating the analysis.

If we could solve equation (3.5) we would find that ψ_n and E_n are functions of λ. Let us therefore expand these quantities in a power series in λ:

$$\psi_n = \psi_n^{(0)} + \lambda\psi_n^{(1)} + \lambda^2\psi_n^{(2)} + \cdots \tag{3.6}$$

$$E_n = E_n^{(0)} + \lambda E_n^{(1)} + \lambda^2 E_n^{(2)} + \cdots \tag{3.7}$$

Our object now is to find $E_n^{(k)}$ and $\psi_n^{(k)}$ in terms of the known quantities E_n^0 and ψ_n^0. On substituting the above expansions into equation (3.5) and arranging the result in powers of λ we have

$$\mathbf{H}^{(1)}\psi_n^{(0)} + \lambda(\mathbf{H}^{(0)}\psi_n^{(1)} + \mathbf{H}^{(1)}\psi_n^{(0)}) + \lambda^2(\mathbf{H}^{(0)}\psi_n^{(2)} + \mathbf{H}^{(1)}\psi_n^{(1)}) + \cdots$$
$$= E_n^{(0)}\psi_n^{(0)} + \lambda(E_n^0\psi_n^{(1)} + E_n^{(1)}\psi_n^{(0)}) + \lambda^2(E_n^{(0)}\psi_n^{(2)} + E_n^{(1)}\psi_n^{(1)} +$$
$$E_n^2\psi_n^{(0)}) + \cdots \tag{3.8}$$

This equation will hold for all values of λ provided the coefficients of like powers of λ on either side of the equation are equal:

$$\mathbf{H}^{(0)}\psi_n^{(0)} = E_n^{(1)}\psi_n^{(0)} \tag{3.9}$$

$$(\mathbf{H}^{(0)} - E_n^0)\psi_n^{(1)} = E_n^{(1)}\psi_n^{(0)} - \mathbf{H}^{(1)}\psi_n^{(0)} \tag{3.10}$$

$$(\mathbf{H}^{(0)} - E_n^{(0)})\psi_n^{(2)} = E_n^{(2)}\psi_n^{(2)} + (E_n^{(1)} - \mathbf{H}^{(1)})\psi_n^{(1)} + E_n^{(2)}\psi_n^{(0)} \tag{3.11}$$

In order to determine the first-order perturbation terms $\psi_n^{(1)}$ and $E_n^{(1)}$ we expand $\psi_n^{(1)}$ in terms of the known orthonormal set of functions $\psi_n^{(0)}$:

$$\psi_n^{(1)} = \sum_{k=1}^{\infty} \alpha_k \psi_k^{(0)} \tag{3.12}$$

and we also expand the function $\mathbf{H}^{(1)}\psi_n^{(0)}$ in terms of $\psi_n^{(0)}$ or

$$\mathbf{H}^{(1)}\psi_n^{(0)} = \sum_{k=1}^{\infty} H_{kn}^{(1)} \psi_k^{(0)} \tag{3.13}$$

where the coefficients $H_{kn}^{(1)}$ are given by the scalar product

$$H_{kn}^{(1)} = \int (\psi_k^{(0)})^* \mathbf{H}^{(1)}\psi_n^{(0)} \, d\tau = (\psi_k^0, \mathbf{H}^{(1)}\psi_n^0) \tag{3.14}$$

are referred to as matrix elements. Introducing (3.12) and (3.13) into (3.10) we find that

$$\sum_{k=1}^{\infty} \alpha_k (E_k^{(0)} - E_n^{(0)})\psi_k^{(0)} = E_n^{(1)}\psi_n^{(0)} - \sum_{k=1}^{\infty} H_{kn}^{(1)}\psi_k^{(0)} \tag{3.15}$$

In order for this equality to hold, the coefficients of ψ_k on the left-hand side of (3.15) must be equal to the coefficients of ψ_k on the right-hand side. We note that when $k = n$, the coefficient of ψ_n vanishes on the left so that we must have

$$E_n^{(1)} - H_{nn}^{(1)} = 0 \tag{3.16}$$

or

$$E_n^{(1)} = H_{nn}^{(1)} = (\psi_n^{(0)}, \mathbf{H}^{(1)}\psi_n^{(0)}) \tag{3.17}$$

This last result permits us to calculate the first-order energy perturbation. Equating the other coefficients we find that

$$\alpha_k = \frac{H_{kn}^{(1)}}{E_n^0 - E_k^{(0)}} \tag{3.18}$$

This last result obviously does not hold when $k = n$. However, α_n may be determined by means of the normalizing condition on ψ_n:

$$\int \psi_n^* \psi_n \, d\tau = 1 \tag{3.19}$$

We see, on introducing (3.12) into (3.6), we have

$$\psi_n = \psi_n^{(0)} + \lambda\left(\sum_{\substack{k \\ k \neq n}} \alpha_k \psi_k^{(0)} + \alpha_n \psi_n \right) \tag{3.20}$$

If now (3.20) is introduced into (3.19), and we recall that the functions $\psi_k^{(0)}$ are an orthonormal set, we find that

$$\int \psi_n^* \psi_n \, d\tau = 1 + 2\lambda\alpha_n + \lambda^2(\quad) + \cdots \tag{3.21}$$

It is clear from the last result that if ψ_n is to be normalized, then for any value of λ, α_n must be zero.

We conclude, therefore, that the first-order perturbation solution is given by

$$E_n = E_n^{(0)} + \lambda H_{nn}^{(1)} + \cdots \tag{3.22}$$

and from (3.18) and (3.20)

$$\psi_n = \psi_n^{(0)} + \lambda \sum_{\substack{k \\ k \neq n}}^{\infty} \frac{H_{kn}^{(1)}}{E_n^{(0)} - E_k^{(0)}} \psi_k^{(0)} + \cdots \tag{3.23}$$

where

$$H_{kn}^{(1)} = (\psi_k^{(0)}, \mathbf{H}^{(1)}\psi_n^{(0)}) \tag{3.24}$$

The above arguments may be extended to obtain the second-order perturbation terms. Proceeding as before we expand $\psi_n^{(2)}$ in terms of the $\psi_k^{(0)}$:

$$\psi_n^{(2)} = \sum_{k=1}^{\infty} \beta_k \psi_k^{(0)} \tag{3.25}$$

On introducing this expansion into (3.11) and proceeding as before it is found that

$$E_n = E_n^{(0)} + \lambda H_{nn}^{(1)} + \lambda^2 \sum_{\substack{k \\ k \neq n}} \frac{H_{nk}^{(1)} H_{kn}^{(1)}}{E_n^{(0)} - E_k^{(0)}} + \lambda^3(\quad) + \cdots \tag{3.26}$$

and

$$\psi_n = \psi_n^0 + \lambda \sum_k \frac{H_{kn}^{(1)}}{E_n^{(0)} - E_k^{(0)}} \psi_k^{(0)}$$

$$+ \lambda^2 \sum_{\substack{l=1 \\ l \neq n}}^{\infty} \left[\sum_{\substack{k=1 \\ k \neq n}}^{\infty} \frac{H_{lk}^{(1)} H_{kn}^{(1)}}{(E_n^{(0)} - E_l^{(0)})(E_n^{(0)} - E_k^{(0)})} - \frac{H_{nn}^{(1)} H_{ln}^{(1)}}{(E_n^{(0)} - E_0^{(0)})^2} \right] \psi_l^{(0)}$$

$$+ \lambda^3(\quad) + \cdots \tag{3.27}$$

In order to illustrate the essential features of a first-order perturbation calculation, we consider the one-dimensional box bounded by an infinite potential barrier discussed in section 2.3. The perturbation is taken to be a small constant potential V_1 over a narrow interval, a to $a + d$, in the interior of the box as shown in figure 3.1.

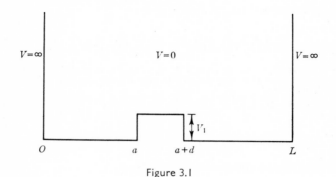

Figure 3.1

We have seen in (1.5) that

$$\psi_n^{(0)} = \sqrt{\frac{2}{L}} \sin \frac{n\pi x}{L} \tag{3.28}$$

and

$$E_n^{(0)} = \frac{\pi^2 \hbar^2 n^2}{2mL^2} \tag{3.29}$$

the perturbation is

$$\begin{aligned}
\mathbf{H}^{(1)} &= V^{(1)} && a < x < a + d \\
\mathbf{H}^{(1)} &= 0 && 0 < x < a \quad a + d < x < L
\end{aligned} \tag{3.30}$$

with $\lambda = 1$.

The matrix elements appearing in the first-order perturbation theory are found to be

$$E_n^{(1)} = H_{nn}^{(1)} = \frac{2V^{(1)}}{L} \int_a^{a+d} \sin^2 \frac{n\pi x}{L} \, dx \tag{3.31}$$

and

$$H_{kn}^{(1)} = \frac{2V^{(1)}}{L} \int_a^{a+d} \sin \frac{k\pi x}{L} \sin \frac{n\pi x}{L} \, dx \tag{3.32}$$

These may be readily evaluated and substituted into the first-order expressions for E_n and ψ_n:

$$E_n = E_n^{(0)} + E_n^{(1)}$$

$$\psi_n = \psi_n^{(0)} + \sum_{\substack{k=1 \\ k \neq n}}^{1} \frac{H_{kn}^{(1)}}{E_n^{(0)} - E_k^{(0)}} \tag{3.33}$$

3.2 *PERTURBATION THEORY WITH DEGENERACY*

We now consider the case when the eigenfunctions are degenerate so that corresponding to the eigenvalue $E_1^{(0)}$ we have n linearly independent eigenfunctions $\psi_1^{(0)}, \psi_2^{(0)}, \ldots, \psi_n^{(0)}$. We introduce the function ϕ defined by

$$\phi = c_1\psi_1^{(0)} + c_2\psi_2^{(0)} + \cdots c_n\psi_n^{(0)} \tag{3.34}$$

It is clear that ϕ is an eigenfunction of $\mathbf{H}^{(0)}$

$$\mathbf{H}^{(0)}\phi = \mathbf{H}^{(0)} \sum_{j=1}^{n} c_j\psi_j^{(0)} = E_1^{(0)} \sum_{j=1}^{n} c_j\psi_j^{(0)} \tag{3.35}$$

since

$$E_1^{(0)} = E_2^{(0)} = E_n^{(0)} \tag{3.36}$$

We now consider the first-order solution to the perturbed equation

$$(\mathbf{H}^{(0)} + \lambda\mathbf{H}^{(1)})\psi = E_1\psi \tag{3.37}$$

Proceeding as before, we expand E_1 and ψ in powers of λ:

$$E_1 = E_1^{(0)} + \lambda E_1^{(1)} + \lambda^2 E_1^{(2)} + \cdots \tag{3.38}$$

$$\psi = \phi + \lambda\psi^{(1)} + \lambda^2\psi^{(2)} + \cdots \tag{3.39}$$

Substituting (3.38) and (3.39) into (3.37) we find that, to the first order in λ,

$$(\mathbf{H}^{(0)} - E_1^{(0)})\psi^{(1)} = \sum_{j=1}^{n} c_j(E_1^{(1)} - \mathbf{H}^{(1)})\psi_j^{(0)} \tag{3.40}$$

As before, we expand the functions $\psi^{(1)}$ and $\mathbf{H}^{(1)}\psi_j^{(0)}$ in terms of the eigenfunctions of the unperturbed equations:

$$\psi^{(1)} = \sum_{j=1}^{\infty} \alpha_j\psi_j^{(0)} \tag{3.41}$$

$$\mathbf{H}^{(1)}\psi_j^{(0)} = \sum_{k=1}^{\infty} H_{kj}^{(1)}\psi_k^{(0)} \tag{3.42}$$

We may now write (3.40) as

$$\sum_{j=1}^{\infty} (E_j^{(0)} - E_1^{(0)})\alpha_j \psi_j^{(0)} = \sum_{j=1}^{n} E_1^{(1)} c_j \psi_j^{(0)} - \sum_{j=1}^{\infty} \left(\sum_{k=1}^{n} c_k \mathbf{H}_{jk}^{(1)} \right) \psi_j^{(0)} \quad (3.43)$$

On recalling that $E_1^{(0)} = E_2^{(0)} = \cdots = E_n^{(0)}$, we find that for $j \leqslant n$ the left-hand side of (3.43) vanishes, and hence each coefficient of ψ_j^0 must also vanish, i.e.,

$$\sum_{k=1}^{n} c_k H_{jk}^{(1)} - E_1^{(1)} c_j = 0 \quad (3.44)$$

The above holds for $j = 1, 2, \ldots, n$ so that we have the system of equations

$$
\begin{aligned}
(H_{11}^{(1)} - E_1^{(1)})c_1 + & \quad H_{12}^{(1)}c_2 \quad + \cdots + \quad H_{1n}^{(1)}c_n \quad = 0 \\
H_{21}^{(1)}c_1 \quad & + (H_{22}^{(1)} - E_1^{(1)})c_2 + \cdots + \quad H_{2n}^{(1)}c_n \quad = 0 \quad (3.45) \\
\vdots \quad & \\
H_{n1}^{(1)}c_1 \quad & + \quad H_{n2}^{(1)}c_2 \quad + \cdots + (H_{nn}^{(1)} - E_1^{(1)})c_n = 0
\end{aligned}
$$

By well-known arguments, a solution to (3.45) exists (such that not all c_j vanish) if, and only if, the secular equation vanishes:

$$\begin{vmatrix} (H_{11}^{(1)} - E^{(1)}) & H_{12}^{(1)} & \ldots & H_{1n}^{(1)} \\ \vdots & & & \\ H_{1n}^{(1)} & H_{n2}^{(1)} & \ldots & (H_{nn}^{(1)} - E^{(1)}) \end{vmatrix} = 0 \quad (3.46)$$

Since (3.46) is an equation in degree n, we see therefore that in general there will be n different values of $E^{(1)}$ unless of course some of the roots are equal. The eigenfunctions ϕ_q, corresponding to any particular root $E_q^{(1)}$, can be found by substituting this root into (3.45) and solving for the ratio of c_j. The normalizing condition

$$\sum_{j=1}^{n} c_j c_j^* = 1 \quad (3.47)$$

provides the additional equation required for the complete determination of c_j.

Having determined ϕ_q, corresponding to $E_q^{(1)}$, we must next find $\psi^{(1)}$ which appears in (3.39). The coefficients α_j appearing in the expansions (3.41) can be obtained from (3.43) by equating the coefficients of $\psi_j^{(1)}$ when $j > n$

$$(E_j^{(0)} - E_1^{(0)})\alpha_j = -\sum_{k=1}^{n} c_k H_{jk}^{(1)} \qquad j > n \quad (3.48)$$

so that

$$\alpha_j = \frac{\sum_{k=1}^{n} c_k H_{jk}^{(1)}}{E_1^{(0)} - E_j^{(0)}} \tag{3.49}$$

The first order approximations are therefore

$$\psi_q = \phi_q + \lambda \sum_{j=n+1}^{\infty} \frac{\sum_{k=1}^{n} c_k H_{jk}^{(1)}}{E_1^{(0)} - E_j^{(0)}} \psi_j^{(0)} \tag{3.50}$$

and

$$E_q = E_1^{(0)} + \lambda E_q^{(1)} \tag{3.51}$$

As an example of first-order perturbation theory in the degenerate case we consider the particle in a three-dimensional box bounded by an infinite potential barrier, as was discussed in section 2.3. If we consider the first triply degenerate case with $n_x = 2$, $n_y = 1$, $n_z = 1$, then the unperturbed energy is

$$E_1^0 = \frac{6\hbar^2\pi^2}{2mL^2} \tag{3.52}$$

and the three wave functions corresponding to this eigenvalue are

$$\psi_1^{(0)} = \sqrt{\frac{8}{L^3}} \sin \frac{2\pi x}{L} \sin \frac{\pi y}{L} \sin \frac{\pi z}{L}$$

$$\psi_2^{(0)} = \sqrt{\frac{8}{L^3}} \sin \frac{\pi x}{L} \sin \frac{2\pi y}{L} \sin \frac{\pi z}{L} \tag{3.53}$$

$$\psi_3^{(0)} = \sqrt{\frac{8}{L^3}} \sin \frac{\pi x}{L} \sin \frac{\pi y}{L} \sin \frac{2\pi z}{L}$$

Suppose that a perturbing field of the form λx^2 is applied, where λ is a small constant, so that the Hamiltonian inside the potential box is now of the form

$$-\frac{\hbar^2}{2m} \nabla^2 \psi + \lambda x^2 \psi = E\psi \tag{3.54}$$

and

$$\mathbf{H}^{(1)} = \lambda x^2 \tag{3.55}$$

we now obtain the first order perturbation on $E_1^{(0)}$ from (3.46). The matrix elements are of the form

$$\mathbf{H}_{lk}^{(1)} = \int_0^L \int_0^L \int_0^L \psi_l^{(0)*} x^2 \psi_k^{(0)} \, dx \, dy \, dz \tag{3.56}$$

where ψ is given by the degenerate eigenfunctions (3.53). Because of the orthogonal properties of the sine functions

$$\mathbf{H}_{lk}^{(1)} = 0 \qquad l \neq k \tag{3.57}$$

When $l = k$ we find, on integrating by parts, that

$$H_{11}^{(1)} = L^2(\tfrac{1}{3} - \tfrac{1}{8}\pi^2)$$
$$H_{22}^{(1)} = H_{33}^{(1)} = L^2\left(\frac{1}{3} - \frac{1}{2\pi^2}\right) \tag{3.58}$$

the secular equation is then

$$\begin{vmatrix} (H_{11}^{(1)} - E^{(1)}) & 0 & 0 \\ 0 & (H_{22}^{(1)} - E^{(1)}) & 0 \\ 0 & 0 & (H_{33}^{(1)} - E^{(1)}) \end{vmatrix} = 0 \tag{3.59}$$

which obviously has the roots $E_1^{(1)} = H_{11}^{(1)}$ and $E_2^{(1)} = H_{22}^{(1)} = H_{33}^{(1)}$. The second root is doubly degenerate. The perturbed energy levels, due to the first order, given by (3.51) are:

$$E_1 = \frac{6h^2\pi^2}{2mL^2} + \lambda L^2\left(\frac{1}{3} - \frac{1}{8\pi^2}\right)$$
$$E_2 = \frac{6h^2\pi^2}{2mL^2} + \lambda L^2\left(\frac{1}{3} - \frac{1}{2\pi^2}\right) \tag{3.60}$$

3.3 THE VARIATIONAL METHOD

When the perturbation is too large to be approximated by the perturbation technique described above, the *variational method* can provide an estimate of the lowest eigenvalue. This method requires the choice of a trial function $\phi(\lambda_1, \lambda_2, \ldots, \lambda_n)$ which depends on a set of parameters $\lambda_1, \lambda_2, \ldots, \lambda_n$, and are to be determined. The integral

$$E = \frac{\int \phi^* \mathbf{H}\phi \, d\tau}{\int \phi^* \phi \, d\tau} \tag{3.61}$$

is minimized with respect to the parameters to provide the equations

$$\frac{\partial E}{\partial \lambda_1} = 0$$

$$\frac{\partial E}{\partial \lambda_2} = 0$$

$$\vdots$$

$$\frac{\partial E}{\partial \lambda_n} = 0 \qquad (3.62)$$

These equations determine the parameters. On substituting the trial function into (2.48) the energy of the system can be estimated. This estimate will be greater or equal to the lowest eigenvalue, E_0, of $\mathbf{H}$. The procedure rests on the theorem that if E_0 is the lowest eigenvalue of $\mathbf{H}$, then

$$\int \phi^* \mathbf{H} \phi \, d\tau \geqslant E_0 \qquad (3.63)$$

assuming that ϕ has been normalized.

In order to prove the theorem we must show that

$$\int \phi^* (\mathbf{H} - E_0) \phi \, d\tau \geqslant 0 \qquad (3.64)$$

This is readily proven by expanding ϕ in terms of the eigenfunctions, ψ_j, of $\mathbf{H}$:

$$\int \phi^* (\mathbf{H} - E_0) \phi \, d\tau = \int \sum c_j^* \psi_j^* (\mathbf{H} - E_0) \sum c_j \psi_j \, d\tau$$

$$= \int \sum c_j^* \psi_j^* \left[\sum_j (E_j - E_0) c_j \psi_j \right] d\tau$$

$$= \sum c_j^* c_j (E_j - E_0) \qquad (3.65)$$

Since $c_j^* c_j$ is positive and $E_j \geqslant E_0$, the statement given by (3.63) follows.

As an example we consider the harmonic oscillator and select as the trial function

$$\phi = a e^{-\lambda x^2} \qquad (3.66)$$

This function is normalized by $a = \sqrt[4]{2\lambda/\pi}$. The Hamiltonian is

$$\mathbf{H} = -\frac{\hbar^2}{2m} \frac{d^2}{dx^2} + \frac{k}{2} x^2 \qquad (3.67)$$

On substituting (3.66) and (3.67) into (3.61) we find

$$E = \frac{\hbar^2 \lambda}{2m} + \frac{k}{8\lambda} \tag{3.68}$$

Applying the condition (3.62) for the minimum it is readily found that

$$\lambda = \frac{1}{2\hbar} \sqrt{mk} \tag{3.69}$$

The wave function is then

$$\phi = \left(\frac{1}{\pi\hbar} \sqrt{mk}\right)^{1/4} \exp\left(-\frac{1}{2\hbar} \sqrt[4]{mk}\, x^2\right) \tag{3.70}$$

and on substituting into the expression for E it is found that

$$E = \frac{\hbar}{2} \sqrt{\frac{k}{m}} \geqslant E_0 \tag{3.71}$$

3.4 *ADDITION OF ANGULAR MOMENTUM*

It is interesting to consider the angular momentum of a central field system made up of two noninteracting systems. Suppose that the wave functions for the latter are designated by $\phi(j_1 m_1)$ and $\phi(j_2 m_2)$ and the wave equation of the system is given by

$$\left[-\frac{\hbar^2}{2m}(\nabla_1^2 + \nabla_2^2) - \frac{Ze^2}{r_1} - \frac{Ze^2}{r_2} + \frac{e^2}{r_{12}}\right]\psi = E\psi \tag{3.72}$$

In the above ∇_1^2 and r_1 refer to the coordinates of one particle and ∇_2^2 and r_2 to the coordinates of the other particle while r_{12}, the repulsive term, involves the mutual distance of the particles. In the present approximation we neglect the repulsive term and it is clear that the product $\phi(j_1 m_1)\phi(j_2 m_2)$ satisfies the unperturbed equation. The approximate wave function of the system is therefore taken to be

$$\phi(j_1 j_2 m_1 m_2) = \phi(j_1 m_1)\phi(j_2 m_2) \tag{3.73}$$

or more generally a linear combination of the above products.

Suppose that the wave functions of the constituent systems are each rotated through an angle θ, then we require that the wave function representing the combined system be also rotated through the same angle, i.e.,

$$e^{i\theta \mathbf{J}}(j_1 j_2 m_1 m_2) = e^{i\theta \mathbf{J}_1}\phi(j_1 m_1)e^{i\theta \mathbf{J}_z}\phi(j_2 m_2) \tag{3.74}$$

$$\therefore \; \mathbf{J} = \mathbf{J}_1 + \mathbf{J}_2$$

Hence the angular momentum operator of the combined system **J** is equal to that of the sum of the constituent systems. Further $\mathbf{J}_1$ and $\mathbf{J}_2$ commute since each acts only on its respective coordinates; it is therefore, easy to show that **J** satisfies the proper commutator relationship

$$\mathbf{J} \times \mathbf{J} = i\hbar\mathbf{J} \tag{3.75}$$

as is required for a vector operator.

The individual functions in (3.73) are eigenfunctions of $\mathbf{J}_{z1}$, $\mathbf{J}_{z2}$, $\mathbf{J}_1^2$, and $\mathbf{J}_2^2$. It is easily shown that the product functions are also eigenfunctions of $\mathbf{J}_z$ with eigenvalues $m_1 + m_2$:

$$\mathbf{J}_z\phi(j_1 j_2 m_1 m_2) = (\mathbf{J}_{1z} + \mathbf{J}_{2z})\phi(j_1 m_1)\phi(j_2 m_2)$$
$$= (m_1 + m_2)\mathbf{J}_z\phi(j_1 m_1)\phi(j_2 m_2) \tag{3.76}$$

However, the product functions are not eigenfunctions of $\mathbf{J}^2$ since the individual functions are not eigenfunctions of $\mathbf{J}_{x1}$, $\mathbf{J}_{y1}$, $\mathbf{J}_{x2}$, and $\mathbf{J}_{y2}$. This last statement follows from the fact that, for example, $\mathbf{J}_{x1}$ and $\mathbf{J}_{z1}$ do not commute, as is indicated by expressions (2.234).

Using the results given in section 2.8 we seek to construct a linear combination of $\phi(j_1 j_2 m_1 m_2)$ which will simultaneously be an eigenfunction of $\mathbf{J}_z$ and $\mathbf{J}^2$. We designate such a linear combination by $\psi(jm)$. We note that there can be only $(2j_1 + 1)(2j_2 + 1)$ linearly independent functions $\psi(jm)$, corresponding to the fact that there are available only $(2j_1 + 1)(2j_2 + 1)$ linearly independent functions $\phi(j_1 j_2 m_1 m_2)$. We may form these linear combinations by starting with the highest value of j corresponding to the eigenvalue $j_1 + j_2$ of $\mathbf{J}_z$ and proceeding to successively smaller values of j, i.e., $j_1 + j_2, j_1 + j_2 - 1, j_1 + j_2 - 2, \ldots$. We recall that corresponding to each value of j there will be $2j + 1$ functions

$$\psi(j, j), \quad \psi(j, j - 1), \ldots, \quad \psi(j, -j)$$

In all, however, we can have only $(2j_1 + 1)(2j_2 + 1)$ eigenfunctions $\psi(jm)$ as pointed out above. Hence there must be at least $j = j_1 + j_2 - k$ such that

$$\sum_{j=j_1+j_2}^{j=j_1+j_2-k} 2j + 1 = (2j_1 + 1)(2j_2 + 1) \tag{3.77}$$

On rearranging the terms on the left-hand side of (3.77) we find

$$\sum_{j=j_1+j_2}^{j_1+j_2-k} 2j + 1 = (k + 1)2(j_1 + j_2) + (k + 1) - 2\sum_{n=0}^{k} n \tag{3.78}$$

and introducing the well-known expression for the summation of integers

$$\sum_{n=0}^{k} n = \frac{k(k+1)}{2} \tag{3.79}$$

we find that (3.77) can be expressed as

$$(k+1)[(2j_1 + 2j_2) - k + 1] = (2j_1 + 1)(2j_2 + 1) \tag{3.80}$$

This expression is satisfied by choosing k equal to $2j_1$ or $2j_2$. If $j_1 > j_2$ and since j is chosen as positive, we must take k equal to $2j_2$, and hence the least value of j is $j_1 + j_2 - 2j_2 = j_1 - j_2$. In summary, we see that on combining two noninteracting systems the individual states $\phi(j_1 m)$ and $\phi(j_2 m)$ give rise to a combined state $\psi(jm)$, where j has the values $j_1 + j_2, j_1 + j_2 - 1, \ldots,$ $j_1 - j_2$.

As an example illustrating the use of this rule we consider the simple case of the coupling between the orbital and spin momentum for a p-electron, for which $l = 1$, as discussed in section 2.4. We have

$$
\begin{aligned}
j_1 = l = 1 \qquad & j_2 = \frac{1}{2} \\
m_l = -1, 0, +1 \qquad & s = \frac{1}{2}, -\frac{1}{2}
\end{aligned}
\tag{3.81}
$$

The wave functions $\phi(j, m)$ corresponding to the various m_l for $l = 1$ are the spherical harmonics given in Section 2.4, but for purposes of exposition we shall use the above notation, i.e., $\phi(j, m)$. The spin functions may be designated by α for $s = 1/2$, and β for $s = -1/2$. We then have the single system functions $\phi(1, 1)$, $\phi(1, 0)$, $\phi(1, -1)$, α, and β. From these we can form six linearly independent products of the form $\phi(jm)\alpha$. These will be eigenfunctions of $\mathbf{J}_z$ but not of $\mathbf{J}^2$. In order to obtain eigenfunctions of the latter we form linear combinations of the products. The highest value of j in $\psi(j, m)$ corresponds to $m_l = 1$ and $s = 1/2$; these give rise to the functions $\psi(3/2, 3/2)$, $\psi(3/2, 1/2)$, $\psi(3/2, -1/2)$, and $\psi(3/2, -3/2)$. The next highest value of j is given by $j = 3/2 - 1 = j_1 - j_2$; this gives rise to $\psi(1/2, 1/2)$ and $\psi(1/2, -1/2)$.

As a second example we consider the states arising from two electrons. Let one electron be a d-electron with $l_1 = 2$, $s = \pm 1/2$, and the second a p-electron with $l_2 = 1$, $s = \pm 1/2$. Two possibilities are presented as to the manner by which the coupling occurs. In one scheme, *the LS or Russell-Saunders* coupling, the spins combine with spins and the orbital momentum also combine with themselves. The resulting terms are then combined to form the J-states:

$$S = s_1 + s_2, s_1 + s_2 - 1, \ldots, s_1 - s_2$$
$$L = l_1 + l_2, l_1 + l_2 - 1, \ldots, l_1 - l_2 \quad \text{(for } l_1 > l_2) \quad (3.82)$$
$$J = L + S, L + S - 1, \ldots, L - S \quad (l > S)$$

Thus with the above l and d-electrons we find that $S = 1, 0$ while $L = 3$, 2, 1. On adding, say $S = 1$ to $L = 3$, we obtain the states $J = 4, 3, 2$ and similarly for the other J-states. It is convenient to represent the various resultant states obtained with LS-coupling by means of the symbol

$$^{2S+1}L_J \tag{3.83}$$

introducing the spectroscopic notation

$$L = 0, 1, 2, 3, 4, 5, 6, \ldots$$
$$\text{S \ P \ D \ F \ G \ H \ I} \ldots \tag{3.84}$$

Thus, the term corresponding to $S = 1$, $L = 3$, and $J = 4$ may be written as $^3F_4$. Terms for which $2S + 1 = 3$ are referred to as *triplet states*, while terms for which $2S + 1 = 1$ are referred to as *singlet states*. It should be recalled that corresponding to a term of the form (3.83) there are $2J + 1$ eigenfunctions $\psi(Jm)$ with eigenvalues

$$\mathbf{J}^2\psi(J, m) = J(J + 1)\hbar^2\psi(J, m)$$
$$\mathbf{J}_z\psi(J, m) = m\hbar\psi(J, m) \quad m = J, J - 1, \ldots, J \tag{3.85}$$
$$\mathbf{S}_z^2\psi(J, m) = S(S + 1)\hbar^2\psi(J, m)$$

A second form of coupling, known as *jj-coupling*, occurs with the heavier elements. This type of coupling for two electrons is expressed by the relationships

$$j_1 = l_1 + s_1, l_1 + s_1 - 1, \ldots, l_1 - s_1 \quad l_1 > s_1$$
$$j_2 = l_2 + s_2, l_2 + s_2 - 1, \ldots, l_2 - s_2 \quad l_2 > s_2 \tag{3.86}$$
$$J = j_1 + j_2, j_1 + j_2 - 1, \ldots, j_1 - j_2 \quad j_1 > j_2$$

Thus for an s and p-electron we have $j_1 = 1/2$ and $j_2 = 3/2, 1/2$, and therefore for $j_1 = 1/2$, $j_2 = 3/2$, then $J = 2, 1$, and for $j_1 = 1/2$, $j_2 = 1/2$, then $J = 1, 0$.

3.5 *MAGNETIC EFFECTS*

It is well known from classical physics that associated with the flow of a current I about a closed path enclosing an area A, there is a magnetic moment μ given by

$$\mu = AI$$

This moment is normal to the plane of the current loop with a positive direction given by the right-hand rule.

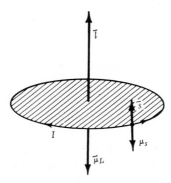

Figure 3.2: Relationship between orbital angular momentum $\bar{l}$ and the magnetic dipole, μ_L. The spin momentum s and dipole μ_s are also indicated.

Consider now an orbital electron with angular momentum $\bar{l}$. Since the current due to the motion of the electron flows in the opposite sense to the motion of the electron, the magnetic moment of the loop μ_L is directed oppositely to $\bar{l}$, as indicated in figure 3.2. It is easy to make a classical calculation of μ_L. Thus, if the electron has a velocity and traverses a circular path of radius r in a time t, then the corresponding current is given by

$$I = \frac{e}{tc} \qquad \text{(electromagnetic units)}$$

where e is the electrostatic charge on the electron, and c is the ratio of the electrostatic to the electromagnetic unit of charge. The magnetic dipole vector is given by

$$\bar{\mu}_L = -AI\bar{e}_e = -\pi r^2\left(\frac{ev}{2\pi rc}\right)\bar{e}_e = -\frac{e}{2mc}\left(mrv\bar{e}_e\right)$$

so that for a single electron

$$\bar{\mu}_L = -\frac{e}{2mc}\,\bar{l}\ \mathrm{erg/gauss}$$

where $\bar{e}_e$ is a unit vector in the direction of the classical angular momentum $\bar{l}$. The proportionality constant relating the dipole moment to the angular momentum is referred to as the gyromagnetic ratio. A dipole moment μ_s is also associated with the spin angular momentum s, but experiments show that the proportionality constant is just twice that calculated above so that for a single electron

$$\bar{\mu}_s = -\frac{e}{mc}\,\bar{s}$$

On introducing the quantum mechanical values of the orbital and spin momentum we have for the magnitude of the magnetic dipoles

$$\mu_L = -\frac{e\hbar}{2mc}\,\sqrt{l(l+1)}$$

$$\mu_s = -\frac{e\hbar}{2mc}\,\sqrt{3}$$

while the total magnetic dipole due to the orbital and spin contributions is given by

$$\bar{\mu}_J = -\left(\frac{e\hbar\bar{l}}{2mc} + \frac{e\hbar\bar{s}}{mc}\right)$$

$$= -\frac{e\hbar}{2mc}\,(\bar{l} + 2\bar{s}) = -\mu_0(\bar{j} + \bar{s})$$

where μ_0, the *Bohr magneton*, is given by

$$\mu_0 = 9.273 \times 10^{-21}\ \mathrm{erg/gauss}$$

In a magnetic field $\bar{H}$ the classical energy of a magnetic dipole is given by the well-known result for a system of electrons

$$E_z = -\sum \bar{H}\cdot\bar{\mu}_J = \mu_0 \sum_i \bar{H}\cdot(\bar{j}_i + \bar{s}_i)$$

$$= \mu_0 \bar{H}\cdot(\bar{J} + \bar{S})$$

From the last result it is clear that in the presence of a magnetic field the energy levels of the atom are split by an amount depending on the magnetic field strength and the angular momentum. This is the Zeeman effect which is discussed in a later section.

The spin magnetic dipole also interacts with the orbital dipole. In order to derive the expression for this effect, we consider the electron to be at rest and the nucleus to be moving at a velocity $\bar{v}$ relative to the electron. If the charge on the nucleus is Ze and the radius of the orbit $\bar{r}$, then the magnetic field at the electron is given by the familiar expression, on introducing $\bar{E} = Ze/r^2$,

$$\bar{H} = \frac{\bar{E} \times \bar{v}}{c} = \frac{Ze}{cr^3} \bar{r} \times \bar{v} = \frac{Ze}{mcr^3} \bar{l}$$

where $\bar{l}$ is the orbital momentum. The energy due to the interaction with the spin is now given for a system of electrons by

$$E_s = - \sum \bar{H} \cdot \bar{\mu}_s = \sum_i \frac{Ze^2}{2m^2c^2r_i^3} \bar{l}_i \cdot \bar{s}_i$$

A factor of one-half has been introduced because of relativistic considerations.

Corresponding to the interaction energies above we may define the following operators

$$\mathbf{H}_z = \mu_0 \bar{H} \cdot (\mathbf{J} + \mathbf{S})$$

$$\mathbf{H}_s = \sum_i \frac{Ze^2}{2m^2c^2r_i^3} \mathbf{l}_i \cdot \mathbf{s}_i$$

3.6 *SYSTEMS OF IDENTICAL PARTICLES*

We now consider in somewhat greater detail a system composed of identical particles. Let $\mathbf{H}$ be the system Hamiltonian and $\psi(r_1, r_2)$ the wave function of a system consisting of two identical particles. Clearly an interchange in position of the two particles results in a system which is indistinguishable from the original system, hence

$$\mathbf{H}\psi(r_1, r_2) = E\psi(r_1 r_2) \tag{3.87}$$

$$\mathbf{H}\psi(r_2, r_1) = E\psi(r_2 r_1) \tag{3.88}$$

If E is not degenerate, equations (3.87) and (3.88) imply that

$$\psi(r_1, r_2) = a\psi(r_2, r_1) \tag{3.89}$$

where a is a constant. Thus, the permutation of two identical particles can, at the most, merely multiply the wave function by a constant. However, since this is so, then

$$\psi(r_1 r_2) = a\psi(r_2, r_1) = a^2\psi(r_1, r_2) \tag{3.90}$$

so that $a^2 = 1$ or $a = \pm 1$. We conclude that if E is not degenerate *all wave functions must be either symmetric* ($a = 1$) *or antisymmetrical* ($a = -1$) *with respect to an interchange of identical particles.* The same conclusion is obtained in the degenerate case on introducing a linear combination of the degenerate eigenfunctions.

PROBLEM

Prove the above assertion for the degenerate case.

We also note that since the square of the function enters into the calculation of observables, both symmetric and antisymmetric functions give identical results in accordance with the principle that interchanging the role of identical particles results in physically indistinguishable systems. In accordance with this principle we must also have for the Hamiltonian operator $H(1, 2) = H(2, 1)$. This requirement is obviously satisfied with the Hamiltonian given in (3.72). It is therefore easy to show that $\psi(1, 2)$ and $H\psi(1, 2)$ have the same symmetry. Thus if $\psi(1, 2)$ is symmetrical then

$$\begin{aligned} f(1, 2) &= H(1, 2)\psi(1, 2) \\ f(2, 1) &= H(2, 1)\psi(2, 1) = H(1, 2)\psi(2, 1) \end{aligned} \tag{3.91}$$

since $\psi(1, 2) = \psi(2, 1)$ then

$$f(1, 2) = f(2, 1) \tag{3.92}$$

Using this result we can also establish the important fact that the symmetry properties of a function do not change with time, i.e., a symmetrical function remains symmetrical, and similarly for the antisymmetrical case. Consider the change in $\psi(t)$ in a time interval dt:

$$\psi(t + dt) = \psi(0) + \frac{\partial\psi}{\partial t} dt \tag{3.93}$$

$$\frac{\partial\psi}{\partial t} = \frac{1}{i\hbar} H\psi \tag{3.94}$$

so that the time derivative has the same symmetry properties as ψ and the above assertion follows.

3.7 PAULI PRINCIPLE

The question now arises as to what symmetry is to be associated with electron wave functions. The answer is provided by the *Pauli principle*, which states that particles with half integral spins (electrons, protons, neutrons) have antisymmetrical functions while particles with integral spin (photons) have symmetrical wave functions. Since in the case of electron $s = 1/2$, the wave functions of electron systems must be antisymmetric.

We now apply this principle to a collection of N-electrons. As shown in section 3.4 the approximate wave functions are of the form

$$\phi_1(1)\phi_2(2), \ldots, \phi_N(N) \tag{3.95}$$

when $\phi_i(i)$ represents the ith state (including spin) occupied by the ith particle. In view of the Pauli principle these functions are not acceptable since they are not antisymmetric. However, it is possible to obtain an antisymmetric function from each function of the form (3.95) by forming a linear combination of the functions obtained by permuting the particles among the various states. In the case of a two-particle system the antisymmetric function is

$$\phi_1(1)\phi_2(2) - \phi_1(2)\phi_2(1) \tag{3.96}$$

More generally we have

$$\psi = \sum_P (-1)^P \mathbf{P}\phi_1(1)\phi_2(2), \ldots, \phi_N(N) \tag{3.97}$$

where $\mathbf{P}$ is a permutation operator which interchanges the particles two at a time while the sum is taken over all such permutations, and P is the number of permutations associated with the pth term. Equation (3.97) may also be written in the form of a determinant

$$\psi = \frac{1}{\sqrt{N!}} \begin{vmatrix} \phi_1(1) & \phi_1(2) & \cdots & \phi_1(N) \\ \phi_2(1) & \phi_2(2) & \cdots & \phi_2(N) \\ \vdots & & & \\ \phi_N(1) & \phi_N(2) & \cdots & \phi_N(N) \end{vmatrix} \tag{3.98}$$

where $(N!)^{1/2}$ is a normalizing factor derived on the assumption that the ϕ is orthonormal.

PROBLEM

Verify the normalization factor by direct normalization of (3.97) in the case $N = 3$.

We now make the important observation that if two electrons occupy the same state function, then two columns in the determinant are equal and the determinant vanishes. We conclude, therefore, that *two or more electrons cannot occupy the same quantum state.* This conclusion holds for all particles of half-integral spin which are referred to, in general, as *fermions.* On the other hand this restriction does not hold for particles with integral spin, referred to, in general, as *bosons.* Since the wave functions for bosons are symmetrical these are of the form

$$\sum_p \mathbf{P}\phi_1(1)\phi_2(2), \ldots, \phi_M(M) \tag{3.99}$$

which does not give rise to a determinantal wave function. We conclude, therefore, that any number of bosons may occupy the same quantum state.

The Pauli exclusion principle is of great value in constructing the permissible states for an atom. We have seen in the solution of the central-field problem that the quantum numbers n, l, m_l are restricted by the relationships that for any n $(1, 2, 3, 4, \ldots)$ l may assume the values $0, 1, \ldots, n - 1$, and m_l may range from $-l$, $-l + 1, \ldots, +l$. The latter restriction is in accord with the more general results given by (2.255). Electrons with the same n, the principle quantum number, are said to occupy the same *shell,* while electrons with the same n and l are said to occupy the same *subshell.* It is sometimes convenient to designate a single electron state corresponding to a given subshell by the notation $1s$, $2s$, $2p$, $3s$, etc., where the integer represents the value of n and the letter the value of l in terms of the spectroscopic designation, i.e.,

$$
\begin{array}{cccccc}
0, & 1, & 2, & 3, & 4, & 5, \ldots \\
s & p & d & f & g & h \ldots
\end{array}
\tag{3.100}
$$

A distribution of electrons among the subshells is referred to as a *configuration.* The symbol $(1s)^1(2p)^2$, for example, represents a configuration with one electron in the $1s$-state and two electrons in the $2p$-state.

A single electron state is completely specified by the quantum numbers,

TABLE 3.1

The Electron Structure of the Atoms

ATOMIC NUMBER	ELEMENT	NUMBER OF ELECTRONS IN EACH QUANTUM GROUP										
		$1s$	$2s$	$2p$	$3s$	$3p$	$3d$	$4s$	$4p$	$4d$	$4f$	$5s$
1	H	1										
2	He	2										
3	Li	2	1									
4	Be	2	2									
5	B	2	2	1								
6	C	2	2	2								
7	N	2	2	3								
8	O	2	2	4								
9	F	2	2	5								
10	Ne	2	2	6								
11	Na				1							
12	Mg				2							
13	Al				2	1						
14	Si	1s to 2p			2	2						
15	P	groups filled.			2	3						
16	S				2	4						
17	Cl				2	5						
18	A				2	6						
19	K							1				
20	Ca							2				
21	Sc						1	2				
22	Ti						2	2				
23	V						3	2				
24	Cr	1s to 3p groups filled.					5	1				
25	Mn						5	2				
26	Fe						6	2				
27	Co						7	2				
28	Ni						8	2				
29	Cu						10	1				
30	Zn								1			
31	Ga								1			
32	Ge								2			
33	As	1s to 4s groups filled.							3			
34	Se								4			
35	Br								5			
36	Kr								6			
37	Rb											1
38	Sr											2
39	Y									1		2
40	Zr									2		2
41	Cb									4		1
42	Mo	1s to 4p groups filled.								5		1
43	Tc									5		2
44	Ru									7		1
45	Rh									8		1
46	Pd									10		

TABLE 3.1 *Continued*

The Electron Structure of the Atoms

ATOMIC NUMBER	ELEMENT		4f	5s	5p	5d	5f	5g	6s	6p	6d	7s
		NUMBER OF ELECTRONS IN EACH QUANTUM GROUP										
47	Ag			1								
48	Cd			2								
49	In			2	1							
50	Sn			2	2							
51	Sb			2	3							
52	Te			2	4							
53	I			2	5							
54	Xe			2	6							
55	Cs			2	6				1			
56	Ba			2	6				2			
57	La	1s to 4d groups filled.		2	6	1			2			
58	Ce		2	2	6				2			
59	Pr		3	2	6				2			
60	Nd		4	2	6				2			
61	Pm		5	2	6				2			
62	Sa		6	2	6				2			
63	Eu		7	2	6				2			
64	Gd		7	2	6	1			2			
65	Tb		9	2	6				2			
66	Dy		10	2	6				2			
67	Ho		11	2	6				2			
68	Er		12	2	6				2			
69	Tm		13	2	6				2			
70	Yb		14	2	6				2			
71	Lu		14	2	6	1			2			
72	Hf	1s to 5p groups filled.				2			2			
73	Ta					3			2			
74	W					4			2			
75	Re					5			2			
76	Os					6			2			
77	Ir					7			2			
78	Pt					9			1			
79	Au					10			1			
80	Hg	1s to 5d groups filled.							2			
81	Tl								2	1		
82	Pb								2	2		
83	Bi								2	3		
84	Po								2	4		
85	At								2	5		
86	Rn								2	6		
87	Fr								2	6		1
88	Ra								2	6		2
89	Ac								2	6	1	2
90	Th								2	6	2	2
91	Pa						2		2	6	1	2
92	U						3		2	6	1	2
93	Np						4		2	6	1	2
94	Pu						5		2	6	1	2
95	Am						7		2	6		2
96	Cm						7		2	6	1	2

n, l, m_l, and s. Thus we have for $n = 1, 2, 3$ the single electron states shown below

n	1	2			3								
l	0(s)	0(s)	1(p)			0(s)	1(p)			2(d)				
m_l	0	0	-1	0	$+1$	0	-1	0	$+1$	-2	-1	0	1	2
s	$\pm\frac{1}{2}$	$\pm\frac{1}{2}$	$\pm\frac{1}{2}$	$\pm\frac{1}{2}$	$\pm\frac{1}{2}$	$\pm\frac{1}{2}$	$\pm\frac{1}{2}$	$\pm\frac{1}{2}$	$\pm\frac{1}{2}$	$\pm\frac{1}{2}$	$\pm\frac{1}{2}$	± 1	$\pm\frac{1}{2}$	$\pm\frac{1}{2}$

According to the Pauli principle, each state can accommodate only one electron so that the ns-subshells can accommodate 2 electrons, the np-subshells six electrons, the nd-subshells 10 electrons, and so on. Starting with the $1s$-states and proceeding to states of successively higher energy, we obtain the configurations for the elements shown in table 3.1.

3.8   *SYSTEMS OF COMMUTING OPERATORS*

In the perturbation treatment of atomic structure it is desirable to work with a simultaneous set of eigenfunctions ψ_n of the commuting operators **H**, **J**$_z$, and **J**^{2}. The advantages of this procedure are several:

a. From the single set ψ_n we can calculate the constants of motion E, λ, and m_j, since

$$\mathbf{H}\psi = E\psi_n$$
$$\mathbf{J}^2\psi = j(j+1)\hbar^2\psi = \lambda\psi \qquad (3.102)$$
$$\mathbf{J}_z\psi = m_j\hbar\psi$$

b. The solution of the secular equation arising in perturbation theory is greatly facilitated.

The second item follows from theorem IV given in Chapter 1. Thus, if two functions ψ_k and ψ_l of the common set have different eigenvalues corresponding to $\mathbf{J}^2$ or $\mathbf{J}_z$, then the matrix element $H^{(1)}_{lk}$ vanishes. In this way, most or all of the off-diagonal elements in the secular equation

$$|H^{(1)}_{lk} - E^{(1)}| = 0 \qquad (3.103)$$

vanish. The solution is then greatly facilitated as will be shown below. If no two eigenfunctions have a common set of eigenvalues (E, λ, m_j), then the secular equation will be diagonalized, i.e.,

$$|H_{jj}^{(1)} - E^{(1)}| = 0 \tag{3.104}$$

and therefore

$$E^{(1)} = H_{jj}^{(1)} \tag{3.105}$$

so that the secular equation is immediately solvable. We recall still a third advantage of employing a common set of eigenfunctions, namely the matrix representation of the corresponding operators are diagonal.

We have already seen from theorem III that a commuting set of operators have a common set of eigenfunctions. Consequently, as the first step toward simplifying the secular equation, we must determine the operators which commute with $\mathbf{H}$. We consider first the central-field Hamiltonian for which the repulsive force between two electrons is taken as the perturbation. The Hamiltonian is

$$\mathbf{H} = -\left(\frac{\hbar^2}{2m}\nabla^2 + \frac{\hbar^2}{2m}\nabla^2\right) - \frac{ze^2}{r_1} - \frac{ze^2}{r_2} + \frac{e^2}{r_{12}} \tag{3.106}$$

where we take

$$\mathbf{H}^{(1)} = \frac{e^2}{r_{12}} \tag{3.107}$$

Since (3.106) does not contain spin coordinates it is clear that $\mathbf{S}_z$ and $\mathbf{S}^2$ commute with $\mathbf{H}$, and hence have common eigenfunctions. It should be noted, however, that since $\mathbf{S}_x$ and $\mathbf{S}_y$ do not, according to (2.234), commute with $\mathbf{S}_z$ that these eigenfunctions are not simultaneously eigenfunctions of $\mathbf{S}_x$ and $\mathbf{S}_y$. We can show that $\mathbf{L}_z$ and $\mathbf{L}^2$ also commute with $\mathbf{H}$ by representing the operators in polar coordinates

$$
\begin{aligned}
x &= r \sin \theta \cos \phi \\
y &= r \sin \theta \sin \phi \\
z &= r \cos \theta
\end{aligned} \tag{3.108}
$$

so that

$$
\begin{aligned}
\mathbf{L}_z = \mathbf{l}_{1z} + \mathbf{l}_{2z} &= i\hbar\left[\left(y_1 \frac{\partial}{\partial x_1} - x_1 \frac{\partial}{\partial y_1}\right) + \left(y_2 \frac{\partial}{\partial x_2} - x_2 \frac{\partial}{\partial y_2}\right)\right] \\
&= -i\hbar\left[\frac{\partial}{\partial \phi_1} + \frac{\partial}{\partial \phi_2}\right]
\end{aligned} \tag{3.109}
$$

If we now examine the expression for ∇^2 given by (2.112) we see that the only term involving ϕ occurs as $\partial^2/\partial\phi^2$, which commutes with $\partial/\partial\phi$. Similarly, the term $1/r$ also commutes with $\partial/\partial\phi$. The repulsive term $1/r_{12}$ in the Hamiltonian (3.106) involves ϕ only in the form $\phi_1 - \phi_2$. This suggests that we transform the operator (3.109) so that $\phi_1 - \phi_2$ is the independent variable and we have

$$-i\hbar\left(\frac{\partial}{\partial\phi_1} + \frac{\partial}{\partial\phi_2}\right)\frac{e^2}{r_{12}} = -i\hbar e^2\left[\frac{\partial(\phi_1 - \phi_2)}{\partial\phi_1} + \frac{\partial(\phi_1 - \phi_2)}{\partial\phi_2}\right]$$

$$\times \frac{\partial}{\partial(\phi_1 - \phi_2)}\frac{1}{r_{12}} = 0 \quad (3.110)$$

hence the operators commute. Since $\mathbf{L}_z$ and $\mathbf{H}$ commute, then by symmetry $\mathbf{L}_x$ and $\mathbf{L}_y$ must also commute with $\mathbf{H}$, hence we have

$$[\mathbf{L}, \mathbf{H}] = 0 \quad (3.111)$$

It also follows that

$$[\mathbf{L}^2, \mathbf{H}] = 0 \quad (3.112)$$

and since $\mathbf{S}$ and $\mathbf{L}$ commute with $\mathbf{H}$, then $\mathbf{J} = \mathbf{L} + \mathbf{S}$ must also:

$$[\mathbf{J}, \mathbf{H}] = 0$$
$$[\mathbf{J}^2, \mathbf{H}] = 0 \quad (3.113)$$

If the spin-orbital coupling term

$$\mathbf{H}^{(1)} = f(r_1)\mathbf{l}_1 \cdot \mathbf{s}_1 + f(r_2)\mathbf{l}_2 \cdot \mathbf{s}_2 \quad (3.114)$$

is added to (3.106), then $\mathbf{L}$ and $\mathbf{S}$ no longer commute with $\mathbf{H}$. This may be seen directly by expressing the operators in terms of the $x, y,$ and z components of the single electron momenta ($\mathbf{l}_1, \mathbf{s}_1$, etc.) and applying the usual commutator relationships. Similar conclusions follow for $\mathbf{L}^2$ and $\mathbf{S}^2$. We see, therefore, that none of these operators correspond to constants of motion when spin-orbital interactions are included. However, $\mathbf{J}_z$ and hence by symmetry $\mathbf{J}_x$ and $\mathbf{J}_y$ do commute with the spin-orbital Hamiltonian, as does also $\mathbf{J}^2$. This assertion may be verified directly by expressing the operators in terms of their single-electron components, and using the commutator relationships. It follows that with spin-orbital interactions $\mathbf{J}_z$ and $\mathbf{J}^2$ are constants of motion, but not $\mathbf{L}$ and $\mathbf{S}$.

3.9 TWO-ELECTRON ATOMS

The application of first-order perturbation theory and determinantal wave functions will be illustrated by means of an atom consisting of two electrons. Helium atoms provide an example of such a system. As will be discussed in a later chapter, the excited states of helium are involved in the helium-neon laser.

In the following discussion we shall neglect spin-orbital coupling so that the Hamiltonian is given by (3.106). The unperturbed, or zero-order, wave functions are simply the product of the single-electron wave functions, some of which are listed in (2.139), multiplied by an appropriate spin function, $\alpha(\xi)$ or $\beta(\xi)$. We shall represent the single-electron state occupied by, say, particle 1 by $\psi(r_1)$, and similarly for the other particle. The simplest case arises when both electrons occupy the ground state with the configuration $(1s)^2$. Since there is only one such state, then according to the Pauli exclusion principle the electrons must have opposite spins. For convenience let us introduce the notation

$$\chi^+ = \alpha$$

$$\chi^- = \beta$$

so that for the two values of the spin coordinate ($\xi = \pm 1$) we have

$$\alpha(1) = 1 \qquad \beta(1) = 0$$

$$\alpha(-1) = 0 \qquad \beta(-1) = 1$$

The appropriate antisymmetrical wave function is

$$\Phi = \frac{1}{\sqrt{2}} \begin{vmatrix} \psi(r_1)\alpha(\xi_1) & \psi(r_2)\alpha(\xi_2) \\ \psi(r_1)\beta(\xi_1) & \psi(r_2)\beta(\xi_2) \end{vmatrix} \tag{3.115}$$

Equation (3.115) may also be expressed as

$$\Phi = \frac{1}{\sqrt{2}} \psi(r_1)\psi(r_2) \begin{vmatrix} \alpha(\xi_1) & \alpha(\xi_2) \\ \beta(\xi_1) & \beta(\xi_2) \end{vmatrix} \tag{3.116}$$

The 0th order energy $E_1^{(0)}$ of the ground state is given by

$$\mathbf{H}^{(0)}\Phi = 2E_1^{(0)}\Phi \tag{3.117}$$

where $E_1^{(0)}$ is given by (2.137a). The first-order energy term is given by

$$E_1^{(1)} = \sum_{\xi_1 \xi_2} \int \Phi^* H^{(1)} \Phi \, d\tau$$

$$= \frac{1}{2} \sum_{\xi_1 \xi_2} \int \psi^*(r_1)\psi^*(r_2) \frac{e^2}{r_{12}} \psi(r_1)\psi(r_2) \, d\tau_1 \, d\tau_2 [\alpha(\xi_1)\beta(\xi_2) - \alpha(\xi_2)\beta(\xi_1)]^2$$

(3.118)

Since the spin functions are orthonormal we have

$$\sum_{\xi_1 \xi_2 = \pm 1} [\alpha(\xi_1)\beta(\xi_2) - \alpha(\xi_2)\beta(\xi_1)]^2 = 2 \tag{3.119}$$

We can then express (3.118) as

$$E_1^{(1)} = \int \psi^*(r_1)\psi^*(r_2) \frac{e^2}{r_{12}} \psi(r_1)\psi(r_2) \, d\tau_1 \, d\tau_2 \tag{3.120}$$

The evaluation of integrals of the form (3.120) is discussed in Slater, vol. 1. It is clear that since $S = s_1 + s_2 = 0$ and $L = m_{l_1} + m_{l_2} = 0$ that the ground state term is $^1S_0$. In general, with closed shell structures we can have only one determinantal wave function which corresponds to the term $^1S_0$, since all the states are occupied, and hence $S = \sum m_s = 0$ and $L = \sum m_l = 0$.

When the atoms are excited so that the electrons no longer necessarily occupy a closed shell, the calculations become somewhat more involved. A number of antisymmetric wave functions are now possible. Denoting the single-electron state occupied by the ith electron by the symbol $(nlm_l|i)\alpha(i)\beta(i)$ we have for, say, the configuration $(1s)(2p)$ the following single electron functions

$$
\begin{array}{cc}
1s & 2p \\
(100|1)\alpha(1) & (211|2)\alpha(2) \\
(100|1)\beta(1) & (210|2)\alpha(2) \\
 & (21\bar{1}|2)\alpha(2) \\
 & (211|2)\beta(2) \\
 & (210|2)\beta(2) \\
 & (21\bar{1}|2)\beta(2)
\end{array}
\tag{3.121}
$$

Here the symbol $(nl\bar{m}_l|i)$ denotes a negative value of m_l. Because n is different for the two electrons, all of the possible wave functions are permitted in this case. There are now twelve antisymmetric wave functions of the form

$$\Phi_1 = \frac{1}{\sqrt{2}} [(100|1)\alpha(1)(21\bar{1}|2)\beta(2) - (100|2)\alpha(2)(21\bar{1}|1)\beta(1)] \tag{3.122}$$

This may be abbreviated by indicating only the main diagonal of the corresponding determinant:

$$
\begin{array}{cccc}
& & M_L & M_S \\
\Phi_1 = \frac{1}{\sqrt{2}}\,|(100|1)\alpha(1)(211|2)\beta(2)| & & 1 & 1 \\[2mm]
\Phi_2 = \frac{1}{\sqrt{2}}\,|(100|1)\alpha(1)(211|2)\beta(2)| & & 1 & 0 \\[2mm]
\Phi_3 = \frac{1}{\sqrt{2}}\,|(100|1)\beta(1)(211|2)\alpha(2)| & & 1 & 0 \\[2mm]
\Phi_4 = \frac{1}{\sqrt{2}}\,|(100|1)\beta(1)(211|2)\beta(2)| & & 1 & -1 \\[2mm]
\Phi_5 = \frac{1}{\sqrt{2}}\,|(100|1)\alpha(1)(210|2)\alpha(2)| & & 0 & 1 \\[2mm]
\Phi_6 = \frac{1}{\sqrt{2}}\,|(100|1)\alpha(1)(210|2)\beta(2)| & & 0 & 0 \\[2mm]
\Phi_7 = \frac{1}{\sqrt{2}}\,|(100|1)\beta(1)(210|2)\alpha(2)| & & 0 & 0 \\[2mm]
\Phi_8 = \frac{1}{\sqrt{2}}\,|(100|1)\beta(1)(210|2)\beta(2)| & & 0 & -1 \\[2mm]
\Phi_9 = \frac{1}{\sqrt{2}}\,|(100|1)\alpha(1)(21\bar{1}|2)\alpha(2)| & & -1 & 1 \\[2mm]
\Phi_{10} = \frac{1}{\sqrt{2}}\,|(100|1)\alpha(1)(21\bar{1}|2)\beta(2)| & & -1 & 0 \\[2mm]
\Phi_{11} = \frac{1}{\sqrt{2}}\,|(100|1)\beta(1)(21\bar{1}|2)\alpha(2)| & & -1 & 0 \\[2mm]
\Phi_{12} = \frac{1}{\sqrt{2}}\,|(100|1)\beta(1)(21\bar{1}|2)\beta(2)| & & -1 & -1
\end{array}
\tag{3.123}
$$

On applying $\mathbf{L}_z$ and $\mathbf{J}_z$ to the above functions it is readily confirmed that they are eigenfunctions of the operators with eigenvalues given by

$$
\begin{aligned}
\mathbf{L}_z \Phi_i &= (m_{l_1} + m_{l_2})\hbar\Phi_i = M_L\hbar\Phi_i \\
\mathbf{S}_z \Phi_i &= (m_{s_1} + m_{s_2})\hbar\Phi_i = M_S\hbar\Phi_i
\end{aligned}
\tag{3.124}
$$

The antisymmetric functions have been arranged in order of decreasing M_L, and for a given M_L in terms of decreasing M_S. With this labelling the secular equation becomes, in view of our previous discussion of theorem IV,

$$\begin{vmatrix}
H_{11}-E^{(1)} & 0 & 0 & 0 & 0 & 0 & 0 & 0 & 0 & 0 & 0 & 0 \\
0 & \multicolumn{2}{c}{\boxed{A}} & 0 & 0 & 0 & 0 & 0 & 0 & 0 & 0 & 0 \\
0 & & & 0 & 0 & 0 & 0 & 0 & 0 & 0 & 0 & 0 \\
0 & 0 & 0 & H_{44}-E^{(1)} & 0 & 0 & 0 & 0 & 0 & 0 & 0 & 0 \\
0 & 0 & 0 & 0 & H_{55}-E^{(1)} & 0 & 0 & 0 & 0 & 0 & 0 & 0 \\
0 & 0 & 0 & 0 & 0 & \multicolumn{2}{c}{\boxed{B}} & 0 & 0 & 0 & 0 & 0 \\
0 & 0 & 0 & 0 & 0 & & & 0 & 0 & 0 & 0 & 0 \\
0 & 0 & 0 & 0 & 0 & 0 & 0 & H_{88}-E^{(1)} & 0 & 0 & 0 & 0 \\
0 & 0 & 0 & 0 & 0 & 0 & 0 & 0 & H_{99}-E^{(1)} & 0 & 0 & 0 \\
0 & 0 & 0 & 0 & 0 & 0 & 0 & 0 & 0 & \multicolumn{2}{c}{\boxed{C}} & 0 \\
0 & 0 & 0 & 0 & 0 & 0 & 0 & 0 & 0 & & & 0 \\
0 & 0 & 0 & 0 & 0 & 0 & 0 & 0 & 0 & 0 & 0 & H_{12,12}-E^{(1)}
\end{vmatrix} = 0 \quad (3.125)$$

where

$$|A| = \begin{vmatrix} H_{22} & -E^{(1)} & H_{23} & -E^{(1)} \\ H_{32} & -E^{(1)} & H_{33} & -E^{(1)} \end{vmatrix}$$

$$|B| = \begin{vmatrix} H_{66} & -E^{(1)} & H_{67} & -E^{(1)} \\ H_{76} & -E^{(1)} & H_{77} & -E^{(1)} \end{vmatrix} \qquad (3.126)$$

$$|C| = \begin{vmatrix} H_{10,10} & -E^{(1)} & H_{10,11} & -E^{(1)} \\ H_{11,10} & -E^{(1)} & H_{11,11} & -E^{(1)} \end{vmatrix}$$

The determinant may be factored with the result

$$|A| \, |B| \, |C|(H_{11} - E^{(1)})(H_{44} - E^{(1)})(H_{55} - E^{(1)})$$
$$\times (H_{88} - E^{(1)})(H_{99} - E^{(1)})(H_{12,12} - E^{(1)}) = 0 \quad (3.127)$$

The roots $E^{(1)}$ of this equation can be obtained by straightforward procedures.

It is interesting, however, to carry the problem a little further and seek the eigenfunctions θ of $\mathbf{L}^2$ and $\mathbf{S}^2$ which are also the eigenfunctions of $\mathbf{L}_z$ and $\mathbf{S}_z$. Such a common set must exist since all of these operators commute with one another. By applying $\mathbf{L}^2$ and $\mathbf{S}^2$ to Φ it is clear that these functions are not necessarily eigenfunctions of $\mathbf{L}_z$ and $\mathbf{S}_z$. It is possible, however, to construct the required eigenfunctions by forming linear combinations of Φ. If θ is such a linear combination then

$$\begin{aligned}
\mathbf{L}^2\theta &= L(L + 1)\hbar^2\theta \\
\mathbf{S}^2\theta &= S(S + 1)\hbar^2\theta \\
\mathbf{L}_z\theta &= M_L\hbar\theta \qquad M_L = L_1, L - 1, \ldots, -L \\
\mathbf{S}_z\theta &= M_s\hbar\theta \qquad M_S = S, S - 1, \ldots, -S
\end{aligned} \qquad (3.128)$$

We can show that for a θ, with a given S and L, the energy associated with different values of M_L and M_s is the same if $\mathbf{L}$ and $\mathbf{S}$ commutes with $\mathbf{H}$, which is the case here. Applying $\mathbf{L}_-$ to $\theta(LSM_LM_s)$ we have from (2.261)

$$\mathbf{L}_-\theta(L, M_L) = [L(L + 1) - M_L(M_L - 1)]^{1/2}\hbar\theta(L, M_L - 1) \quad (3.129)$$

hence the energy of the state $\theta(L_1M_L - 1)$ is given by the scalar product

$$\begin{aligned}
[\theta(L, M_L - 1)\mathbf{H}\theta(L, M_L - 1) &= [L(L + 1) - M_L(M_L - 1)]^{-1}\hbar^{-2} \\
&\quad \times [\mathbf{L}_{-1}\theta(L, M_L), \mathbf{H}\mathbf{L}_{-1}\theta(L, M_L)] \\
&= [L(L + 1) - M_L(M_L - 1)]^{-1}\hbar^{-2} \\
&\quad \times [\mathbf{L}_+\mathbf{L}_-\theta(L, M_L), \mathbf{H}\theta(L, M_L)] \quad (3.130)
\end{aligned}$$

In order to obtain the last expression we have used the fact that $\mathbf{L}_-$ and $\mathbf{H}$ commute and $\mathbf{L}_-^\dagger = \mathbf{L}_+$. Finally, on applying the Hermitian operator $\mathbf{L}_+\mathbf{L}_-$ in (3.130) we have the desired result

$$[\theta(L_1M_L - 1), \mathbf{H}\theta(L_1M_L - 1)] = [\theta(LM_L), \mathbf{H}(L_1M_L)]. \quad (3.131)$$

Similar procedures can be used to prove the above assertion for M_s.

PROBLEMS

1. In obtaining (3.131) we have used $\mathbf{L}_+\mathbf{L}_- = \mathbf{L}^2 - \mathbf{L}_z^2 + \mathbf{L}_z$. Obtain this relationship and complete the derivation.

2. Carry through the above proof for M_s.

It follows from this result that the energy depends only on L and S for a given value of the principle quantum number, n. This conclusion, of course holds only when spin-orbital interaction is neglected as well as external fields.

We can now find the number of energy levels for the $(1s)$ $(2p)$ configuration without solving (3.127). If we assume Russell-Saunders coupling as discussed earlier, then we see that $L = 1$ and $S = 0$ and 1 so that there will be a singlet state (^1P) energy level and a triplet state (^3P) energy level. The function θ can be assigned to one or the other of these two levels. Though we cannot enter into the details for forming the required linear combinations, a general idea of the procedure can be obtained from some qualitative considerations. It is clear from (3.128) that only Φ functions of the same M_L and M_s can be used in forming the required θ functions. On inspecting our list of Φ functions we see that Φ_1, Φ_4, Φ_5, Φ_8, and Φ_{12} each have a unique set of M_s and M_L. Hence these cannot be combined with any other function and must be θ functions. This may be verified by applying $\mathbf{L}^2$ and $\mathbf{S}^2$ to each of the above functions. We find, for example, that for Φ_1 we have $L = 1$ and $S = 1$ so that Φ_1 must correspond to the term ^3P. By noting the value of M_s it is clear that Φ_4, Φ_5, Φ_8, and Φ_{12} also belong to ^3P. On the other hand Φ_2 and Φ_3 turn out not to be eigenvalues of $\mathbf{L}^2$ and $\mathbf{S}^2$ and we must form appropriate linear combinations.

In order to obtain the energies associated with each term the integrals must be evaluated. It then develops that the terms with the highest multiplicity (i.e., the triplet term in our case) have the lowest energy. This is the so-called *Hund's rule* from spectroscopy. Hund's rule is also apparent in the build-up of the electron configurations shown in table 3.1 where the electrons tend to occupy orbitals so as to remain unpaired.

3.10 *SPIN-ORBIT COUPLING*

Under the influence of spin-orbit coupling there is further splitting of multiple terms so that, for example, the triplet term is divided into three energy levels $^3P_2$, $^3P_1$, $^3P_0$ in accordance with the Russell-Saunders' coupling

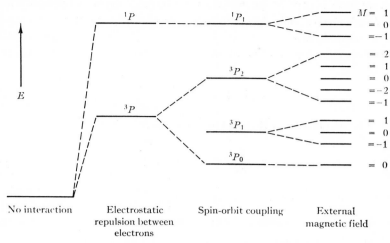

^1P		$^1P_1$	$M = 1$	
			$= 0$	
			$= -1$	

Figure 3.3: Interactions for the (is) (2p) configuration.

scheme, i.e., J through $L + S$, $L + S - 1, \ldots, (L - S)$. The effects of electrostatic repulsion and spin-orbit interaction are shown in Figure 3.3. As pointed out previously, when spin-orbit interactions are included in the Hamiltonian then J rather than L or S is a constant of motion. Since $\mathbf{J}$ commutes with $\mathbf{H}$ we can prove by exactly the same procedure used to establish (3.131) that for a given L, S, and J the energy is independent of M_J. This results in a $2J + 1$ degeneracy in the energy which is removed in a magnetic field, as shown in figure 3.1. The splitting of energy levels in a magnetic field is referred to as the *Zeeman effect*.

Expressions may be readily derived for both spin-orbit and Zeeman splitting. In the instance of spin-orbit interaction the contribution to the Hamiltonian is of the form

$$\mathbf{H}^{(1)} = f(r)\mathbf{LS} \tag{3.132}$$

Using the identity

$$\mathbf{LS} = \tfrac{1}{2}(\mathbf{J}^2 - \mathbf{L}^2 - \mathbf{S}^2) \tag{3.133}$$

We have for the energy shift

$$\Delta E = \langle \mathbf{H}^{(1)} \rangle = [J(J + 1) - L(L + 1) - S(S + 1)]\frac{\hbar^2}{2} \langle f(r) \rangle \tag{3.134}$$

For a given term the L and S values are the same so that the separation between the states with quantum numbers J and $J + 1$ is given by

$$(J + 1)\hbar^2 \langle f(r) \rangle \tag{3.135}$$

The separation is thus proportional to the larger J value, a relation known as the *Landé interval rule*. As an example, the relative separation between the states $^3P_1$ and $^3P_2$ is $1:2$.

The Zeeman effect may be treated in a similar way. The perturbation is given by

$$\mathbf{H}^{(1)} = -\mu_0 \bar{H} \cdot (\mathbf{L} + 2\mathbf{S}) = -\mu_0 \bar{H} \cdot (\mathbf{J} + \mathbf{S}) \qquad (3.136)$$

where $\bar{H}$ is the magnetic field intensity and

$$\mu_0 = \frac{e\hbar}{2mc} \qquad \text{(Bohr magneton)} \qquad (3.137)$$

Since $\mathbf{J}$ and $\mathbf{S}$ commute we have the identity

$$\mathbf{SJ} = \mathbf{JS} \qquad (3.138)$$

Therefore

$$\mathbf{SJ}^2 = \mathbf{JS} \cdot \mathbf{J} \qquad (3.139)$$

hence

$$\langle \mathbf{S} \rangle = \left\langle \frac{\mathbf{JS} \cdot \mathbf{J}}{J(J+1)} \right\rangle \qquad (3.140)$$

Equation (3.140) may be transformed by introducing

$$\mathbf{S} \cdot \mathbf{J} = \tfrac{1}{2}(\mathbf{J}^2 + \mathbf{S}^2 - \mathbf{L}^2) \qquad (3.141)$$

which is obtained from

$$\mathbf{J} - \mathbf{S} = \mathbf{L} \qquad (3.142)$$

We now find that

$$\Delta E = \langle H^{(1)} \rangle = \mu_0 \langle \bar{H} \cdot \mathbf{J} \rangle \left[1 + \frac{J(J+1) + S(S+1) - L(L+1)}{2J(J+1)} \right] \qquad (3.143)$$

If the direction of $\bar{H}$ is taken along the z-axis then $\bar{H} \cdot \mathbf{J} = H\mathbf{J}_z$ and therefore

$$\Delta E = -\mu_0 H g M_J \qquad (3.144)$$

where g is the *Landé g-factor* given by

$$g = 1 + \frac{J(J+1) + S(S+1) - L(L+1)}{2J(J+1)} \qquad (3.145)$$

3.11 COUPLED OSCILLATORS AND PHONONS

As a final topic relating to many-body systems we shall consider the important problem of coupled oscillators. An example of such a system is the crystal lattice where the atoms, which are bonded to one another, undergo oscillations about their equilibrium position. In this section we shall formulate the general problem of coupled systems which undergo small oscillations using the results relating to normal coordinates derived in appendix II. We consider a coupled system of N particles each of mass m_k. In terms of the generalized coordinates q_i, the kinetic T, and potential V, energies are given by (see appendix III).

$$T = \frac{1}{2} \sum_{i,j=1}^{3N} m_{ij} \dot{q}_i \dot{q}_j \qquad (3.146)$$

$$V = \frac{1}{2} \sum_{i,j=1}^{3N} k_{ij} q_i q_j \qquad (3.147)$$

where

$$m_{ij} = \sum_{k=1}^{N} m_k \left(\frac{\partial x_k}{\partial q_i} \frac{\partial x_k}{\partial q_j} + \frac{\partial y_k}{\partial q_i} \frac{\partial y_k}{\partial q_j} + \frac{\partial z_k}{\partial q_i} \frac{\partial z_k}{\partial q_j} \right) \qquad (3.148)$$

$$k_{ij} = \left(\frac{\partial^2 V}{\partial q_i \partial q_j} \right)_0 \qquad (3.149)$$

It is desirable to reduce (3.146) and (3.147) to a form involving only the sum of the square terms. This transformation can be achieved by means of normal coordinates Q_i which are related to the generalized coordinates q_i by the matrix equation

$$(q_i) = (R_{ij})(Q_j) \qquad (3.150)$$

where (R_{ij}) is the transformation matrix. For any particular coordinate q_i, (3.150) gives

$$q_i = \sum_{j=1}^{3N} R_{ij} Q_j$$

In terms of the normal coordinates the kinetic and potential energies become

$$T = \frac{1}{2} \sum_{i=1}^{3N} \dot{Q}_i^2 \qquad (3.151)$$

$$V = \frac{1}{2} \sum_{i=1}^{3N} \frac{Q_i^2}{\lambda_i} \qquad (3.152)$$

where the λ_i are the roots of the secular equation

$$|(m_{ij}) - \lambda(k_{ij})| = 0$$

the generalized momentum is

$$P_i = \frac{\partial L}{\partial \dot{Q}_i} = \frac{\partial T}{\partial \dot{Q}_i} = \dot{Q}_i$$

so that the Hamiltonian of the coupled system is

$$H = T + V = \frac{1}{2} \sum_i \left(P_i^2 + \frac{Q_i^2}{\lambda_i} \right)$$

$$= \frac{1}{2} \sum_i (P_i^2 + \omega_i^2 Q_i^2) \qquad (3.153)$$

where

$$\omega_i^2 \equiv \lambda_i^{-1}$$

where w_i is the frequency of the normal mode.

The Hamiltonian operator corresponding to (3.153) is found by the usual procedure of substituting, for P_i, the operator

$$\mathbf{P}_i = \frac{\hbar}{i} \frac{\partial}{\partial Q_i}$$

and the resulting wave equation is

$$\sum_{i=1}^{3N} \left(\frac{\partial^2 \psi}{\partial Q_i^2} \right) + \frac{2}{\hbar^2} \left(E - \frac{1}{2} \sum_i \omega_i^2 Q_i^2 \right) \psi = 0 \qquad (3.154)$$

This equation may be solved by substituting

$$\psi = \prod_{i=1} \psi_i \quad \text{and} \quad E = \sum_i E_i$$

so that we find

$$\frac{\partial^2 \psi_i}{\partial Q_i^2} + \frac{2}{\hbar^2} \left(E_i - \frac{\omega_i^2}{2} Q_i^2 \right) \psi_i = 0$$

Clearly this last result is of the same form as the harmonic oscillator discussed in chapter 2 (see 2.87) with

$$m = 1$$

$$\omega_i^2 = k$$

$$\beta_i = \frac{\omega_i}{\hbar}$$

so that

$$E_i = \hbar\omega_i\left(n + \frac{1}{2}\right) \qquad n = 0, 1, 2, \ldots \tag{3.155}$$

$$\psi_i = \left[\frac{\left(\frac{\beta_i}{\pi}\right)^{1/2}}{2^n n!}\right]^{1/2} H_n(\sqrt{\beta_i}\, Q_i)e^{-(\beta_i Q_i^2/2)} \tag{3.156}$$

We see that the energy associated with each normal mode is quantized and the allowed values are given by (3.155). It is customary to refer to these quantized energy states associated with the lattice vibrations as *phonons*. The energy of a phonon of frequency ω_i is $\hbar\omega_i$ so that if we have n phonons this is equivalent to exciting the normal lattice mode of frequency ω_i to the energy state $\hbar\omega_i(n + \frac{1}{2})$. If all the phonons were to disappear then the mode corresponding to ω_i is left with the zero-point energy of $\frac{1}{2}\hbar\omega_i$.

Phonons may be regarded as a quantized energy unit or "particle" associated with the elastic field of the lattice as, similarly, photons are the quantized energy units associated with the electromagnetic field. Indeed, a number of other quantized energy fields arise in solid state physics. For example, the *exciton* is the energy packet associated with the electrically neutral excited states of a dielectric, the *polaron* arises from the coupled electron-phonon field, while the *magnon* is associated with the coupled electron spins.

We may therefore consider the phonon as a wave packet with energy $\hbar\omega_i$ and a wave vector K_s. These packets may interact, under certain conditions, to produce new phonons, thus

$$\underset{\text{phonon}}{K_1} + \underset{\text{phonon}}{K_2} \rightarrow \underset{\text{phonon}}{K_3}$$

For such a three-phonon process it can be shown that the conservation of both energy and wave vectors must hold:

$$\hbar\omega_1 + \hbar\omega_2 = \hbar\omega_3$$

$$\overline{K}_1 + \overline{K}_2 = \overline{K}_3$$

Such phonon-phonon interaction may result in the production of a new phonon with a motion in the direction opposite to the original phonons. It is this type of process (an Umklapp process) which accounts in part for the thermal resistance of solids. In addition, phonon-electron interactions may occur, contributing to the electrical resistance of a solid. Detailed accounts of these and other interactions are given in the book by Ziman.

PROBLEMS

1. Verify 3.75 and show that if $\mathbf{J}_1$ and $\mathbf{J}_2$ are constants of motion then $\mathbf{J}$ is a constant of motion.

2. Show that the matrix representation of $\mathbf{L}_z$ and $\mathbf{L}^2$ may be expressed as

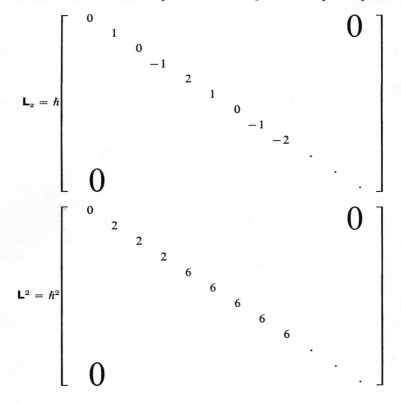

4 / Statistical and

Thermodynamic Approaches

Statistical considerations play an important role in the discussion of systems consisting of a large number of particles. In this chapter we present a brief introduction to statistical mechanics and then discuss a number of important applications to electron physics.

4.1 STATISTICAL DISTRIBUTIONS

We have seen in chapter 3 that no two fermions can occupy the same single particle state. This restriction does not apply to bosons, any number of which can occupy the same single particle state. It was also shown that the system wave function ψ of a collection of noninteracting particles is a linear combination of the products of the single particle wave functions, i.e.,

$$\psi = \sum a_r P^r \phi_1^{(1)} \phi_2^{(2)} \ldots \qquad (4.1)$$

(ϕ_k^i indicates that the ith electron is in state ϕ_k). Where P^r signifies the operation of permuting the particles among the single particle states ϕ, and a_r is chosen to make (4.1) symmetric ($a_r = 1$) or antisymmetric [$a_r = (-1)^r$]. We now ask the question, given a system of n identical particles with a total energy E, how will these particles distribute themselves among the available energy states at equilibrium? We require that the energy E and the number of particles remain fixed:

$$\sum_i E_i n_i = E$$

$$\sum_i n_i = n \qquad (4.2)$$

where E_i is the energy associated with the ith state and n_i the number of particles in the ith state. In general E_i will be degenerate with g_i wave functions $\phi_{i1}, \phi_{i2}, \ldots, \phi_{ig}$ corresponding to E_i:

$$
\begin{array}{ccc}
E_1 & E_2 & E_3 \ldots \\
g_1 & g_2 & g_3 \\
n_1 & n_2 & n_3
\end{array}
\tag{4.3}
$$

We shall refer to any particular distribution $n_1, n_2, n_3, \ldots$ of the particles as a configuration. Clearly each configuration has associated with it a certain number of states ψ. The number of ψ associated with a configuration varies with the configuration as shown for a simple example of fermions in figure 4.1. For simplicity we ignore any constraints on the total energy. In the case $n_1 = 3, n_2 = 0, n_3 = 0$ we can have only one state for the system. In the case of electrons this state is

$$
\psi = \sum (-1)^r P^r \phi_{11}^{(1)} \phi_{12}^{(2)} \phi_{13}^{(3)}
\tag{4.4}
$$

The other configuration shown can be similarly treated.

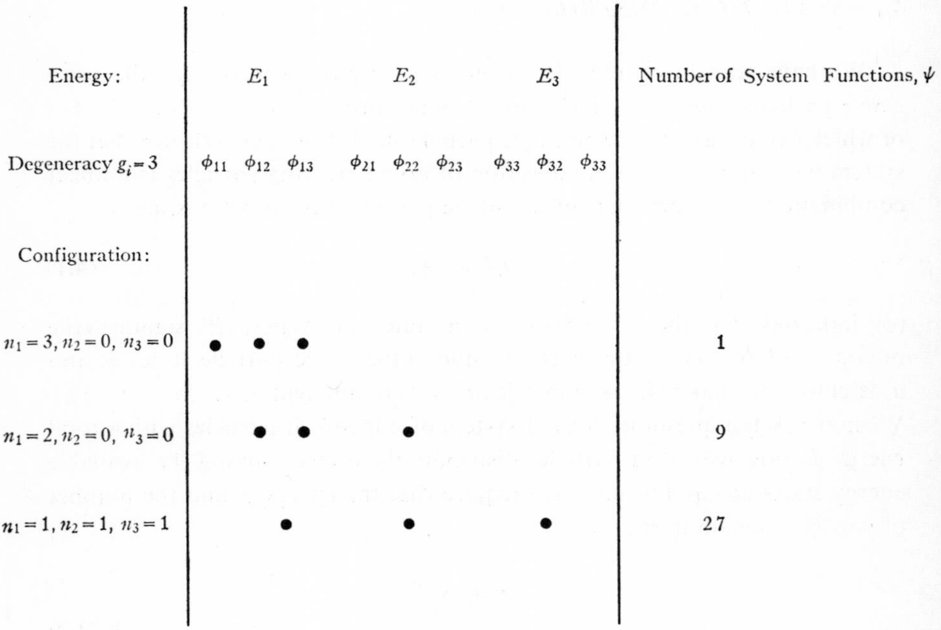

Energy:	E_1			E_2			E_3			Number of System Functions, ψ
Degeneracy $g_i = 3$	ϕ_{11}	ϕ_{12}	ϕ_{13}	ϕ_{21}	ϕ_{22}	ϕ_{23}	ϕ_{33}	ϕ_{32}	ϕ_{33}	
Configuration:										
$n_1 = 3, n_2 = 0, n_3 = 0$	●	●	●							1
$n_1 = 2, n_2 = 0, n_3 = 0$	●	●				●				9
$n_1 = 1, n_2 = 1, n_3 = 1$			●			●			●	27

Figure 4.1: The states ψ associated with various fermion configurations with no constrain on the total energy.

In order to find the equilibrium configuration, we use a fundamental postulate of statistical mechanics, namely, *the states ψ have an equal probability of occurring.* Hence the most likely configuration at equilibrium is that corresponding to the maximum number of states ψ, subject to the constraints (4.2).

In order to apply this postulate we must find an expression for the number of states associated with a given configuration. In the case of fermions only one particle may occupy a single particle state ϕ. Consider the energy E_i. If there are n_i fermions associated with this energy then the number of different ways t_i of assigning identical particles to the g_i functions is

$$t_i = \frac{g_i(g_i - 1)\ldots(g_i - n_i - 1)}{n_i!}$$

$$t_i = \frac{g_i!}{n_i!(g_i - n_i)!}$$

(4.5)

since we may assign the first particle in g_i ways, the second in $(g_i - 1)$, and so on, while the last particle may be assigned in $g_i - n_i - 1$ ways. Since we are not interested in the order of the particles associated with the assignments we divide by $n_i!$. The total number of assignments corresponding to the configuration $n_1, n_2, \ldots$ is then

$$t_{FD} = \prod^i \frac{g_i!}{n_i!(g_i - n_i)!}$$

(4.6)

On maximizing (4.6) we shall obtain the Fermi-Dirac distribution which holds for electrons and other fermions. Before proceding however, we wish to obtain the corresponding expression for bosons. In this case any number of bosons may be assigned to a given ϕ. The problem is then the familiar one of distributing n_i identical objects among g_i identical boxes. As may be seen from figure 4.2 this problem is equivalent to finding the permutations of n_i identical objects with $g_i - 1$ identical partitions between the boxes:

$$t_i = \frac{(n_i + g_i - 1)!}{n_i!(g_i - 1)!}$$

(4.7)

The factors $n_i!$ and $(g_i - 1)!$ appear since we are not interested in the ordering of the particles or partitions. For the entire configuration the total number of system wave functions or assignments is given by

$$t_{BE} = \prod^i \frac{(n_i + g_i - 1)!}{n_i!(g_i - 1)!}$$

(4.8)

This assignment leads to the Bose–Einstein statistics.

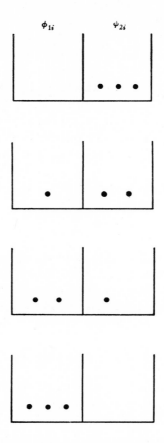

Figure 4.2: The possible ways of assigning $ni = 3$ bosons to $gi = 2$ states.

We next must find the maximum of t_{FD} and t_{BE}, with respect to n_i, subject to the restrictions (4.2). Since t will be maximum when $\ln t$ is maximum we have the more convenient expressions

$$\ln t_{FD} = \sum \ln g_i! - \sum \ln n_i! - \sum \ln (g_i - n_i)!$$
$$\ln t_{BE} = \sum \ln (n_i + g_i - 1)! - \sum \ln n_i! - \sum \ln (g_i - 1)! \tag{4.9}$$

Introducing the Sterling approximation

$$\ln n! = n \ln n - n \tag{4.10}$$

and setting $(g_i - 1) \approx g_i$ we have

$$\ln t_{FD} = \sum_i \left(-g_i \ln \frac{g_i - n_i}{g_i} + n_i \ln \frac{g_i - n_i}{n_i} \right) \qquad (4.11)$$

$$\ln t_{BE} = \sum_i \left(g_i \ln \frac{g_i + n_i}{g_i} + n_i \ln \frac{g_i + n_i}{n_i} \right) \qquad (4.12)$$

In order to maximize (4.11) and (4.12) we apply the condition

$$d \ln t = 0 \qquad (4.13)$$

subject to the restraints

$$\sum_i dn_i = 0 \qquad (4.13a)$$

$$\sum_i E_i \, dn_i = 0 \qquad (4.13b)$$

This type of problem is best handled by means of Lagrangian multipliers, i.e., we multiply (4.13a) by α and (4.13b) by β and add the result to (4.13). We find that

$$\sum_i \left(\ln \frac{n_i}{g_i - n_i} + \alpha + \beta E_i \right) dn_i = 0 \qquad (FD) \qquad (4.14)$$

$$\sum_i \left(\ln \frac{n_i}{g_i + n_i} + \alpha + \beta E_i \right) dn_i = 0 \qquad (BE) \qquad (4.15)$$

Since dn_i is independent and arbitrary we must have

$$\ln \frac{n_i}{g_i - n_i} + \alpha + \beta E_i = 0$$

$$\ln \frac{n_i}{g_i + n_i} + \alpha + \beta E_i = 0 \qquad (4.16)$$

or

$$n_i = \frac{g_i}{e^{\alpha + \beta E_i} + 1} \qquad (FD) \qquad (4.17)$$

and

$$n_i = \frac{g_i}{e^{\alpha + \beta E_i} - 1} \qquad (BE) \qquad (4.18)$$

Equations (4.17) and (4.18) are the desired results for the equilibrium distribution in the Fermi–Dirac and Bose–Einstein cases.

We note from (4.17) and (4.18) that if $g_i/n_i \gg 1$, both expressions become identical and reduce to the Boltzmann distribution:

$$n_i = \frac{g_i}{e^{\alpha + \beta E_i}} \quad \text{(Boltzmann)} \tag{4.19}$$

In general the Boltzmann distribution may be expected to hold, provided concentration of the particles is not too great and the system not too near absolute zero, since then the lower energy levels tend to become crowded and the inequality given above may no longer apply. However, with these restrictions in mind the Boltzmann approximation has been found to be useful.

We now consider the quantities α and β appearing in the above distributions. Since βE_i must be unitless, β must have the dimensions of reciprocal energy. Now the energy of a system of free noninteracting particles, the so-called perfect gas, depends directly on kT, where k is the Boltzmann constant (1.38×10^{-16} ergs/deg) and T is the absolute temperature. These considerations lead us to identify β with $1/kT$. The identification is justified in much greater detail in all standard works on statistical mechanics. In order to obtain a relationship for α we introduce (4.19) into (4.2) and we find that

$$e^{\alpha} = \frac{1}{n} \sum_i g_i e^{-E_i/kT} = \frac{Q}{n} \tag{4.20}$$

the summation Q is referred to as the *partition function* of the system. We also can express (4.20) as

$$\alpha = \ln \frac{Q}{n} \tag{4.21}$$

On substituting (4.20) into (4.19) we find

$$n_i = \frac{n g_i e^{-E_i/kT}}{Q} \tag{4.22}$$

Another relationship of importance is obtained by substituting (4.22) into (4.2) which gives the result

$$E = \frac{n \sum_i E_i g_i e^{-E_i/kT}}{\sum g_i e^{-E_i/kT}} = \frac{n}{Q} \sum E_i g_i e^{-E_i/kT} \tag{4.23}$$

This last result can also be expressed in terms of the partition function on recognizing that

$$\frac{\partial Q}{\partial T} = \frac{1}{kT^2} \sum g_i E_i e^{-E_i/kT} \tag{4.24}$$

so that

$$E = \frac{nkT^2}{Q} \frac{\partial Q}{\partial T} \tag{4.25}$$

Equation (4.25) permits us to express the total internal energy in terms of the partition function.

4.2 ENTROPY

According to the second law of thermodynamics the entropy of an isolated system undergoing an irreversible change always increases until equilibrium is achieved, at which the entropy remains at a constant maximum value. This fundamental property of entropy is exactly that of the function t. As we have seen, the number of system states t also tends to a maximum at equilibrium consistent with the constraints (4.2). We expect that there must be a functional relationship between entropy S and t, i.e., $S = f(t)$. The nature of this relationship is made clear by considering what happens when two systems which are in equilibrium with each other are converted into a single system. Since entropy is an extensive property, the entropy of the combined system S_{12} must equal the sum of the individual entropies S_1 and S_2:

$$S_{12} = S_1 + S_2 \tag{4.26}$$

hence

$$f(t_{12}) = f(t_1) + f(t_2) \tag{4.27}$$

On the other hand, the total number of states t_{12} of the combined system must equal $t_1 t_2$ since any state of one system may be taken in combination with a state from the other. It follows that

$$f(t_{12}) = f(t_1 \times t_2) \tag{4.28}$$

hence we require that

$$f(t_1 \times t_2) = f(t_1) + f(t_2) \tag{4.29}$$

This functional relationship is clearly satisfied by choosing $f(t) = k \ln t$ hence

$$S = k \ln t \tag{4.30}$$

Since entropy has the dimensions of energy per degree absolute and $\ln t$ is dimensionless, the proportionality constant k must also have the dimensions of energy per degree absolute. This last requirement is satisfied by identifying k with the Boltzmann constant.

We now shall evaluate (4.30) for the case $g_i/n_i \gg 1$. With this assumption both (4.11) and (4.12) become

$$\ln t = \sum_i (n_i \ln g_i - n_i \ln n_i + n_i) \tag{4.31}$$

and hence

$$S = k \sum_i n_i \left(\ln \frac{g_i}{n_i} + 1 \right) \tag{4.32}$$

On introducing (4.22) we obtain

$$S = nk \left(\ln \frac{Q}{n} + 1 \right) + \frac{E}{T} \tag{4.33}$$

or from (4.25)

$$S = nk \left(\ln \frac{Q}{n} + 1 \right) + \frac{nkT}{Q} \frac{\partial Q}{\partial T}$$

$$= nk \left(\ln \frac{Q}{n} + 1 \right) + nkT \frac{\partial \ln Q}{\partial T} \tag{4.34}$$

The free energy of the system F is defined by

$$F = H - TS \tag{4.35}$$

where the enthalpy H is given by

$$H = E + pV \tag{4.36}$$

Here p is the pressure and V the volume of the system. On introducing (4.25) and (4.34) into (4.35) and recalling that for an ideal gas $pV = nkT$ we find that

$$F = -nkT \ln \frac{Q}{n} \tag{4.37}$$

as the free energy of a system of noninteracting particles. This last result permits us to relate α to the free energy since from (4.21) we find that

$$\alpha = -\frac{F}{nkT} \tag{4.38}$$

In the theory of conductors the free energy per electron F/n is referred to as the *Fermi level* and will be represented here by E_F. With this notation we can write the Fermi–Dirac distribution for a system of electrons as

$$n_i = \frac{g_i}{1 + e^{(E_i - E_F)/kT}} \tag{4.39}$$

In many instances the energy levels may be regarded as forming a continuum so that g, the number of single particle states associated with E, may be written

$$g = N(E)\, dE \tag{4.40}$$

where $N(E)$ is the number of single particle states per unit energy in the interval dE about E. Introducing (4.40) into (4.39) gives the useful result

$$dn = \frac{N(E)\, dE}{1 + e^{(E - E_F)/kT}} = f(E)N(E)\, dE \tag{4.41}$$

where

$$f(E) = \frac{1}{1 + e^{(E - E_F)/kT}} \tag{4.42}$$

The factor $f(E)$ is referred to as the Fermi function and is the probability of finding an electron with energy E. The significance of E_F is apparent from (4.42), since when $E = E_F$ the probability is just one-half. The Fermi function is shown in figure 4.3. At absolute zero, the states with energy less than E_F

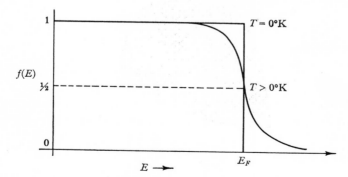

Figure 4.3: Fermi function $f(E)$.

are fully occupied while those with energy greater than E_F have zero probability of occupancy. At temperatures greater than $0°K$ the curve indicates a more gradual transition in the neighborhood of $E_F = \frac{1}{2}$.

4.3 *FREE ELECTRON THEORY OF METALS*

An interesting and important application of the above results is provided by the free electron theory of metals in which the conductor is regarded as consisting of a collection of free electrons in a three-dimensional box. As we have seen (2.67) the energy levels for a particle in a box with a side of length a is given by

$$E = \frac{\hbar^2\pi^2}{2ma^2} (l^2 + q^2 + n^2)$$

$$= \frac{\hbar^2\pi^2 r^2}{2ma^2} \qquad (r^2 = l^2 + q^2 + n^2) \qquad (4.43)$$

where the quantum number l, q, and n can assume only positive integral values. Each set of numbers l, q, n determines a single particle state function, and associated with each such state there are two electrons with different spins. In order to calculate the total number single electron states corresponding to E we make a three-dimensional plot shown in figure 4.4 by placing a point at integral values of l, q, and n. The space is thus resolved into cubes of unit volume with one point per unit volume since each point is

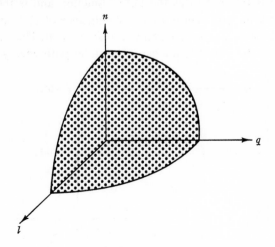

Figure 4.4: Distribution of quantum numbers.

shared by eight cubes and there are eight points per cube. For large E we find, to a good approximation, that the total number of states $G(E)$, excluding spin, is simply the volume of one octant of a sphere of radius r where r is given by (4.43):

$$G(E) = \tfrac{1}{8}(\tfrac{4}{3}\pi r^3)$$

$$= \frac{V}{6\pi^2\hbar^3}(2mE)^{3/2} \tag{4.44}$$

where V is the volume of the electron box given by a^3. The number of states per unit energy interval is simply the derivative of $G(E)$ with respect to E and the result must be multiplied by two because of spin degeneracy:

$$N(E) = \frac{mV}{\pi^2\hbar^3}(2mE)^{1/2} \tag{4.45}$$

The total number of electrons n is from (4.41)

$$n = \frac{(2m)^{3/2}V}{2\pi^2\hbar^3}\int\limits_0^\infty \frac{E^{1/2}\,dE}{1 + e^{(E-E_F)/kT}} \tag{4.46}$$

At zero degrees Kelvin the Fermi function is a step function as shown in figure 4.3. It is easy to see that (4.46) gives the result

$$n = \frac{(2mE_{F0})^{3/2}V}{3\pi^2\hbar^3} \tag{4.46a}$$

or

$$E_{F0} = \frac{\hbar^2}{2m}\left(\frac{3\pi^2 n}{V}\right)^{2/3}$$

where E_{F0} is the Fermi level at zero degrees Kelvin. Introducing (4.46a) into (4.46) we have the convenient result

$$n = \frac{3m}{2E_{F0}^{3/2}}\int\limits_0^\infty \frac{E^{1/2}\,dE}{1 + e^{(E-E_F)/kT}} \tag{4.46b}$$

The average value of the energy may be calculated from

$$\langle E \rangle = \int\limits_0^\infty EN(E)f(E)\,dE = \frac{3m}{2E_{F0}^{3/2}}\int\limits_0^\infty \frac{E^{3/2}\,dE}{1 + e^{(E-E_F)/kT}} \tag{4.46c}$$

The evaluation of (4.46) would be greatly facilitated if the quantity unity could be neglected in the denominator of the integral. Under these circumstances the distribution would correspond to the classical Boltzmann distribution, given by equation (4.19). Unfortunately this approximation cannot be made with the free electron model of a metal as we shall now show. An electron system is said to be *degenerate* if the classical Boltzmann statistics does not apply. In order for a system to be nondegenerate, and hence for the Boltzmann statistics to apply, we require that

$$e^{-E_F/kT} = e^{\alpha} \gg 1 \tag{4.47}$$

From (4.20) we have

$$e^{\alpha} = \frac{1}{n} \sum_i g_i e^{-E_i/kT} \tag{4.48}$$

On introducing the expression (4.43) for the translational energy E_i and replacing the sum by an integral, after introducing 4.45, we have on simplifying

$$e^{\alpha} = \frac{2V}{n} \left(\frac{8mkT}{h} \right)^{3/2} \left[\int_0^\infty e^{-y^2 dy} \right]^3 \tag{4.49}$$

where

$$y = \left(\frac{h}{8mkT} \right)^{3/2} l \qquad l = 1, 2, \dots$$
$$h = 2\pi\hbar \tag{4.50}$$

The integral is evaluated using

$$\int_0^\infty e^{-y^2 dy} = \frac{\sqrt{\pi}}{2} \tag{4.51}$$

so that

$$e^{\alpha} = \frac{2V}{n} \left(\frac{2m\pi kT}{h} \right)^{3/2} \tag{4.52}$$

For a typical metal we may assume that one electron per atom is ionized so that we expect an Avogadro number of electrons per gram atom of metal, i.e., 6×10^{23} electrons per gram atom. Assuming that $V \approx 10 \text{ cm}^3$ we find that

$$e^{\alpha} \approx 8 \times 10^{-8} T^{3/2} \tag{4.53}$$

so that condition (4.47) requires that $T \approx 10^6\,°K$. This temperature is well above the melting point of all metals and we conclude that the electrons inside a metal must be degenerate.

In order to integrate (4.46) in the case $E_F/kT \gg 1$, we make use of the general result proved in section 3.5, that

$$\int_0^\infty q(E)f(E)\,dE = \int_0^{E_F} q(E)\,dE + \frac{\pi^2}{6}(kT)^2\left(\frac{\partial q(E)}{\partial E}\right)_{E_F}$$

$$+ \frac{7\pi^4}{360}(kT)^4\left(\frac{\partial^3 q(E)}{\partial E^3}\right)_{E_F} + \cdots \quad (4.54)$$

for any well behaved $q(E)$ such that the above integral exists. In the present case we have $q(E) = E^{1/2}$ and $E^{3/2}$ for (4.46) and (4.46c) respectively. In the case of (4.46) we obtain the following result by straightforward calculation

$$\left(\frac{E_F}{E_{F0}}\right)^{3/2}\left[1 + \frac{\pi^2}{8}\left(\frac{kT}{E_F}\right)^2 + \frac{7\pi^4}{640}\left(\frac{kT}{E_F}\right)^4 + \cdots\right] = 1 \quad (4.55)$$

This expression may be put into a more useful form by writing

$$\left(\frac{E_F}{E_{F0}}\right)^{3/2}[1 + Z(E_F)] = 1 \quad (4.56)$$

and using the expansion

$$\frac{1}{(1+Z)^{2/3}} = 1 - \frac{2}{3}Z + \frac{5}{9}Z^2 \quad (4.57)$$

we obtain

$$E_F = E_{F0}\left[1 - \frac{\pi^2}{12}\left(\frac{kT}{E_F}\right)^2 + \frac{\pi^4}{720}\left(\frac{kT}{E_F}\right)^4 + \cdots\right] \quad (4.58)$$

By similar arguments (4.46c) gives the result

$$\langle E \rangle = \frac{3}{5}n\frac{E_F^{5/2}}{E_{F0}^{3/2}}\left[1 + \frac{5\pi^2}{8}\left(\frac{kT}{E_F}\right)^2 - \frac{7\pi^4}{384}\left(\frac{kT}{E_F}\right)^4 + \cdots\right] \quad (4.59)$$

One of the main results of the free electron theory is the explanation of the low atomic heat (specific heat per gram atom) of metals. If we assume that each atom of the metal provides one electron to the electron gas, and consider one gram atom of metal, then with the classical theory we have

$$\langle E \rangle = \frac{3}{2}RT \quad (4.60)$$

so that the atomic heat should be

$$\frac{d\langle E \rangle}{dT} = \frac{3}{2} R \qquad (4.61)$$

However, actual measurements indicate that the atomic heat is much lower.

The atomic heat may be calculated from (4.59) after substituting the value for E_F given by the first two terms of (4.58), and assuming that $E_F \approx E_{F0}$. We obtain

$$\langle E \rangle = \frac{3nE_{F0}}{5} \left[1 + \frac{5\pi^2}{12} \left(\frac{kT}{E_{F0}} \right)^2 + \cdots \right] \qquad (4.62)$$

which gives, to a first approximation, the result

$$\frac{d\langle E \rangle}{dT} = \frac{3R}{2} \left(\frac{\pi^2 kT}{3E_{F0}} \right) \qquad (4.63)$$

Comparison with (4.61) shows the last result to be considerably smaller. The electronic contribution to the specific heat is much less than that due to atomic vibrations and can be measured only at very low temperatures.

4.4 TRANSPORT PHENOMENA

Our previous discussion has been concerned with systems in equilibrium. We now consider the nonequilibrium situation which arises when, for example, a system of electrons in a metal or semiconductor is subjected to a system of forces $\bar{F}$. We have seen (in section 2.7) that an electron moving through a crystal may be represented by a wave packet with an energy determined by the wave number $\bar{k}$. The wave number is related to the expected value of the momentum, the *crystal momentum* $\bar{P}$, by means of the relationship

$$\hbar\bar{k} = \langle p \rangle = \bar{P} \qquad (4.64)$$

However, from (2.183) we have

$$\hbar\dot{\bar{k}} = \langle \dot{p} \rangle = \bar{F} \qquad (4.65)$$

In order to analyze the nonequilibrium situation it is convenient to introduce the probability distribution function $f(\bar{k}, \bar{r}, t)$ defined as the probability, at time t, of finding an electron with wave number $\bar{k}$ and position vector

$\bar{r}$ centered in the volume elements $d\bar{k}$ and $d\bar{r}$. The number of electrons dN in the element $d\bar{k} \, d\bar{r}$ at time t is

$$dN = f(\bar{k}, \bar{r}, t)N(\bar{k}, \bar{r}) \, d\bar{k} \, d\bar{r} \qquad (4.66)$$

where

$$\begin{aligned} d\bar{k} &= dk_x \, dk_y \, dk_z \\ d\bar{r} &= dx \, dy \, dz \end{aligned} \qquad (4.67)$$

and $N(\bar{k}, \bar{r})$ is the number of states at $\bar{k}$ and $\bar{r}$ per unit volume element in $\bar{k}$ and $\bar{r}$ space. It is convenient to think of the electrons as occupying a generalized volume $d\bar{k} \, d\bar{r}$. When the system is at equilibrium $f(\bar{k}, \bar{r}, t)$ becomes the Fermi distribution function $f(E)$ given by (4.42).

We now derive the differential equation governing the change in the distribution $f(\bar{k}, \bar{r}, t)$. This equation is of fundamental importance in the analysis of transport phenomena. Consider dN particles which at time t occupy a volume $d\bar{k} \, d\bar{r}$. We first consider the case where there are no collisions which may scatter the particles into or out of $d\bar{k} \, d\bar{r}$. The number of particles in this element of volume centered about $\bar{k}$ and $\bar{r}$ is for an isotropic material with uniform density of states N,

$$dN = f(\bar{k}, \bar{r}, t)N \, d\bar{k} \, d\bar{r} \qquad (4.68)$$

At time $t + dt$ these particles will have moved into a volume $d\bar{k}' \, d\bar{r}'$ at $\bar{k} + d\bar{k}$ and $\bar{r} + d\bar{r}$ and we have

$$dN = f(\bar{k} + d\bar{k}, \bar{r} + d\bar{r}, t + dt)N \, d\bar{k}' \, d\bar{r}' \qquad (4.69)$$

However $\bar{k}$, and hence $\langle p \rangle$, of the set of particles under consideration is very nearly the same as that at t. If $d\bar{r}$ is taken to be small in comparison with the variation in applied force, then to a first approximation all the particles in $dk \, dr$ will undergo equal increments in $\bar{k}$ and $\bar{r}$ and $d\bar{k}' \, d\bar{r}' \approx d\bar{k} \, d\bar{r}$. It follows therefore that

$$f(\bar{k} + dh, \bar{r} + d\bar{r}, t + dt) = f(\bar{k}, \bar{r}, t) \qquad (4.70)$$

or

$$\frac{df}{dt} = 0 \qquad (4.71)$$

Hence, if we neglect collisions and the resulting scattering, then (4.71) holds. This is one form of Liouville's theorem. If collisions occur, however, then particles will be scattered into or out of $d\bar{k}\ d\bar{r}$, and (4.71) no longer holds. The total change in $f(\bar{k}, \bar{r}, t)$ is then given by

$$\frac{df}{dt} = \frac{\partial f}{\partial t}\Bigg)_{\text{coll.}} \tag{4.72}$$

However, we can also express the total change in $f(\bar{k}, \bar{r}, t)$ in the form

$$\frac{df}{dt} = \frac{\partial f}{\partial t} + \sum_{i=1}^{3} \frac{\partial f}{\partial k_i} \cdot \frac{dk_i}{dt} + \sum_{i=1}^{3} \frac{\partial f}{\partial x_i} \cdot \frac{dx_i}{dt} \tag{4.73}$$

where k_i and x_i represent the components of $\bar{k}$ and $\bar{r}$. Equation (4.73) can also be written in vector notation, and on introducing (4.65) we have the *Boltzmann equation*

$$\frac{\partial f}{\partial t}\Bigg)_{\text{coll.}} = \frac{\partial f}{\partial t} + \frac{\bar{F}}{\hbar} \cdot \nabla_k f + \bar{v} \cdot \nabla_r f \tag{4.74}$$

where $\bar{v}$ is the velocity of the particles.

In the following we shall be interested in the *steady state* solutions to (4.74) for which $\partial f/\partial t = 0$. Under steady state conditions the perturbing effects of the collisions must be offset by a restoring tendency which, for small disturbances, may be taken as proportional to the deviation from equilibrium:

$$\frac{\partial f}{\partial t}\Bigg)_{\text{coll.}} = -\frac{f - f_0}{\tau} \tag{4.75}$$

where τ is referred to as the relaxation time. The distribution function in this case is then

$$f = f_0 + (f' - f_0)e^{-t/T} \tag{4.76}$$

where f_0 is the Fermi–Dirac function given by (4.42) and f' is the value of f at $t = 0$.

In the case of a homogeneous crystal, f does not depend on the position vector $\bar{r}$, and (4.74) may be written

$$f - f_0 = -\frac{\tau}{\hbar} \bar{F} \cdot \nabla_k f \tag{4.77}$$

If we assume that the deviation from equilibrium is small, f may be replaced by f_0 in the right-hand side and we obtain

$$f = f_0 - \frac{\tau}{\hbar} \bar{F} \cdot \nabla_k f_0 \tag{4.78}$$

The last result may be put into a more convenient form by recalling that f_0 is a function of the energy

$$f = f_0 - \frac{\tau}{\hbar}\frac{\partial f_0}{\partial E}(\bar{F}\cdot\nabla_k E) \qquad (4.79)$$

Since f_0, in the case of electrons, is the Fermi–Dirac function, we have

$$\frac{\partial f_0}{\partial E} = -\frac{f_0(1 - f_0)}{kT} \qquad (4.80)$$

and from (2.184), on setting $\langle v \rangle \equiv \bar{v}$,

$$\nabla_k E = \hbar\bar{v} \qquad (4.81)$$

so that (4.79) can also be written

$$f = f_0 + \frac{\tau}{kT}f_0(1 - f_0)(\bar{F}\cdot\bar{v}) \qquad (4.82)$$

4.5   FERMI–DIRAC INTEGRAL

We shall evaluate the Fermi–Dirac integral for the case $E_F/kT \gg 1$. In general we may deal with the integral

$$F = \int_0^\infty q(E)f(E)\, dE \qquad (4.83)$$

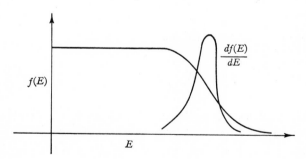

Figure 4.5: The Fermi-Dirac function and its first derivative.

where $q(E)$ is such that the integral exists. We observe from figure 4.5 that $\partial f(E)/\partial E$ vanishes for E considerably removed from E_F. It is easily seen on integrating by parts that

$$F = \int_0^\infty q(E)f(E)\, dE = -\int_0^\infty Q(E)\frac{\partial f(E)}{\partial E}\, dE \qquad (4.84)$$

where

$$Q(E) = \int_0^E q(E') \, dE' \tag{4.85}$$

In obtaining (4.84) we have used the relationship $Q(0) = 0$.
On introducing

$$x = \frac{E - E_F}{kT} \tag{4.86}$$

and expanding $Q(E)$ about $x = 0$ (i.e., $E = E_F$) we have

$$Q(x) = \sum_{n=0}^{\infty} \frac{x^n}{n!} \frac{\partial^n Q(x)}{\partial x^n}\bigg)_{x=0} \tag{4.87}$$

The partial derivatives may be easily shown to be given by

$$Q(x = 0) = \int_0^{E_F} q(E) \, dE$$

$$\frac{\partial^n Q(x)}{\partial x^n}\bigg)_{x=0} = (kT)^n \frac{\partial^{n-1} q(E)}{\partial E^{n-1}}\bigg)_{E_F} = B_n(E_F) \tag{4.88}$$

On introducing (4.87) into (4.84) we find that

$$F = -Q(0) \int_0^{\infty} \frac{\partial f(E)}{\partial E} \cdot dE - \sum_{n=1}^{\infty} \frac{B_n(E_F)}{n!} \int_{E_F/kT}^{\infty} x^n \frac{\partial f(x)}{\partial E} \, dx \tag{4.89}$$

The first integral is readily evaluated:

$$-\int_0^{\infty} \frac{\partial f(E)}{\partial E} \cdot dE = f(0) - f(\infty) = (1 + e^{-E_F/kt})^{-1} \approx 1 \tag{4.90}$$

since $E_F/kT \gg 1$. The remaining integral may be evaluated on noting that E_F/kT is large and that the lower limit may be replaced by $-\infty$ in view of our remarks concerning the behavior of the derivative of $f(x)$. Introducing

$$\frac{\partial f(x)}{\partial x} = -\frac{1}{kT} \frac{e^x}{(e^x + 1)^2} = \frac{1}{kT} \frac{1}{(e^x + 1)(e^{-x} + 1)} \tag{4.91}$$

We note that this function is symmetric in x. The integral of interest may now be written

$$\int_{-\infty}^{\infty} \frac{x^n \, dx}{(e^{-x} + 1)(e^x + 1)} \tag{4.92}$$

In view of the symmetry of the denominator, the integral is antisymmetric if n is odd, and hence vanishes. We require, therefore, only the value for even n for which the integral is symmetric, and hence is just twice the value of the integral taken from zero to infinity. The integral for even n is found by using the expression

$$\frac{1}{(e^{-x} + 1)(e^x + 1)} = \frac{e^{-x}}{(1 + e^{-x})^2} = e^{-x} - 2e^{-2x} + 3e^{-3x} + \cdots$$

$$= -\sum_{s=1}^{\infty} (-1)^s s e^{-sx} \tag{4.93}$$

On introducing (4.93) into (4.92) we have

$$\int_{=\infty}^{+\infty} \frac{x^n \, dx}{(e^{-x} + 1)(e^x + 1)} = -2 \sum_{s=1}^{\infty} (-1)^s s \int_0^{\infty} x^n e^{-sx} \, dx$$

$$= -2n! \sum_{s=1}^{\infty} \frac{(-1)^s}{s^n} \tag{4.94}$$

for n even. The sums may be expressed as

$$-\sum_{s=1}^{\infty} \frac{(-1)^s}{s^2} = \frac{\pi^2}{12}; \qquad -\sum_{s=1}^{\infty} \frac{(-1)^s}{s^4} = \frac{7\pi^4}{720} \tag{4.95}$$

for $n = 2$ and $n = 4$ respectively. Introducing (4.94) and (4.95) into (4.89) we have, finally,

$$F = \int_0^{E_F} q(E) f(E) \, dE + \frac{\pi^2}{6} (kT)^2 \left(\frac{\partial q}{\partial E}\right)_{E_F} + \frac{7\pi^4}{360} (kT)^4 \left(\frac{\partial^3 q}{\partial E^3}\right)_{E_F} + \cdots \tag{4.96}$$

PROBLEMS FOR CHAPTER 4

1. Generalize the equations of motion given by (2.182) and (2.183) to the case of a particle moving in an electromagnetic field characterized by a vector potential $\bar{A}$ for which the momentum operator is given by

$$P_m = \mathbf{P} - \frac{e}{c} \bar{A}$$

as will be shown in chapter 8. [See equation (8.16).]

Hint: We have

$$i\hbar \frac{d\langle \mathbf{A} \rangle}{dt} = \langle [\mathbf{A}, \mathbf{H}] \rangle + i\hbar \left\langle \frac{\partial \mathbf{A}}{\partial t} \right\rangle$$

Let

$$\mathbf{A} = \mathbf{P}_m = \mathbf{P} - \frac{e}{c}\,\bar{A} = -\left(i\hbar\nabla + \frac{e}{c}\,\bar{A}\right)$$

$$\mathbf{H} = \frac{1}{2m}\,\mathbf{P}_m^2 + e\phi$$

and show that

$$\frac{d\langle\bar{r}\rangle}{dt} = \frac{\langle\mathbf{P}_m\rangle}{m}$$

$$\frac{d}{dt}\langle\mathbf{P}_m\rangle = \langle\text{Lorentz force}\rangle$$

2. Show that for the Fermi-Dirac distribution $f(E)$

$$\frac{\partial f}{\partial E} = -f(1 - f)/kT$$

3. It is sometimes convenient to express the collision term in equation (4.74) as an integral. Show that if $T(k, k')$ is the probability that a fermion in state k is scattered to an unoccupied state specified by the wave number k', and $f(k)$ are the distribution functions expressed in terms of k, then

$$P(kk')\,dk = f(k)[1 - f(k')]T(kk')\,dk'$$

where $P(kk')\,dk'$ is the probability, for a system of particles, that a particle is scattered from k to k' in the interval dk'.

4. Use the above result to show that if $T(kk') = T(k'k)$ then

$$\left.\frac{\partial f(k)}{\partial t}\right)_{\text{coll.}} = \int \{f(k')[1 - f(k)] - f(k)[1 - f(k')T(kk')]\}\,dk'$$

and

$$\left.\frac{\partial f(k)}{\partial t}\right)_{\text{coll.}} = \int \{[f(k') - f_0(k)] - [f(k) - f_0(k)]\}T(kk')\,dk'$$

where $f_0(k)$ is the Fermi-Dirac distribution function corresponding to equilibrium.

CHAPTER 5 / *Electron Emission*

*I*n the present chapter we apply the previous considerations to the emission of electrons from solids. In particular, we shall discuss thermionic emissions arising from the emissions of electrons from hot surfaces, field emission due to the influence of electrical fields at a surface, photoemission induced by the adsorption of light, and secondary emission caused by collision of electrons with a surface. All of these processes are of immense importance in electronics particularly in the field of vacuum tube physics. A very extensive literature has developed in each of the above indicated areas and the interested reader is referred to the sources in the bibliography.

5.1 *THERMIONIC EMISSION*

As we have seen in our discussion of the free electron theory of metals, most electrons have energies lying below the Fermi level. However, a small fraction of the electrons have energies in excess of the Fermi level and indeed some electrons possess sufficient energy so as to permit them to overcome the natural potential barrier at the surface and so be emitted. As might be expected, the number of electrons capable of emission increases with temperature and it is the purpose of the present discussion to derive this temperature dependency.

We assume that the electrons in a metal consist of a gas so that all the energy is kinetic. The surface of the metal presents a potential barrier to the electrons as indicated in figure 5.1. It is assumed that the surface of the metal is clean and exposed to a vacuum. The energy states somewhat below the Fermi level are all occupied and the occupancy decreases rapidly on passing

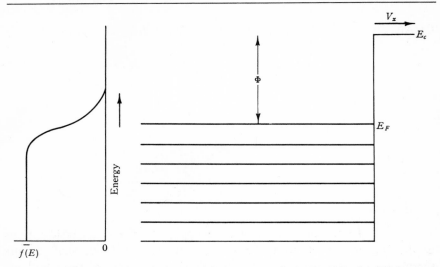

Figure 5.1: Energy levels at the surface of a metal. Here E_F is the Fermi level and Φ the work function.

to the energy levels above the Fermi level, as indicated in figure 5.1. The work function Φ is also shown in figure 5.1, and is defined as the energy required to move an electron from the Fermi level E_F to a large distance outside of the metal, i.e., the energy required for a Fermi electron to escape into a vacuum.

We shall take the surface of the metal to be perpendicular to the x-axis. As a first approximation we shall assume that only those electrons can escape whose velocity v_x along the x-direction is such that $1/2mv_x^2 \geqslant \Phi + E_F$. The expression for the x component of the current due to electrons with velocities in the interval v_x to $v_x + dv_x$ is

$$dJ_x = ev_x \, dn = \frac{e}{m} p_x \, dn \tag{5.1}$$

where dn is the number of electrons with velocities in the interval v_x to $v_x + dv_x$ or, if the momentum expression is used, in the interval p_x to $p_x + dp_x$. If we assume that the system is at thermodynamic equilibrium, then from (4.41) we can write

$$dn = \left\{ \int_{-\infty}^{+\infty} \int_{-\infty}^{+\infty} f(p)N(p) \, dp_y \, dp_z \right\} dp_x \tag{5.2}$$

The expression $f(p)$ is the Fermi–Dirac function in terms of momentum.

The latter is readily obtained from $f(E)$ on introducing the relationship

$$E = \frac{\bar{p}^2}{2m} \tag{5.3}$$

so that

$$f(p) = \{1 + e^{[(p_x^2 + p_y^2 + p_z^2)/2m - E_F]/kT}\}^{-1} \tag{5.4}$$

This of course is the probability that the electron will have the indicated values of momentum. The quantity $N(p)$ is the density of states corresponding to a momentum in the interval $\bar{p}$ to $\bar{p} + d\bar{p}$. To obtain the total thermionic current we must integrate (5.2) from p_{xc}, corresponding to $\Phi + E_F$, to infinity:

$$J_x = \frac{e}{m} \int_{-\infty}^{+\infty} \int_{-\infty}^{+\infty} \int_{p_{xc}}^{\infty} f(p)N(p)p_x \, dp_x \, dp_y \, dp_z \tag{5.5}$$

We must now evaluate $N(p)$. From (2.67) we have

$$E_x = \frac{\hbar^2 \pi^2 l^2}{2ma^2} \tag{5.6}$$

where the quantum number can assume only positive integral values. Combining the last expression with (5.3) we have

$$|p_x| = \frac{hl}{2a} \qquad l = 1, 2, 3, \ldots \tag{5.7}$$

and therefore

$$l = \frac{2a}{h} |p_x| \tag{5.8}$$

where $h = 2\pi\hbar$. The absolute value occurs here since l can assume only positive integral values; however, it is clear that $\bar{p}_x$ may be either positive or negative depending on the direction of motion. The quantum number l appearing in (5.8) is the total number of states corresponding to an x-component of momentum equal to or less than $|p_x|$. The number of energy states (excluding spin) in the interval $|p_x|$ to $|p_x| + d|p_x|$ is

$$dl = \frac{2a}{h} dp_x \tag{5.9}$$

These states include electrons with both positive and negative momentum components. However, we are only interested in the electrons moving in the positive x-direction since only these electrons contribute to the thermionic current. The number of such states is just one-half that given by (5.9) and we have

$$dl = \frac{a}{h} dp_x \qquad (5.10)$$

By similar arguments we can show that

$$dp = \frac{2a}{h} dp_y \qquad p = 1, 2, \ldots$$

$$dq = \frac{2a}{h} dp_z \qquad q = 1, 2, \ldots \qquad (5.11)$$

These states again correspond to electrons moving in both directions along the y and z-axes. However, on inspecting (5.2) it is clear that the limits of the appropriate integrals have already taken both positive and negative values of momentum into account. Consequently in order to obtain the expressions corresponding to electrons moving in only one direction we must divide the integrands (5.11) and (5.12) by two:

$$dp = \frac{a}{h} dp_y$$

$$dq = \frac{a}{h} dp_z \qquad (5.12)$$

The total number of states including spin is

$$dl \, dp \, dq = 2 \frac{V}{h^3} dp_x \, dp_y \, dp_z \qquad (5.13)$$

where V has been substituted for the volume of the system a^3. The density of states *per unit volume* in momentum space is

$$N(p) = \frac{2}{h^3} \qquad (5.14)$$

and (5.2) can be written

$$J_x = \frac{2e}{mh^3} \int_{-\infty}^{+\infty} \int_{-\infty}^{+\infty} \int_{p_{xc}}^{\infty} f(p) p_x \, dp_x \, dp_y \, dp_z \qquad (5.15)$$

The evaluation of this integral is considerably simplified by the fact that the exponent in $(E - E_F)/kT$ occurring in the Fermi–Dirac distribution is usually sufficiently large so that unity may be neglected. We then have the result

$$J_x = \frac{2e}{mh^3} e^{+E_F/kT} \int_{-\infty}^{+\infty} \int_{-\infty}^{+\infty} \int_{p_{xc}}^{+\infty} e^{-(p_x^2 + p_y^2 + p_z^2)/2mkT} p_x \, dp_x \, dp_y \, dp_z$$

$$J_x = \frac{4\pi emk^2T^2}{h^3} e^{-(E_c - E_F)/kT} \tag{5.16}$$

$$= \frac{4\pi emk^2T^2}{h^3} e^{-\Phi/kT},$$

on using

$$\int_{-\infty}^{+\infty} e^{-au^2} \, du = \left(\frac{\pi}{a}\right)^{1/2}. \tag{5.17}$$

and recalling that

$$E_c = \frac{p_{xc}}{2m} = \Phi + E_F \tag{5.18}$$

In practical work it is customary to set $\Phi = e\phi$ where ϕ is in electron volts and to write the Richardson equation

$$J_x = AT^2 e^{-e\phi/kT} \tag{5.19}$$

where $A = 1.20 \times 10^6$ amperes per square meter per degree K^2.

TABLE 5.1

Electron Emission Properties of Various Materials

	ϕ (electron-volts)	A (amp/m²/°K²)	MELTING POINT (°K)
Cu	3.9	0.65×10^6	1356
Ta	4.2	0.55×10^6	3123
W	4.5	0.60×10^6	3655
Ni	4.6	0.30×10^6	1725
Pt	5.3	0.32×10^6	2047
Thoriated Tungsten W + 1.5% ThO₂	2.6–2.9	0.03×10^6	—
Oxide Coated Cathode (Ba, Sr)O coated onto Ni sleeve	1.6–1.4	1.00×10^2	—

Some experimentally determined values of ϕ and A are listed in table 5.1. It is apparent that the measured values of A for the pure metals are about one-half the value calculated above. Much of this discrepancy can be accounted for by assuming that some electrons may be reflected at the surface barrier and so returned to the bulk material.

5.2   *REFLECTION AT POTENTIAL BARRIERS*

In order to explore the consequences of reflection at the surface we shall apply the considerations given in chapter 2. We consider the case of an electron, with energy E, in a field of zero potential energy which encounters a potential field of magnitude $V_0 < E_x$, as shown in figure 5.2.

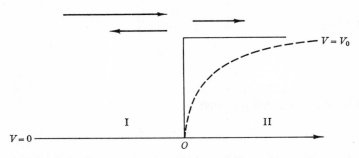

Figure 5.2: Reflection at a potential barrier. The potential barrier at the surface of a metal. The image barrier is indicated by a dashed curve.

The wave equations are

$$\frac{d^2\psi_1}{dx^2} + \frac{2m}{\hbar^2} E_x\psi_1 = 0 \qquad\qquad x < 0 \qquad\qquad (5.20)$$

$$\frac{d^2\psi_2}{dx^2} = \frac{2m}{\hbar^2}(E_x - V_0)\psi_2 = 0 \quad x > 0 \qquad (5.21)$$

These have the solution

$$\psi_1 = A_1 e^{ik_1 x} + A_2 e^{-ik_1 x} \qquad\qquad (5.22)$$

$$\psi_2 = B_1 e^{ik_2 x} + B_2 e^{-ik_2 x} \qquad\qquad (5.23)$$

where

$$k_1 = \sqrt{\frac{2mE_x}{\hbar^2}} \qquad\qquad (5.24)$$

$$k_2 = \sqrt{\frac{2m(E_x - V_0)}{\hbar^2}} \qquad\qquad (5.25)$$

The exponentials in (5.22) and (5.23) when multiplied by $(\exp - E_x/\hbar i t)$, according to postulate ψ, represent traveling waves. Thus the exponential corresponding to A_1 may be regarded as representing the incident electron moving in the positive x-direction in region I, while the term in A_2 represents an electron moving in the negative x-direction in region I, i.e., the reflected electron. Similarly in region II the term corresponding to B_1 represents the transmitted electron moving in the positive x-direction while B_2 represents an electron in region II moving in the negative x-direction. Since the latter is not of interest in the present discussion we may set B_2 equal to zero.

Applying the continuity conditions on the wave function and its first derivatives at $x = 0$ we have

$$\psi_1(0) = \psi_2(0)$$
$$\left. \frac{d\psi_1}{dx} \right)_{x=0} = \left. \frac{d\psi_2}{dx} \right)_{x=0} \tag{5.26}$$

or

$$A_1 + A_2 = B_1$$
$$k_1(A_1 - A_2) = k_2 B_1 \tag{5.27}$$

These expressions permit us to solve for A_2 and B_1 in terms of the coefficient of the incident wave, A_1:

$$A_2 = \frac{k_1 - k_2}{k_1 + k_2} A_1$$
$$B_1 = \frac{2k_1}{k_1 + k_2} A_1 \tag{5.28}$$

Equations (5.22) and (5.23) now become

$$\psi_1 = A_1 e^{ik_1 x} + \frac{k_1 - k_2}{k_1 + k_2} A_1 e^{-ik_1 x} \tag{5.29a}$$

$$\psi_2 = \frac{2k_1 A_1}{k_1 + k_2} e^{ik_2 x} \tag{5.29b}$$

The incident current J_i, the reflected current J_r, and the transmitted current J_t may be calculated from (2.33) and the appropriate terms of (5.29a) and (5.29b):

$$J_i = \frac{e\hbar}{m} A_1^2 k_1$$

$$J_r = -\frac{e\hbar}{m} A_1^2 k_1 \left[\frac{k_1 - k_2}{k_1 + k_2} \right]^2 \tag{5.30}$$

$$J_t = \frac{e\hbar}{m} A_1^2 k_2 \left[\frac{2k_1}{k_1 + k_2} \right]^2$$

The ratio of the reflected-to-incident current is the reflection coefficient R, given by,

$$R = \frac{J_r}{J_i} = \left[\frac{k_1 - k_2}{k_1 + k_2}\right]^2 \tag{5.31}$$

and the transmission coefficient is given by

$$T = \frac{J_t}{J_i} = \frac{4k_1k_2}{(k_1 + k_2)^2} \tag{5.32}$$

We observe from (5.31) that unless $k_1 = k_2$, which implies $V_0 = 0$, there is always some reflection from the surface barrier. This reflection occurs even though $E > V_0$.

The thermionic current, when the transmission coefficient $T(E_x)$ is taken into account, is, from (5.16),

$$J = \frac{4\pi mekT}{h^3} e^{E_F/kT} \int_{E_c}^{\infty} T(E_x)e^{-E_x/kT} \, dE_x \tag{5.33}$$

Evaluation of this integral gives the result

$$J = \frac{4\pi emk^2T^2}{h^3} e^{-e\phi/kT} \cdot 4\sqrt{kT/E_c} \left[\frac{\sqrt{\pi}}{2} - 2\left(\frac{kT}{E_c}\right)^{1/2} + \cdots\right]$$
$$= F_t(kT/E_c)AT^2e^{-e\phi/kT} \tag{5.34}$$

Substituting typical values of $E_c = 10$ ev and if the temperature is taken as $1000°K$, $kT = 0.01$ ev, then $F_t(kT/E_c)$ is approximately 0.27. This value is clearly in the right order of magnitude.

A more exact treatment requires that we take into account the image force resulting from the positive charge induced in the metal by the emitted electron. This force tends to attract the electron back into the metal and is given in newtons by

$$F = \frac{e^2}{4\pi\varepsilon_0(2x)^2} \tag{5.35}$$

Corresponding to the image force there is a potential given by $e^2/16\pi\varepsilon_0 x$ so that the net potential barrier is given by

$$V = V_0 - \frac{e^2}{16\pi\varepsilon_0 x} \tag{5.36}$$

The resulting potential is shown in figure 5.2. Barriers of this type result in less reflection of the electrons than abrupt barriers.

If a negative electrical potential is applied to the emitting surface then the potential energy barrier is given by

$$V = V_0 - \frac{e^2}{16\pi\varepsilon_0 x} - eE_0 x \qquad (5.37)$$

where E_0 is the electrical field, as shown in figure 5.3. The barrier has a maximum at

$$x_m = \sqrt{\frac{e}{16\pi\varepsilon_0 E_0}} \qquad (5.38)$$

with a maximum V given by

$$V_m = V_0 - \frac{e}{2}\sqrt{\frac{eE_0}{\pi\varepsilon_0}} \qquad (5.39)$$

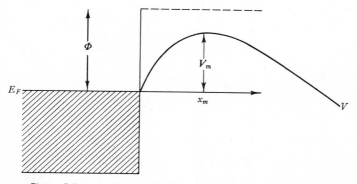

Figure 5.3: Potential barrier in the presence of an applied field.

We see that the barrier is reduced by an amount indicated in (5.39). The new work function $\Phi^{\cdot}$ is given by

$$\Phi^{\cdot} = E_F + V_m = \Phi - \frac{e}{2}\sqrt{\frac{eE_0}{\pi\varepsilon_0}} \qquad (5.40)$$

or, expressed in electron-volts, we have

$$\phi^{\cdot} = \phi - \frac{1}{2}\sqrt{\frac{eE_0}{\pi\varepsilon_0}} = \phi - 3.78 \times 10^{-5}\sqrt{E_0} \qquad (5.41)$$

where E_0 is in volts per meter. The reduction of the effective potential energy barrier at the surface by applied fields is referred to as the *Schottky effect*.

On introducing (5.41) into (5.34) we obtain the expression for the effect of an applied field on the thermionic current

$$J = F_t A T^2 e^{-e\phi \cdot /kT} = F_t A T^2 e^{-e\phi/kT} e^{+0.44\sqrt{E_0}/T} \qquad (5.42)$$

where we have used the value $e/k = 1.16 \times 10^4$.

5.3 FIELD EMISSION AND TUNNELING

When the field at the surface is about 10^9 volt/m, electron emission can occur at room temperatures. This effect is known as field emission. The mechanism of field effect emission is different from thermionic emission. In the latter case the electrons must possess sufficient energy to pass over the surface barrier. With field effect emission, however, the electrons can *tunnel* through the barrier as shown in figure 5.4.

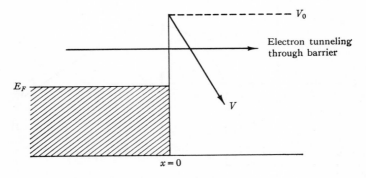

Figure 5.4: Field emission of electrons.

A simpler situation is the rectangular barrier shown in figure 5.5 which we now discuss. It is assumed that the electron with energy $E < V_0$ impinges on the barrier from the left-hand side. Proceeding as before we can write the solutions to the wave equations as

$$
\begin{aligned}
\psi_1 &= A_1 e^{k_1 xi} + A_2 e^{-k_1 xi} & x < 0 \\
\psi_2 &= B_1 e^{k_2 x} + B_2 e^{-k_2 x} & 0 < x < a \\
\psi_3 &= C_1 e^{k_1 xi} & x > a
\end{aligned}
\qquad (5.43)
$$

where

$$k_1 = \sqrt{\frac{2mE}{\hbar}}, \qquad k_2 = \sqrt{\frac{2m(V_0 - E)}{\hbar}} \qquad (5.44)$$

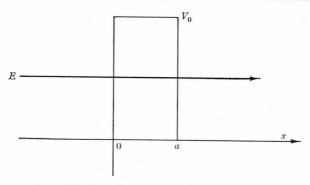

Figure 5.5: Tunneling through a rectangular barrier.

The coefficients are determined by applying the continuity condition on the wave function and its first derivative at $x = 0$ and $x = a$:

$$A_2 + A_1 = B_2 + B_1$$
$$ik_1(A_1 - A_2) = k_2(B_1 - B_2)$$
$$B_1 e^{k_2 a} + B_2 e^{-k_2 a} = C_1 e^{k_1 ai}$$
$$k_2[B_1 e^{ak_2} - B_2 e^{-k_1 a}] = C_1 k_1 i e^{k_1 ai}$$
(5.45)

Since we are primarily interested in the transmission coefficient T, we solve these relationships for C_1 and obtain

$$C_1 = \frac{e^{-ik_1 a} 2u}{2u \cosh k_2 a - i(1 - u^2) \sinh k_2 a}$$
(5.46)

where

$$u = \frac{k_1}{k_2}$$
(5.47)

and the transmission coefficient is found, as before, to be proportioned to

$$|T|^2 = \frac{4u^2}{(1 - u^2) \sinh^2 k_2 a + 4u^2 \cosh^2 k_2 a}$$
(5.48)

It is apparent from this result that transmission or tunneling through the barrier can occur even though $E < V_0$. However, the transmission through the barrier decreases very rapidly with increasing $k_2 a$, i.e., with increasing barrier height and thickness.

In the instance of field emission the barrier is given by

$$V = V_0 - eE_0 x$$
(5.49)

and the wave equations are

$$\frac{d^2\psi}{dx^2} + \frac{2m}{\hbar^2} E\psi = 0 \qquad\qquad x < 0$$

$$\frac{d^2\psi}{dx^2} + \frac{2m}{\hbar^2} (E - V_0 + eE_0 x) = 0 \qquad x > 0$$

(5.50)

Fowler and Nordheim have shown that the transmission coefficient is given by

$$T(E_x) = \frac{4\sqrt{E_x(V_0 - E_x)}}{V_0} \exp\left\{ -\left[\frac{4}{3E_0} \left(\frac{2m}{\hbar^2} \right)^{1/2} (V_0 - E_x)^{3/2} \right] \right\} \quad (5.51)$$

We can write for the current density in the case $E_x < V_0$ where $V_0 = E_F + \Phi$.

$$J = \frac{2e}{mh^3} \int\limits_0^{E_F + \Phi} \int\limits_{-\infty}^{+\infty} \int\limits_{-\infty}^{+\infty} f(p)T(E_x)p_x \, dp_y \, dp_z \, dpx \qquad (5.52)$$

On introducing the assumption that $E_x < E_F$, corresponding to the situation at $T = 0°$K, we have

$$J = \frac{2e}{h^3} \int\limits_0^{E_F} \int\limits_{-\infty}^{+\infty} \int\limits_{-\infty}^{+\infty} \frac{T(E_x) \, dp_y \, dp_z \, dE_x}{1 + e^{(p_y{}^2 + p_z{}^2)/2mkT + (E_x - E_F)/kT}} \qquad (5.53)$$

This last expression may be integrated by introducing the polar coordinates

$$r^2 = p_y^2 + p_z^2$$
$$p_y = r \cos\theta$$
$$p_z = r \sin\theta$$

(5.54)

so that the double integral involving p_x and p_y becomes

$$\int\limits_0^{2\pi} d\theta \int\limits_0^\infty \frac{r \, dr}{1 + \exp\left[r^2/2mkT + (E_x - E_F)/kT \right]} \qquad (5.55)$$

This may be integrated directly on noting that (5.55) may be written as

$$\int\limits_0^{2\pi} d\theta \int\limits_0^\infty \frac{e^{-r^2/2mkT} r \, dr}{e^{-r^2/2mkT} + e^{(E_x - E_F)/kT}}$$

$$= 2\pi mkT \ln \left[1 + e^{(E_F - E_x)/kT} \right]$$

$$\sim 2\pi m(E_F - E_x) \qquad (5.56)$$

since for most of the electrons

$$\frac{E_F - E_x}{kT} \gg 1 \tag{5.57}$$

The integral (5.53) may now be written

$$J = \frac{4\pi e m}{h^3} \int_0^{E_F} T(E_x)(E_F - E_x)\, dE_x \tag{5.58}$$

This may be evaluated by letting $(E_F - E_x) = \xi$ and introducing this new variable into (5.58). We find that (5.58) becomes on expanding the exponential in powers of ξ

$$\frac{16\pi e m}{h^3 V_0} e^{-4u/3E_0 \cdot (V_0 - E_F)^{3/2}} \int_0^{E_F} \xi[(E_F - \xi)(V_0 - E_F + \xi)]^{1/2}$$
$$\times e^{-2u/E_0 \cdot (V_0 - E_F)^{1/2} \cdot \xi}\, d\xi \tag{5.59}$$

where

$$u = \left(\frac{2m}{\hbar^2}\right)^{1/2} \tag{5.60}$$

The radical under the integral sign may be expanded in terms of ξ. On integrating we find that

$$J = \frac{e}{2\pi h V_0} \sqrt{\frac{E_F}{V_0 - E_F}}\, E_0^2 \exp - \left[\frac{4}{3E_0}\left(\frac{2m}{\hbar^2}\right)^{1/2}(V_0 - E_F)^{3/2}\right] \tag{5.61}$$

The last result is clearly of the form

$$J = B E_0^2 e^{-C/E_0} \tag{5.62}$$

where B and C are constants. The last expression is sometimes referred to as the Fowler–Nordheim equation and has been found to be generally applicable to field emission phenomena.

An interesting application of field emission is provided by the field emission microscope shown in figure 5.6. A large voltage of 10–20 kv is applied between single crystal metal point of radius r and a fluorescent screen of radius R. Electrons are emitted by the point and pass to the screen producing fluorescence. This device is useful for the investigation of adsorption onto the surface of the point which will result in local increases or decreases of the work function. Since the work function appears in the exponential of equation

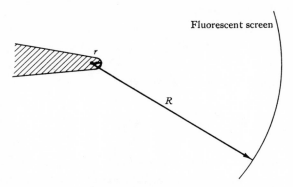

Figure 5.6: Field emission microscope.

(5.61), appreciable changes in the field emission may be expected to result from the local variations in the work function.

The resolving power of the field emission microscope is very high and it is possible to distinguish individual molecules with this device.

5.4 *PHOTO EMISSION*

Photo emission refers to emission of electrons from metals under the influence of light. It has been observed that the emission current depends on both the intensity and frequency of the illumination. There exists a threshold frequency below which no photoemission will occur no matter how intense the illumination. At $0°K$ the threshold frequency ν_0 is related to the work function Φ by the Einstein law

$$h\nu_0 = \Phi \tag{5.63}$$

and the kinetic energy of the emitted electron is given by

$$\frac{1}{2}mv^2 = h(\nu - \nu_0) \tag{5.64}$$

Thus, in order for photo emission to occur at $0°K$, the photon must provide the electron with an amount of energy equal to the work function of the metal. Photons with energy in excess of Φ give the emitted electron a velocity as indicated by (5.64).

As the temperature is raised above $0°K$ the Fermi distribution begins to tail out so that the number of electrons with energies above E_F increases. Emission can then also occur for frequencies below that given by (5.63).

We now calculate the photocurrent as a function of frequency and temperature. If E_x is the x-component of the kinetic energy of the electron in a metal, and E_c the height of the surface barrier, then emission will occur if

$$E_x + h\nu > E_c \qquad (5.65)$$

The photo current in the x-direction is obtained from (5.15) and is easily seen to be

$$J = K \frac{2e}{h^3} \int_{E_c - h\nu}^{\infty} \int_{-\infty}^{+\infty} \int_{-\infty}^{+\infty} \frac{dp_y \, dp_z \, dE_x}{1 + e^{[p_y{}^2 + p_z{}^2]/2mkT + (E_x - E_F)/kT}} \qquad (5.66)$$

where K is a proportionality factor.

On introducing (5.56) we have

$$J = K \frac{4\pi mekT}{h^3} \int_{E_c - h\nu}^{\infty} \log \left[1 + e^{(E_F - E_x)/kT} \right] dE_x \qquad (5.67)$$

On introducing the transformation

$$\omega = e^{(E_F - E_x)/kT} \qquad (5.68)$$

and letting

$$\omega_0 = e^{[E_F - (E_c - h\nu)]/kT} \qquad (5.69)$$

we have

$$\begin{aligned} J &= \frac{K \cdot 4\pi mek^2 T^2}{h^3} \int_0^{\omega_0} \frac{\log(1 + \omega)}{\omega} \, d\omega \\ &= AT^2 \int_0^{\omega_0} \frac{\log(1 + \omega)}{\omega} \, d\omega \end{aligned} \qquad (5.70)$$

This integral is well known and we consider two cases

a. $\nu \leqslant \nu_0$ so that $\omega_0 \leqslant 1$, and we have on recalling $h\nu_0 = E_c - E_F$

$$J = AT^2 \left[e^{-\alpha} - \frac{e^{-2\alpha}}{2^2} + \frac{e^{-3\alpha}}{3^2} + \cdots \right] \qquad (5.71)$$

where

$$\alpha = \frac{h(\nu_0 - \nu)}{kT}$$

b. $\nu > \nu_0$ and $\omega_0 > 1$

$$J = AT^2\left[\frac{\alpha^2}{2} + \frac{\pi^2}{6} - \left(e^\alpha - \frac{e^{2\alpha}}{2^2} + \frac{e^{3\alpha}}{3^2} + \cdots\right)\right] \qquad (5.72)$$

These expressions are of the form

$$J = T^2 A f(x) \qquad (5.73)$$

It is interesting to note that when $\nu = 0$ (5.71) reduces to the Richardson equation for thermionic emission on neglecting the terms beyond $e^{-\alpha}$ and recognizing that $h\nu_0/kT = \Phi$.

Equation (5.73) is useful for obtaining the work function and the constant A from experimental data since this equation may be written in the form

$$\ln \frac{J}{T^2} = \ln A + \ln f(\alpha) \qquad (5.74)$$

The quantity $\ln f(\alpha)$ is plotted as a function of α. This curve is compared to a plot of the experimental results in the form of $\ln J/T^2$ vs. $h\nu/kT$, the so-called Fowler plot. Both the Fowler plot and the curve $\ln f(\alpha)$ vs. α have the same shapes and may be brought into coincidence by shifting the Fowler plot in both the vertical and horizontal directions. The vertical shift permits an estimate of A and the horizontal an estimate of Φ.

Photoemission in metals is a highly inefficient process with yields of 10^{-3} to 10^{-4} electron per incoming photon. The alkali metals have low work functions and are relatively effective emitters with spectral response characteristics shown in figure 5.7. The low quantum yields can be explained by means of the conservation of energy and momentum of the electron-photon system. Initially the electron has an energy E and momentum $\sqrt{2mE}$ while the photon has an energy $h\nu$ and momentum $h\nu/c$. If the electron and photon are proceeding in the same direction, then after interaction has occurred, the electron has an energy given by $E + h\nu$ and a resulting momentum $\sqrt{2m(E + h\nu)}$ which is greater than the sum of the initial momenta $\sqrt{2mE} + h\nu/c$. In order to conserve the momenta, an additional source is required. As we shall see in a later chapter, this additional source of momentum is the lattice atoms, i.e., the photons can promote an electron to a higher energy state provided momentum is made available by the lattice. In the case of metals which approximate the free electron model, coupling between the lattice atoms and the free electrons is relatively weak and hence the quantum yield will be low.

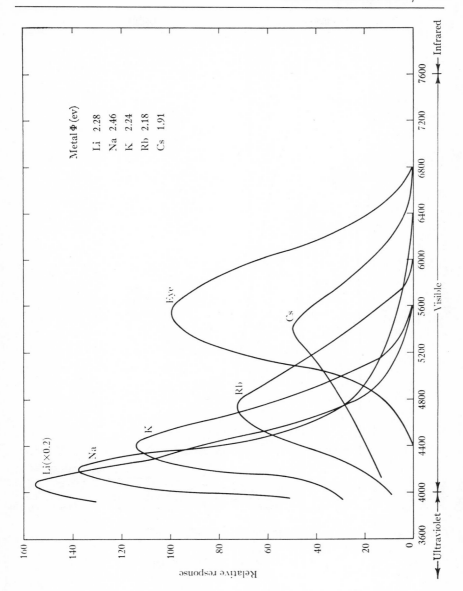

Figure 5.7: Photo emission by alkali metals.

Greatly improved quantum yields, approaching 0.20% in some cases, can be obtained from especially prepared photosurfaces. The spectral response is shown (figure 5.8) of a layer made by depositing cesium on a

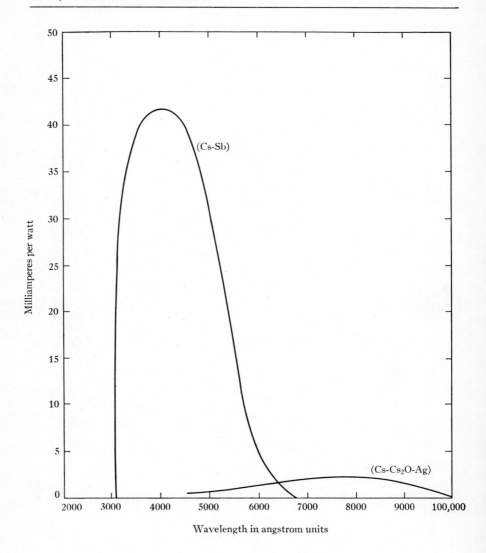

Figure 5.8: Photoresponse of cesium systems.

silver base, oxidizing the cesium, and then subliming a small additional amount of cesium onto the surface. A large number of photosensitive surfaces using various modifications of this technique have been studied. The response of antimony–cesium photosurface is also shown. The surface in this case is actually an intermetallic semiconductor compound Cs_3Sb.

5.5 SECONDARY EMISSION

When the surface of a solid is bombarded with charged particles (ions or electrons) of sufficient energy, electron emission from the surface is observed. This phenomena is termed secondary emission. The bombarding beams of electrons, or primaries, are partially elastically reflected on striking the solid, while the remainder of the primaries penetrate into the solid and lose energy to the lattice electrons. Some of the excited electrons of the lattice will escape from the solid as secondary electrons. A typical energy distribution is shown in figure 5.9 for the case of secondary electrons emitted from silver on bombardment with 155 ev electrons. The elastically scattered primaries appear as a narrow peak P, centered at 155 ev. The vast majority of the secondaries appear as low energy particles with a peak at S. The additional peak at b is due to inelastically scattered primaries.

A second feature of importance is the energy dependency of the secondary yield δ, defined as the ratio of emitted electrons to the incident primary electrons. We note that both the elastically and inelastically scattered primaries are included in the emitted electrons. Figure 5.10 shows the general

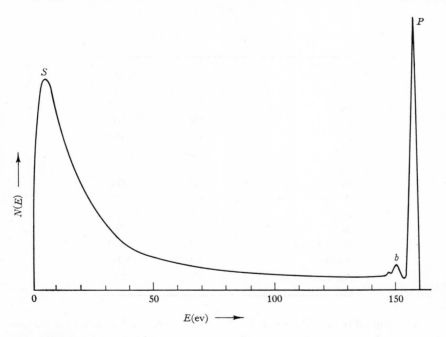

Figure 5.9: Energy distribution of secondary electrons emitted by silver (After Rudberg, *Phys. Rev.*, **4**, 764 (1934)).

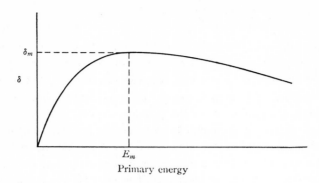

Figure 5.10: General curve of δ vs. E.

form of the δ vs. primary energy, E, curve. We observe that the secondary yield increases to a maximum δ_m at E_m, and on further increase in E, then δ tends to decrease. Some values of δ_m and the corresponding primary energy E_m are given in table 5.2.

TABLE 5.2

Maximum Yield (δ_m) and Primary Energy (E_m)

	δ_m	E_m (ev)
Ag	1.5	800
C	1.0	300
Cu	1.3	600
Mo	1.25	375
Ni	1.3	550
Pt	1.6	800
W	1.4	600
Ge	1.1	400
Si	1.1	250
Hard Glass	2.3	400
Al_2O_3	4.8	1300
Ag–Cs_2O–CS	8.8	550

The general behavior exhibited by the curve in figure 5.10 can be explained in terms of elementary concepts. The secondary yield δ can be expressed in terms of $n(x)$, the number of secondaries produced per primary in the interval

x to $x + dx$, and the probability $f(x)$ that a secondary at a distance x will escape from the surface:

$$\delta = \int_0^x n(x)f(x)\, dx \tag{5.75}$$

We assume that the primaries penetrate the solid in a straight path and we neglect primary scattering.

The energy loss per unit path length of a primary is given by Whiddington's law

$$\frac{dE_p(x)}{dx} = -\frac{k}{E_p(x)} \tag{5.76}$$

where $E_p(x)$ is the energy of the primary at point x, and k is a constant characteristic of the material. If ε is the average energy required to produce a secondary then the number of secondaries per unit path length is

$$n(x) = \frac{k}{\varepsilon E_p(x)} \tag{5.77}$$

In order to obtain an expression for $E_p(x)$ we integrate (5.76) and find that

$$E_p^2(x) = E_p^2(0) - 2kx \tag{5.78}$$

where $E_p(0)$ is the energy of the incident primary electron. The penetration depth x_p is obtained on setting $E_p(x) = 0$;

$$x_p = \frac{E_p^2(0)}{2k} \tag{5.79}$$

and hence

$$E_p^2(x) = 2k(x_p - x) \tag{5.80}$$

We can now write

$$n(x) = \left(\frac{k}{2}\right)^{1/2} \frac{1}{\varepsilon(x_p - x)^{1/2}} \tag{5.81}$$

It is clear from the form of (5.81) that $n(x)$ increases very rapidly in the neighborhood of x_p so that most of the secondaries must be produced at x_p. These secondaries, however, must escape to the surface and we assume that $f(x)$ is given by

$$f(x) = f(0)e^{-\alpha x} \tag{5.82}$$

where $f(0)$ is the probability that a secondary at $x = 0$ will escape and α is a constant. Introducing (5.81) and (5.82) into (5.75) we have

$$\delta = \left(\frac{k}{2}\right)^{1/2} \frac{f(0)}{\varepsilon} \int_0^{x_p} \frac{e^{-\alpha x}}{(x_p - x)^{1/2}} \, dx \qquad (5.83)$$

or on introducing

$$y^2 = \alpha(x_p - x) \qquad (5.84)$$

and

$$z^2 = \alpha x_p \qquad (5.85)$$

the last equation may be written in the form

$$\delta = \left(\frac{2k}{\alpha}\right)^{1/2} \frac{f(0)}{\varepsilon} F(z) \qquad \text{where} \qquad F(z) = e^{-z^2} \int_0^z e^{y^2} \, dy \qquad (5.86)$$

On setting $\partial\delta/\partial E_p(0)$ equal to zero we find that δ has a maximum at $z_m = 0.92$. From the relationship

$$z = \sqrt{\alpha x_p} = \left(\frac{\alpha}{2k}\right)^{1/2} E_p(0) \qquad (5.87)$$

we find that the maximum in $E_p(0)$ corresponding to z_m is given by

$$E_m = 0.92 \left(\frac{2k}{\alpha}\right)^{1/2} \qquad (5.88)$$

We note that

$$z = 0.92 \frac{E_p(0)}{E_m} \qquad (5.89)$$

so that

$$\frac{\delta}{\delta_m} = \frac{F(z)}{F(0.92)} = \frac{1}{1.85} F\left(0.92 \frac{E_p(0)}{E_m}\right) \qquad (5.90)$$

This last equation relates δ and $E_p(0)$ in a manner independent of the specific properties of the solids. Measurements of a variety of different materials indicate that a relationship of the form (5.90) does indeed apply.

A comparison of the theoretical and empirical curves is given in figure 5.11 where it can be seen that there is a fairly large discrepancy for $E > E_m$. One reason for this discrepancy has to do with the scattering of the primaries in the solid which was neglected above. Such scattering may be expected to increase the yield by a direct contribution, and also by decreasing the depth x_p at which the secondaries are generated. The latter effect would tend to increase the escape of secondaries.

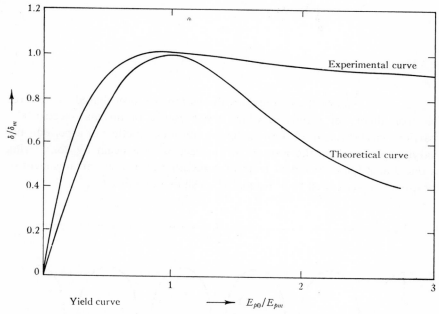

Figure 5.11: Comparison of experimental and theoretical results for secondary emission.

PROBLEMS FOR CHAPTER 5

1. Derive the expression for the energy distribution of thermionically emitted electrons assuming the transmission coefficient is unity.
   Hint: The current density is given by (5.15) while the number of electrons with energy dE in excess of E_c is found from (5.33).
2. Show that the average total energy of an electron thermionically emitted perpendicular to the surface is kT.
3. Using the data in table 5.1 plot the thermionic emission vs. temperature for copper and an oxide coated cathode.
4. Calculate x_m from (5.38) for the fields 10^2 and 10^5 v/m.
5. What is the photoelectric threshold for copper? Use the data of table 5.1.
(b) Explain why a photon cannot give up its energy to a free electron in space.

CHAPTER 6 / *Band Theory of Solids*

Much of our previous discussion has been based on the free electron theory of metals in which the presence of internal electrostatic barriers was neglected. In this chapter we consider the effect of a periodically varying potential on the motion of an electron. We begin by considering a one-dimensional crystal of length L consisting of a linear arrangement of positive ions separated by a distance d, as shown in figure 6.1.

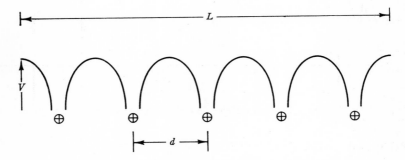

Figure 6.1: The potential energy field in a one-dimensional crystal.

6.1 *PERIODIC BOUNDARY CONDITIONS*

The potential field $V(x)$ is repeated with a period corresponding to the distance between the ions, i.e.,

$$V(x) = V(x + d) \qquad 0 \leqslant x \leqslant L \qquad (6.1)$$

160

We now consider the solution to the wave equation

$$\frac{d^2\psi}{dx^2} + \frac{2m}{\hbar}[E - V(x)] = 0 \tag{6.2}$$

where $V(x)$ is a periodic potential function given by (6.1).

Because of the periodicity of the potential we expect that the probability of finding an electron at x and $x + d$ is the same:

$$|\psi(x)|^2 = |\psi(x + d)|^2 \tag{6.3}$$

If the lattice has N atoms then the length of the crystal is given by $L = Gd$, where $G = N - 1$. It is convenient in discussing problems involving periodic potential functions to introduce the periodic boundary conditions, that is, the linear crystal is regarded as a circle of circumference L. In this way, awkward questions associated with end effects are circumvented. If we are dealing with a long crystal, then the elimination of end effects by forming a circular crystal should not appreciably change the behavior of the electron within the crystal. For a circular crystal, if we start at some point x and traverse the circumference Gd, we must return to x so that

$$\psi(x) = \psi(x + Gd) \tag{6.4}$$

We now shall determine the form of the wave function which satisfies the boundary conditions (6.3) and (6.4) and the wave equation (6.2). In other words we shall determine the form of the solution to the wave equation (6.2) for a crystal of finite length L, but for which surface effects can be neglected.

Now, since

$$|\psi(x)|^2 = |\psi(x + d)|^2$$

we must have

$$\psi(x + d) = \lambda\psi(x) \tag{6.5}$$

where λ is a quantity such that

$$\lambda\lambda^* = 1 \tag{6.6}$$

From equation (6.5) we can also write

$$\psi(x + 2d) = \psi(x + d + d) = \lambda\psi(x + d) = \lambda^2\psi(x)$$

or, in general for an integer g,

$$\psi(x + gd) = \lambda^g\psi(x) \tag{6.7}$$

hence for $g = G$

$$\psi(x + Gd) = \lambda^G \psi(x) \qquad (6.8)$$

but from (6.4) we require that

$$\lambda^G = 1 \qquad (6.9)$$

Conditions (6.6) and (6.9) on the quantity λ are satisfied by choosing

$$\lambda = e^{2\pi g i / G} \qquad g = 0, \pm 1, \pm 2, \ldots \qquad (6.10)$$

The functional relationship (6.5) now may be written

$$\psi(x + d) = e^{2\pi g i / G} \psi(x) \qquad (6.11)$$

and this is satisfied by choosing

$$\psi(x) = \mu_k(x) e^{ikx} \qquad (6.12)$$

where

$$k = \frac{2\pi g}{dG} \qquad (6.12a)$$

and where $\mu(x)$ has the periodicity of the potential

$$\mu(x) = \mu_k(x + d) \qquad (6.13)$$

We note that k may be regarded as increasing in increments proportional to G^{-1} as g changes by unity. If G is very large, as it is in practice, k may be considered to vary in a continuous manner. That (6.12) and (6.13) satisfy (6.11) is easily established since

$$\psi(x + d) = e^{ik(x + d)} \mu_k(x + d) = e^{ikd} e^{ikx} \mu_k(x)$$
$$= e^{2\pi i g / G} \psi(x)$$

We conclude, therefore, that a function of the form (6.12) satisfies the required boundary periodic conditions (6.3) and (6.4). We shall refer to functions of the form (6.12) as *Bloch functions*.

6.2   ONE-DIMENSIONAL CRYSTALS—(KRONIG–PENNY MODEL)

It is interesting to apply the Bloch functions to an ideal one-dimensional crystal. In order to simplify the problem we shall replace the actual potential function with a rectangular potential function shown in figure 6.2. The

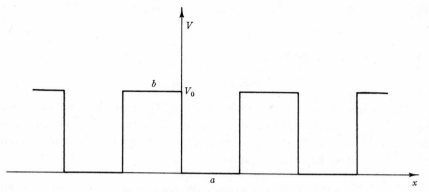

Figure 6.2: A simplified potential scheme.

potential barrier has a spacing a, a thickness b, and a height V_0. We assume that the total energy of the particle $E < V_0$. The wave equations are

$$\frac{d^2\psi_1}{dx^2} + \frac{2m}{\hbar^2} E\psi_1 = 0 \qquad\qquad 0 < x < a \qquad (6.14)$$

$$\frac{d^2\psi_2}{dx^2} + \frac{2m}{\hbar^2}(E - V_0)\psi_2 = 0 \qquad -b < x < 0 \qquad (6.15)$$

Since $V(x)$ is periodic, we have

$$V(x) = V(x + d), \qquad d = a + b \qquad (6.16)$$

This system of equations has, as we have seen a Bloch function solution

$$\psi(x) = \mu_k(x)e^{ikx} \qquad (6.17)$$

We can determine $\mu_k(x)$ by substituting (6.17) into (6.14) and (6.15). We find that

$$\mu_1(x) = A_1 e^{i(\alpha - k)x} + A_2 e^{-i(\alpha + k)x} \qquad 0 < x < a$$
$$\mu_2(x) = B_1 e^{i(\beta - ik)x} + B_2 e^{-i(\beta + ik)x} \qquad -b < x < 0 \qquad (6.18)$$

$$\alpha^2 = \frac{2mE}{\hbar^2} \qquad\qquad \beta^2 = \frac{2m(V_0 - E)}{\hbar^2} \qquad (6.19)$$

Imposing the continuity condition on $\mu(x)$ and its first derivatives leads to the expressions

$$\mu_1(0) = \mu_2(0) \qquad \left.\frac{d\mu_1}{dx}\right)_{x=0} = \left.\frac{d\mu_2}{dx}\right)_{x=0} \qquad (6.20)$$

$$\mu_1(a) = \mu_2(-b) \qquad \left.\frac{d\mu_1}{dx}\right)_{x=0} = \left.\frac{d\mu_2}{dx}\right)_{x=-b} \qquad (6.21)$$

The conditions given in 6.21 must hold, since for a Bloch function

$$\mu_k(x) = \mu_k(x + d) \qquad d = a + b$$

Choosing $x = -b$ we must have

$$\mu_k(a) = \mu_k(-b)$$

The boundary conditions (6.20) and (6.21) determine the allowable values of E in a manner analogous to the particle in the well-known problem discussed in chapter 2 (see equation 2.50). In the present case, (6.20) and (6.21) give rise to the secular equation

$$\frac{\beta^2 - \alpha^2}{2\alpha\beta} \sinh(\beta b) \sin(\alpha a) + \cosh(\beta b) \cos(\alpha a) = \cos k(a + b) \quad (6.22)$$

This equation places conditions on α and β and hence on the allowed energies. However, the discussion of (6.22) is rather cumbersome and nothing essential is lost if we adopt the simplification of Kronig and Penny and assume that V_0 tends to infinity and b approaches zero in such a manner that $V_0 b$ remains constant. In the limit we find that (6.22) becomes

$$\frac{Q}{\alpha a} \sin \alpha a + \cos \alpha a = \cos ka \quad (6.23)$$

where

$$Q = \frac{m V_0 b a}{\hbar^2}$$

The quantity Q may be regarded as a measure of the strength of the barrier $V_0 b$.

Only those values of α, and hence of E, which satisfy (6.23) will give acceptable wave functions. It is of interest to consider some special cases of (6.23). If V_0 vanishes, then so does Q and the condition on α is simply $\alpha = k$. Since k is essentially continuous and ranges over all positive and negative values, it follows that in this case E is also continuous and can assume any positive value. This of course is simply the free particle solution to the wave equation for which E is not quantized.

On the other hand if Q becomes infinitely large, corresponding to a tightly bound electron, then a solution of (6.23) is only possible if

$$\sin \alpha a = 0$$

so that

$$\alpha = \pm \frac{n\pi}{a} \qquad n = 1, 2, 3, \ldots \quad (6.24)$$

or

$$E = \frac{\pi^2 \hbar^2 n^2}{2ma^2}$$

so that E can only assume discrete values. This result is of course the same as the particle-in-the-box problem dealt with in chapter 2.

For intermediary values of V_0, E may be determined from (6.23) by graphical means as shown in figure 6.3. We note, to begin with, that since $\cos ka$ can never exceed ± 1, only those values of αa are permitted for which the left-hand side of (6.23) lies between the indicated limits. The permitted values of

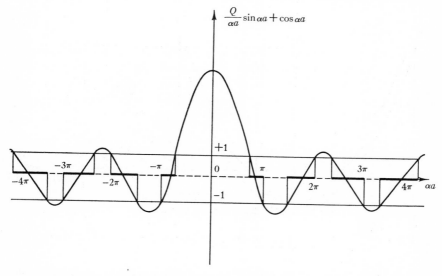

Figure 6.3: Allowed and forbidden energy regions for a one-dimensional crystal.

αa are indicated as heavily drawn line segments in figure 6.3. Thus, the energy is quantized and the permissible energies cover a range of values. We shall refer to a permissible range of energies as an allowed energy band. Separating these allowed energy bands are forbidden energy regions. The discontinuities in allowed energy occur at

$$\cos ka = \pm 1$$

or

$$k = \pm \frac{n\pi}{a} \qquad n = 1, 2, 3, \ldots \qquad (6.25)$$

We note from figure 6.3 that the width of the allowed band increases on proceeding to greater values of αa.

The allowed energy regions may also be exhibited as a function of k as shown in figure 6.4. The region $-\pi/a < k < \pi/a$ is called the first Brillouin zone, while the two regions $\pi/a < k < 2\pi/a$ and $-2\pi/a < k < -\pi/a$ are referred to as the second Brillouin zone, etc. Thus, the Brillouin zones are regions in k-space within which the allowed energy state varies continuously with k. At the edges of the zone there is a discontinuity in the energy state. A second representation of the information in figure 6.4, the *reduced zone*

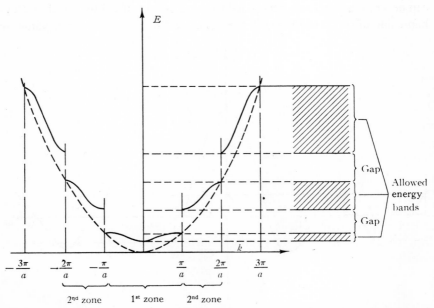

Figure 6.4: Allowed energy regions vs. k is shown on the left-hand side of the diagram while the various energy bands are shown on the right.

scheme, is shown in figure 6.5. Here the various energy bands are represented by values of k confined to the first Brillouin zone. The state of an electron in the Bloch scheme can be designated by specifying k in the extended zone representation or k and the zone number n in the reduced zone representation.

The number of energy states g_m per zone excluding spin can be found from (6.12a), and the fact that $-\pi/a < k < \pi/a$. In the Kronig–Penny model $a \approx d$ so that

$$\frac{2\pi}{a} = \frac{2\pi g_m}{Ga} = \frac{2\pi g_m}{(N-1)a} \qquad (6.26)$$

$$\therefore \; g_m = N - 1 \approx N$$

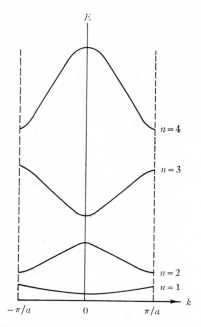

Figure 6.5: Reduced zone representation.

where a is the interatomic distance and N the number of atoms in the crystal. We see, therefore, that each atom contributes two states, including spin, to the zone.

6.3 THREE-DIMENSIONAL CRYSTALS

The previous discussion will now be extended to three-dimensional crystals. In order to facilitate the subsequent discussion we briefly review some of the more important ideas associated with the geometry of crystals.

A crystal is a solid made up of atoms arranged in a periodic pattern in space. It is convenient in the discussion of crystals to distinguish between the basic geometry of the periodic pattern and the atoms themselves. This may be done by replacing the atoms or groups of atoms in the crystal structure by points as shown in figure 6.6. As indicated, the lattice point replaces two atoms in the crystal structure. The essential requirement is that each lattice point must have identical surroundings. The group of atoms associated with a lattice point is referred to as a *basis*, while the array of lattice points is referred to as the lattice. It is clear, therefore, that a given crystal structure

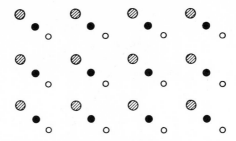

(a) Crystal structure obtained by associating a basis
with the lattice points

(b) Square array of lattice points

Figure 6.6.

may be characterized by designating the type of lattice and the associated basis. The latter is designated by the coordinates of the centers of the atoms with respect to the associated lattice point. Some examples will be given below.

We now consider the specification of the point lattice. As indicated in figure 6.7 the lattice may be regarded as made up of unit cells. However, the resolution of a given lattice into unit cells is by no means unique. Bravais has shown that there are no more than fourteen possible unit cells. These unit Bravais cells are shown in figure 6.8 and described in table 6.1. We

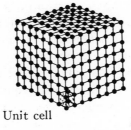

Unit cell

Figure 6.7: Crystal lattice.

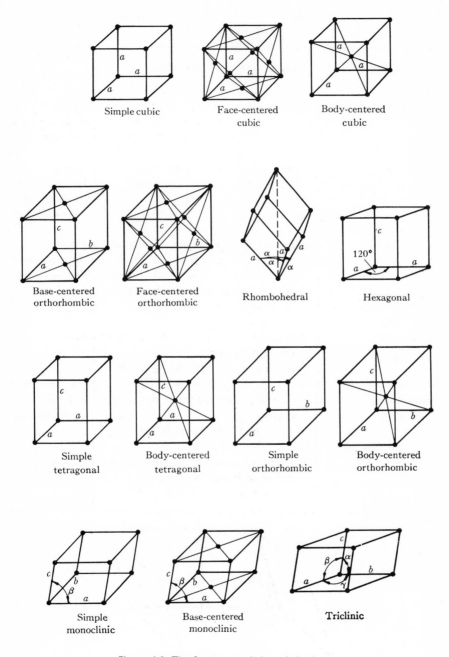

Figure 6.8: The fourteen unit bravais lattices.

TABLE 6.1

Bravais Lattices

SYSTEM	AXIALS, LENGTHS, AND ANGLES	BRAVAIS LATTICE
Cubic	Three equal axes at right angles $a = b = c, \alpha = \beta = \gamma = 90°$	Simple Body-centered Face-centered
Rhombic (Orthorhombic)	Three unequal axes at right angles $a \neq b \neq c, \alpha = \beta = \gamma = 90°$	Simple Body-centered Base-centered Face-centered
Tetragonal	Three axes at right angles, two equal $a = b \neq c, \alpha = \beta = \gamma = 90°$	Simple Body-centered
Trigonal (Rhombohedral)	Three equal axes, equally inclined $a = b = c, \alpha = \beta = \gamma \neq 90°$	Simple
Hexagonal	Two equal coplanar axes at 120°, third axis at right angles $a = b \neq c, \alpha = \beta = 90°, \gamma = 120°$	Simple
Monoclinic	Three unequal axes, one pair not at right angles $a \neq b \neq c, \alpha = \gamma = 90° \neq \beta$	Simple Base-centered
Triclinic	Three unequal axes, unequally inclined and none at right angles $a \neq b \neq c, \alpha \neq \beta \neq \gamma \neq 90°$	Simple

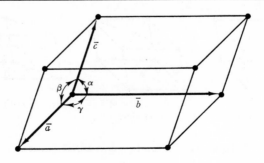

observe that the Bravais cells may be divided into those which have the equivalent of one lattice point per cell (the simple or primitive cell) and those with more than one. It is easy to see that the equivalent number of lattice points per cell is given by

$$N = N_i + \frac{N_f}{2} + \frac{N_c}{8} \tag{6.27}$$

where N_i is the number of interior points, N_f the number of points on a face, and N_c the number of points at the corners.

Lattices made up of simple Bravais cells can be generated by the lattice vector $\bar{r}$, given by

$$r = n_1\bar{a} + n_2\bar{b} + n_3\bar{c} \tag{6.28}$$

where n_1, n_2, and n_3 are integers and $\bar{a}$, $\bar{b}$, $\bar{c}$ are the vectors along the edges of the unit lattice sell.

In the case of nonprimitive cells not all of the points are given by (6.28) and it is necessary to introduce nonintegral multiples of the unit lattice vectors. If the point in the cell is given by the translation $r = x\bar{a} + y\bar{b} + z\bar{c}$, then it is customary to designate the point by the coordinates (x, y, z).

6.4 CRYSTAL STRUCTURES

The simplest structure is that obtained by placing atoms at the lattice points of a simple cubic lattice. Metals do not crystallize in this structure. However, a large number of metals crystallize in the body-centered, face-centered and hexagonal close-packed structures. The body-centered structure occurs with such metals as Na, α-Fe, Cr, Mo, and V. While the crystal may be described in terms of a body-centered cubic lattice, for some purposes it may be more convenient to express the lattice in terms of a primitive rhombohedral cell as shown in figure 6.9a. If we designate the length of the cube edge by a and the unit Cartesian vectors as $\bar{e}_1$, $\bar{e}_2$, and $\bar{e}_3$, it may be seen by simple geometrical arguments that

$$\begin{aligned} \bar{a} &= \tfrac{1}{2}a(-\bar{e}_1 + \bar{e}_2 + \bar{e}_3) \\ \bar{b} &= \tfrac{1}{2}a(\bar{e}_1 - \bar{e}_2 + \bar{e}_3) \\ \bar{c} &= \tfrac{1}{2}a(\bar{e}_1 + \bar{e}_2 - \bar{e}_3) \end{aligned} \tag{6.28a}$$

The volume of the primitive rhombohedral cell is given by the well-known expression

$$\bar{a}\cdot\bar{b} \times \bar{c} = \tfrac{1}{2}a^3$$

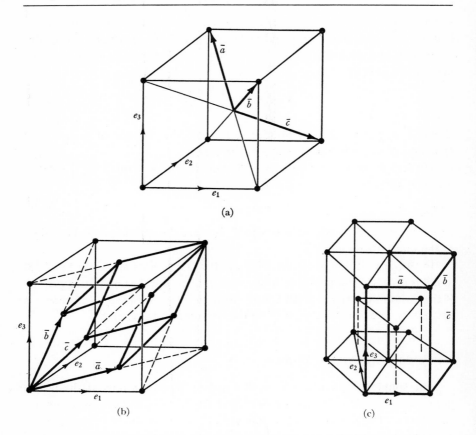

Figure 6.9: (a) Body-centered cubic showing rhombohedral cell. (b) Face-centered cubic showing simple rhombohedral cell. (c) Close-packed hexagonal structure with the simple cell indicated by heavy lines.

The face-centered structure occurs with such metals as γ–Fe, Cu, Pb, Ni, Al, etc. The unit rhombohedral cell is shown in figure 6.9b and the edge vectors are given by

$$\bar{a} = \tfrac{1}{2}a(\bar{e}_1 + \bar{e}_2)$$
$$\bar{b} = \tfrac{1}{2}a(\bar{e}_2 + \bar{e}_3) \qquad\qquad (6.28b)$$
$$\bar{c} = \tfrac{1}{2}a(\bar{e}_3 + \bar{e}_1)$$

The close-packed hexagonal structure is shown in figure 6.9c. With this structure the atoms are arranged in equidistant planes in each of which every atom has six equidistant neighbors. This structure represents one of the two ways in which hard spheres may be most densely packed. The other way is the face-centered cubic. The hexagonal close-packed structure may be resolved into a simple hexagonal Bravais lattice with a basis at $(0, 0, 0)$ and $(1/3, 1/3, 1/2)$. The simple hexagonal lattice has edge vectors

$$
\begin{aligned}
\bar{a} &= a\bar{e}_1 \\
\bar{b} &= \tfrac{1}{2}a\bar{e}_1 + \tfrac{1}{2}\sqrt{3}\, a\bar{e}_2 \\
\bar{c} &= c\bar{e}_3
\end{aligned}
\tag{6.28c}
$$

The interior atom has the position vector with respect to a lattice point of

$$
\tfrac{1}{3}\bar{a} + \tfrac{1}{3}\bar{b} + \tfrac{1}{2}\bar{c}
$$

hence the basis consists of the atom at the lattice point with coordinates $(0, 0, 0)$ and the atom at $(1/3, 1/3, 1/2)$.

The diamond structure shown in figure 6.10(a) is shared by Ge and Si, the most important of the semiconductors. The lattice is a face-centered cubic with a basis at $(0, 0, 0)$ and $(1/4, 1/4, 1/4)$.

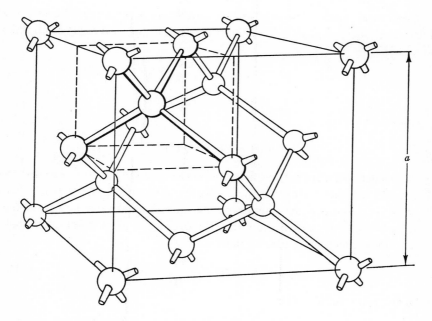

Figure 6.10: Diamond structure characteristic of germanium and silicon.

6.5   *THREE-DIMENSIONAL BLOCH FUNCTION*

We now consider the wave functions associated with an electron moving through a three-dimensional crystal. It is convenient to consider, at first, a simple Bravais lattice. The potential function $V(r)$ has the periodicity of the lattice so that

$$V(\bar{r}) = V(\bar{r} + \bar{R})$$

where $\bar{R}$ is a lattice vector given by

$$\bar{R} = n_1\bar{a} + n_2\bar{b} + n_3\bar{c} \qquad (6.29)$$

and n_1, n_2, and n_3 are integers.

Since all the lattice points are equivalent, we must have, as with the one-dimensional case,

$$|\psi(\bar{r})|^2 = |\psi(\bar{r} + \bar{R})|^2 \qquad (6.30)$$

This requirement is satisfied by a function of the form

$$\psi(r) = e^{i\bar{k}\cdot\bar{r}}\mu_k(r) \qquad (6.31)$$

where $\bar{k}$ is a vector to be determined, and where $\mu_k(r)$ is periodic with the lattice, i.e., $\mu_k(r) = \mu_k(r + R)$. That (6.31) satisfies (6.30) is easily established since

$$\psi(r + R) = e^{i\bar{k}\cdot(r + R)}\mu_k(\bar{r} + \bar{R}) = e^{i\bar{k}\cdot\bar{R}}e^{i\bar{k}\cdot\bar{r}}\mu_k(\bar{r} + \bar{R})$$
$$= e^{i\bar{k}\cdot\bar{R}}\psi(\bar{r}) \qquad (6.32)$$

so that

$$|\psi(\bar{r} + \bar{R})|^2 = |\psi(\bar{r})|^2$$

Consider now a crystal consisting of N_1 atoms in the direction $\bar{a}$ so that the length L_1 of the crystal in the indicated direction is $L_1 = G_1a$ where $G = N_1 - 1$ and a is the interatomic distance. Similarly we find $L_2 = G_2\bar{b}$ and $L_3 = G_3\bar{c}$. We now assume that the cyclic boundary conditions apply in the three-dimensional case so that

$$\psi(\bar{r}) = \psi(\bar{r} + G_1\bar{a}) = e^{i\bar{k}\cdot G_1\bar{a}}\psi(\bar{r}) \qquad (6.32a)$$

The last result implies that

$$e^{i\bar{k}\cdot G_1\bar{a}} = 1 \qquad (6.32b)$$

and hence

$$\bar{k} \cdot \bar{a} = \frac{2\pi g_1}{G_1} \qquad (6.32c)$$

and by similar arguments

$$\bar{k} \cdot \bar{b} = \frac{2\pi g_2}{G_2} \qquad (6.32d)$$

$$\bar{k} \cdot \bar{c} = \frac{2\pi g_3}{G_3} \qquad (6.32e)$$

where g_1, g_2, and g_3 are positive or negative integers.

Equations (6.32a) through (6.32e) serve to determine $\bar{k}$. Let us write

$$\bar{k} = l_1\bar{b}_1 + e_3\bar{b}_2 + l_3\bar{b}_3 \qquad (6.32f)$$

In what follows it is convenient to relabel the lattice vectors of the unit cell as follows

$$\bar{a} \equiv \bar{a}_1$$

$$\bar{b} \equiv \bar{a}_2$$

$$\bar{c} \equiv \bar{a}_3$$

We can now define the vectors $\bar{b}$ by the relationships

$$\bar{a}_i \cdot \bar{b}_j = 2\pi\delta_{ij} \qquad (6.33)$$

and

$$\bar{b}_1 = c_1(\bar{a}_2 \times \bar{a}_3) \qquad (6.33a)$$

$$\bar{b}_2 = c_2(\bar{a}_3 \times \bar{a}_1) \qquad (6.33b)$$

$$\bar{b}_3 = c_3(\bar{a}_1 \times \bar{a}_2) \qquad (6.33c)$$

From (6.33) and (6.33a) we have

$$c_1\bar{a}_1 \cdot (\bar{a}_2 \times \bar{a}_3) = 2\pi$$

and since

$$\bar{a}_1 \cdot (\bar{a}_2 \times \bar{a}_3) = V$$

where V is the volume of the unit of the lattice cell we have

$$c_1 = \frac{2\pi}{V}$$

Similarly we find

$$\bar{b}_1 = \frac{2\pi}{V} (\bar{a}_2 \times \bar{a}_3) \tag{6.34}$$

$$\bar{b}_2 = \frac{2\pi}{V} (\bar{a}_3 \times \bar{a}_1) \tag{6.35}$$

$$\bar{b}_3 = \frac{2\pi}{V} (\bar{a}_1 \times \bar{a}_2) \tag{6.36}$$

The vectors $\bar{b}_1$, $\bar{b}_2$, and $\bar{b}_3$ are referred to as the *reciprocal lattice vectors*.

Returning to (6.32f) we can now determine l since from (6.34) and (6.33)

$$l_1 = \frac{g_1}{G_1}, \qquad l_2 = \frac{g_2}{G_2}, \qquad l_3 = \frac{g_3}{G_3} \tag{6.37}$$

It follows that the vector $\bar{k}$ is given by

$$\bar{k} = \frac{g_1}{G_1} \bar{b}_1 + \frac{g_2}{G_2} \bar{b}_2 + \frac{g_3}{G_3} \bar{b}_3 \tag{6.38}$$

As an example, we calculate the reciprocal lattice vectors for a simple rhombic lattice. In this case we have

$$\begin{aligned}
\bar{a}_1 &= a_1 \bar{e}_1 \\
\bar{a}_2 &= a_2 \bar{e}_2 \\
\bar{a}_3 &= a_3 \bar{e}_3
\end{aligned} \tag{6.38a}$$

where $\bar{e}_i$ is a unit Cartesian vector. From (6.34) through (6.36) we have

$$V = \bar{a}_1 \cdot (\bar{a}_2 \times \bar{a}_3) = a_1 a_2 a_3$$

$$\bar{b}_1 = \frac{2\pi}{V} (\bar{a}_2 \times \bar{a}_3) = \frac{2\pi}{a_1} \bar{e}_1$$

$$\bar{b}_2 = \frac{2\pi}{V} (\bar{a}_3 \times \bar{a}_1) = \frac{2\pi}{a_2} \bar{e}_2$$

$$\bar{b}_3 = \frac{2\pi}{V} (\bar{a}_1 \times \bar{a}_2) = \frac{2\pi}{a_3} \bar{e}_3$$

Applying the above procedure we may obtain the reciprocal lattice vectors for the following lattice types:

a. the body-centered cubic lattice

$$\bar{b}_1 = \frac{2\pi}{a}(\bar{e}_2 + \bar{e}_3)$$

$$\bar{b}_2 = \frac{2\pi}{a}(\bar{e}_1 + \bar{e}_3) \qquad (6.38b)$$

$$\bar{b}_3 = \frac{2\pi}{a}(\bar{e}_1 + \bar{e}_2)$$

b. face-centered cubic

$$\bar{b}_1 = \frac{2\pi}{a}(\bar{e}_1 + \bar{e}_2 - \bar{e}_3)$$

$$\bar{b}_2 = \frac{2\pi}{a}(-\bar{e}_1 + \bar{e}_2 + \bar{e}_3) \qquad (6.38c)$$

$$\bar{b}_3 = \frac{2\pi}{a}(\bar{e}_1 - \bar{e}_2 + \bar{e}_3)$$

c. close-packed hexagonal

$$\bar{b}_1 = \frac{2\pi}{a}\left(\bar{e}_1 - \frac{1}{\sqrt{3}}\,\bar{e}_2\right)$$

$$\bar{b}_2 = \frac{4\pi}{\sqrt{3}\,c}\,\bar{e}_3 \qquad (6.38d)$$

$$\bar{b}_3 = \frac{2\pi}{c}\,\bar{e}_3$$

6.6 ENERGY BANDS—BRILLOUIN ZONES

In this section we shall apply first order perturbation theory to an electron moving in a three-dimensional periodic potential field. The unperturbed wave function is taken to be that of a free electron and it is easily verified that

$$\psi = Ce^{i\bar{k}\cdot\bar{r}} \qquad (6.39)$$

where C is a normalizing constant, and where $\bar{k}$ is given by (6.38), satisfies the periodic boundary conditions (6.32a) through (6.32e) and the wave equation

$$-\frac{\hbar^2}{2m}\nabla^2\psi = E\psi$$

provided that

$$E = \frac{4\pi^2\hbar^2}{2m}\left[\left(\frac{g_1}{L_1}\right)^2 + \left(\frac{g_2}{L_2}\right)^2 + \left(\frac{g_3}{L_3}\right)^2\right]$$

where $g_1 = 0, \pm 1, \pm 2, \ldots$ and similarly for g_2 and g_3. We see that E is eightfold degenerate. If the volume of the solid is v then it is easy to show that ψ normalized over the volume of the solid gives

$$\psi = \frac{1}{\sqrt{v}}\, e^{i\vec{k}\cdot\vec{r}}$$

Suppose now we consider the effect on the electron energy of a perturbation due to small periodic potential $V(r)$. Since E is eightfold degenerate we have from the earlier discussion of first order degenerate perturbation theory that the first order correction $E^{(1)}$ is given by the secular equation

$$|V_{kk'} - E^{(1)}\delta_{kk'}| = 0 \qquad (6.40)$$

where the matrix elements are given by

$$V_{kk'} = \int \psi_k V(r)\psi_{k'}\, d\tau = \frac{1}{v}\int e^{i(\vec{k}-\vec{k}')\cdot\vec{r}}V(r)\, d\tau \qquad (6.40a)$$

where the integral is over the crystal. If the nondiagonal elements of (6.40) vanish then $E^{(1)}$ is merely the average potential energy of the crystal, i.e.,

$$E^{(1)} = \frac{1}{v}\int V(\vec{r})\, d\tau \qquad (6.41)$$

and the energy does not exhibit discontinuities in k-space. In order for an energy gap to occur some diagonal matrix elements must be nonvanishing.

The implications of this requirement can be made clear by recalling that $V(\vec{r})$ has the periodicity of the lattice and on introducing $\vec{r} = \vec{r}' + \vec{R}_n$ into (6.40a) we can easily show that

$$\begin{aligned}
V_{kk'} &= \frac{1}{v}\sum_{\text{all cells}}\int_{\text{cell}} e^{i(\vec{k}-\vec{k}')\cdot\vec{r}}V(\vec{r})\, d\tau \\
&= \frac{1}{v}\sum_{\text{all cells}} e^{i(\vec{k}-\vec{k}')\cdot\vec{R}_n}\int_{\text{cell}} e^{i(\vec{k}-\vec{k}')\cdot\vec{r}'}V(r')\, dr'
\end{aligned} \qquad (6.42)$$

where the integral is taken over a single cell and the result then summed, as indicated, over the crystal. The summation term may be written

$$\sum_{n_1=0}^{G_1-1} e^{2\pi(g_1-g_1')n_1 i/G_1} \sum_{n_2=0}^{G_2-1} e^{2\pi(g_2-g_2')n_2 i/G_2} \sum_{n_3=0}^{G_3-1} e^{2\pi(g_3-g_3')n_3 i/G_3} \quad (6.42a)$$

on introducing (6.29) and (6.38).

Each term in (6.42a) is a geometric series of the form

$$S_n = 1 + R + R^2 + \cdots + R^n$$

The sum S_n is given by

$$S_n = \frac{R^{n+1} - 1}{R - 1}$$

In the present case we have for example

$$R = e^{2\pi(g_1-g_1'/G_1)i}$$

$$n = G_1 - 1$$

so that since g_1 and g_1' are integers

$$S_n = \frac{e^{2\pi(g_1-g_1')} - 1}{e^{2\pi(g_1-g_1')/G_1} - 1} = 0$$

unless

$$g_1 - g_1' = -m_1 G_1$$

where m_1 is a positive or negative integer or zero. Similar arguments apply to the other sums so that

$$g_2 - g_2' = -m_2 G_2$$

$$g_3 - g_3' = -m_3 G_3$$

The above may be written more compactly as

$$\bar{k} = \bar{k}' - \bar{K}_m \quad (6.43)$$

where

$$\bar{K}_m = m_1 \bar{b}_1 + m_2 \bar{b}_2 + m_3 \bar{b}_3 \quad (6.43a)$$

Since $|k| = |k'|$ we have

$$2\bar{k} \cdot \bar{K}_m - |\bar{K}_m|^2 = 0 \tag{6.44}$$

The last result defines as we shall soon see, *the Brillouin zone of a three-dimensional solid.*

We note that if (6.43) is substituted into (6.40a) then

$$V_{kk'} = V_m = \frac{1}{v} \int e^{-i\bar{K}_m \cdot \bar{r}} V(r) \, dr$$

This last is simply the Fourier coefficient in the triple Fourier expansion of $V(r)$:

$$V(r) = \sum_{m=-\infty}^{+\infty} V_m e^{i\bar{K}_m \cdot \bar{r}}$$

More generally, a unit cell may not be simple but consists of atoms with position vectors $\bar{s}_1, \bar{s}_2, \ldots, \bar{s}_l$ with respect to a corner chosen as the origin. The potential at any point $\bar{r}$ within the unit cell may be regarded as the superposition of the contributions from the individual atoms $V(\bar{r} - \bar{s}_j)$ hence

$$V(r) = \sum_{j=1}^{l} V(\bar{r} - \bar{s}_j)$$

Expanding $V(\bar{r} - \bar{s}_j)$ in a Fourier series, we have

$$V(\bar{r} - \bar{s}_j) = \sum_{m=-\infty}^{+\infty} V'_m e^{i\bar{K}_m \cdot (\bar{r} - \bar{s}_j)}$$

so that

$$V(r) = \sum_{j=1}^{l} \sum_{m=-\infty}^{+\infty} V'_m e^{i\bar{K}_m \cdot (\bar{r} - \bar{s}_j)} = \sum_{m} S_m V'_m e^{i\bar{K}_m \cdot \bar{r}}$$
$$= \sum_{m} V_m e^{i\bar{K}_m \cdot \bar{r}} \tag{6.44a}$$

where S_m, referred to as the structural factor, is given by

$$S_m = \sum_{j=1}^{l} e^{-i\bar{K}_m \cdot \bar{s}_j} \tag{6.44b}$$

The determination of S_m may be illustrated by the body-centered cubic cell shown in figure 6.9a. We consider the cell to be a simple cubic lattice with a basis. The position vector for the atom at the origin is $\bar{s}_1 = 0$ while that for the central atom is $\bar{s}_2 = a/2(\bar{e}_1 + \bar{e}_2 + \bar{e}_3)$. We also have for a simple cubic lattice

$$K_m = \frac{2\pi}{a} (m_1\bar{e}_1 + m_2\bar{e}_2 + m_3\bar{e}_3)$$

so that

$$S_m = 1 + e^{-i\pi(m_1 + m_2 + m_3)} \tag{6.44c}$$

where m may be a negative, positive, or zero integer.

In summary, we have seen that energy gaps will occur at values of k which satisfy (6.44) provided that the Fourier coefficients V_m, occurring in the expansion of the potential (6.44a), do not vanish and hence S_m does not vanish for a given set of integers.

6.7 BRILLOUIN ZONE IN THREE DIMENSIONS

In order to provide a geometric interpretation of (6.44) we consider the vectors $\bar{k}$ and $\bar{K}_m$ as shown in figure 6.11. It is clear that the equation of the plane P, which is the perpendicular bisector of $\bar{K}_m$, is given by

$$\bar{k} \cdot \frac{\bar{K}_m}{|K_m|} = \frac{1}{2} |K_m|$$

or

$$|K_m|^2 - 2\bar{k} \cdot \bar{K}_m = 0$$

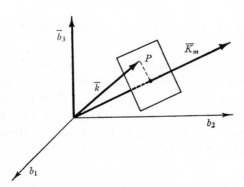

Figure 6.11.

which is identical with (6.44). Hence it is clear that (6.44) defines a set of planes which bound the Brillouin zones since, as we have seen, discontinuities in energy can occur at these planes provided $S_m \neq 0$. The zone is the solid region in k space bounded by the above planes.

As an example of the method for constructing Brillouin zones we consider the body-centered cubic structure. In order to avoid the use of oblique coordinates we shall, as before, consider the body-centered cubic lattice to be a simple cubic lattice with a side a and a basis $(0, 0, 0)$ and $(a/2, a/2, a/2)$. The lattice vectors $\bar{a}_1$, $\bar{a}_2$, $\bar{a}_2$ are a rectangular set and therefore

$$\bar{b}_1 = \frac{2\pi}{a}\,\bar{a}_2$$

$$\bar{b}_2 = \frac{2\pi}{a}\,\bar{a}_2 \tag{6.45}$$

$$\bar{b}_3 = \frac{2\pi}{a}\,\bar{a}_3$$

hence

$$\bar{K}_m = \frac{2\pi}{a}\,(m_1\bar{a}_1 + m_2\bar{a}_2 + m_3\bar{a}_3) \tag{6.46}$$

The structural factor S_m is given by (6.44c):

$$S_m = 1 + e^{-\pi i(m_1 + m_2 + m_3)} \tag{6.47}$$

Introducing (6.46) into (6.44) we obtain the general equation for the surfaces bounding the zone:

$$(m_1 k_1 + m_2 k_2 + m_3 k_3) = -\frac{\pi}{a}\,[m_1^2 + m_2^2 + m_3^2] \tag{6.48}$$

where k_1, k_2, k_3 are the components of $\bar{k}$ on $\bar{a}_1$, $\bar{a}_2$, and $\bar{a}_3$.

We next seek the set of planes consistent with $S_m \neq 0$. Writing $(\pm 1, 0, 0)$ for $m_1 = \pm 1$, $m_2 = 0$, $m_3 = 0$ we see that $S_m = 0$ for $(\pm 1, 0, 0)$, $(0, \pm 1, 0)$, and $(0, 0, \pm 1)$ so that these sets of integers are eliminated. However, $(\pm 1, \pm 1, 0)$ $(\pm 1, 0, \pm 1)$, $(0, \pm 1, \pm 1)$ give $S_{110} = 2$. Hence the first zone is bounded by twelve intersecting planes (figure 6.12a), i.e.,

$$\pm k_1 \pm k_2 = \frac{2\pi}{a}, \qquad \pm k_1 \pm k_3 = \frac{2\pi}{a}, \qquad \pm k_2 \pm k_3 = \frac{2\pi}{a}$$

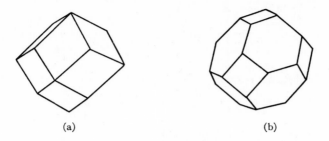

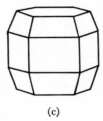

(c)

Figure 6.12: First Brillouin zone in (a) the body-centered lattice, (b) the face-centered lattice, and (c) the hexagonal close-packed lattice.

The face-centered cubic may be treated similarly. The unit cell is taken to be a simple cubic lattice with the basis $(0, 0, 0)$, $(a/2, a/2, 0)$, $(a/2, 0, a/2)$, $(0, a/2, a/2)$ and we find that

$$S_m = 1 + e^{-\pi i(m_1 + m_2)} + e^{-\pi i(m_1 + m_3)} + e^{-\pi i(m_2 + m_3)}$$

which is zero for the $(1, 0, 0)$, $(1, 1, 0)$ planes. However, the first nonvanishing S_m are obtained from $(\pm 1, \pm 1, \pm 1)$, $(\pm 2, 0, 0)$, $(0, \pm 2, 0)$, and $(0, 0, \pm 2)$. The first Brillouin zone is bounded by the planes

$$\pm k_1 \pm k_2 \pm k_3 = \frac{3\pi}{a}, \qquad \pm k_1 = \frac{2\pi}{a}, \qquad \pm k_2 = \frac{2\pi}{a}, \qquad \pm k_3 = \frac{2\pi}{a}$$

The resulting truncated octahedron is shown in figure 6.12b.

The hexagonal close-packed lattice may be treated by taking as the unit cell the simple hexagonal Bravais lattice with a basis. The reciprocal lattice vectors $\vec{b}$ may be referred to the rectangular coordinates $(\vec{e}_1, \vec{e}_2, \vec{e}_3)$ which are given by (6.28c). In the rectangular system the basis is given by $(0, 0, 0)$ and $(a/2, \sqrt{3}\,a/b, c/2)$.

We have from (6.43a) and (6.38d)

$$\bar{K}_m = 2\pi \left[\frac{m_1 \bar{e}_1}{a} + \frac{1}{\sqrt{3}a} (2m_2 - m_1)\bar{e}_2 + \frac{m_3}{2} \bar{e}_3 \right]$$

The structural factor is then

$$S_m = 1 + e^{-\pi i (2m/3 + 2m_2/3 + m_3)} \tag{6.49}$$

and the general equation of the bounding planes is

$$\pi \left[\frac{m_1 \bar{k}_1}{a} + \frac{1}{\sqrt{3}a} (2m_2 - m_1)\bar{k}_2 + \frac{m_3}{c} \bar{k}_3 \right]$$

$$- 4\pi^2 \left[\frac{m_1^2}{a^2} + \frac{1}{3a^2} (2m_2 - m_1) + \frac{m_3}{c^2} \right] = 0$$

where k_1 etc., are the components of $\bar{k}$ on $\bar{e}$. We see from the above that the first planes bounding the zone are given by $(\pm 1, 0, 0)$, $(0, \pm 1, 0)$, $(\pm 1, \pm 1, 0)$, $(\pm 1, 0, \pm 1)$, while the planes $(0, 0, \pm 1)$ are eliminated. The resulting zone is shown in figure 6.12c.

6.8 DENSITY OF ENERGY STATES

The number of energy states per unit volume of $\bar{k}$-space can be readily calculated. We consider a crystal in the form of a cube containing G^3 unit lattice cells. The number of energy states (excluding spin degeneracy) per unit volume of $\bar{k}$-space may be obtained from

$$\bar{k} = \frac{g_1}{G} \bar{b}_1 + \frac{g_2}{G} \bar{b}_2 + \frac{g_3}{G} \bar{b}_3$$

where g is a positive or negative integer. It is clear that if g_1 ranges from $-G/2$ to $G/2$, then $\bar{b}_1$ ranges from $-\bar{b}/2$ to $\bar{b}_1/2$, and similarly for the other two vectors in reciprocal lattice space. It follows that the total number of states in the volume defined by the parallelepiped with sides of length b_1, b_2, and b_3 is G^3. The volume occupied by the G^3 uniformly spaced values of $\bar{k}$ is just,

$$\bar{b}_1(\bar{b}_2 \times \bar{b}_3) = \frac{8\pi^3}{V^3} (\bar{a}_2 \times \bar{a}_3) \cdot (\bar{a}_3 \times \bar{a}_1) \times (\bar{a}_1 \times \bar{a}_2)$$

where V is the volume of the unit lattice cell. Now

$$(\bar{a}_3 \times \bar{a}_1) \times (\bar{a}_1 \times \bar{a}_2) = [\bar{a}_1 \cdot (\bar{a}_2 \times \bar{a}_3)] \cdot \bar{a}_1 = V\bar{a}_1$$

hence, the volume in $\bar{k}$-space is just $(\bar{b}_1 \cdot \bar{b}_2 \times \bar{b}_3) = 8\pi^3/V$. This volume includes G^3-states (neglecting spin degeneracy), hence the number of states per unit volume in $\bar{k}$-space is

$$N(k) = G^3 \times \frac{V}{8\pi^3} = \frac{V_t}{8\pi^3} \qquad (6.50)$$

where V_t is the total physical volume of the crystal. It also follows that the number of states in the volume element dk is

$$N(k)\,dk = \frac{V_t}{8\pi^3}\,dk \qquad (6.51)$$

The last may also be expressed in terms of energy by considering k-space divided up by the surfaces $E(k) = $ constant. The volume element dk between E and $E + dE$ is

$$dk = \frac{dn}{dE}\,dE\,dS$$

where dS is an element of the constant energy surface and n is the normal to that surface. Since

$$\frac{dE}{dn} = |\nabla_k E(k)|$$

we have

$$dk = \frac{dE\,dS}{|\nabla_k E(k)|} \qquad (6.51a)$$

If $N(E)$ is the density of states per unit energy interval then

$$N(E)\,dE = \frac{V_t\,dE}{8\pi^3} \int_s \frac{dS}{\nabla_k E(k)}$$

or

$$N(E) = \frac{V_t}{8\pi^3} \int_s \frac{dS}{\nabla_k E(k)} \qquad (6.52)$$

Finally, we note that the fundamental domain in $\bar{k}$-space contains G^3-states which is just equal to the number of cells in the crystal. It is clear that each unit cell contributes one state to the Brillouin zone so that, including spin, two electrons can be accommodated per cell. If the unit cell contains one atom then the Brillouin zone can accommodate two electrons per atom.

6.9   *EFFECTIVE MASS*

In chapter 2 we discussed the representation of an electron by a wave packet. In the same way an electron moving through a periodic potential field may be represented by a wave packet formed from Bloch functions. Thus on multiplying the Bloch function by the time factor we have

$$\psi(\bar{r}, t) = \mu_k(r)e^{i(\bar{k}\cdot\bar{r} - E(k)/\hbar t)}$$

As before, we can construct a wave packet

$$\psi(r, t) = \int a(k)\mu_k(r)e^{i(\bar{k}\cdot\bar{r} - E(k)/\hbar t)} \, dk \qquad (6.52a)$$

where $a(k)$ is a function with a sharp maximum and a rapid decay to either side of the maximum. As indicated in chapter 2, the group velocity of the packet is

$$v_g = \frac{1}{\hbar} \nabla_k E(k) \qquad (6.25b)$$

Similarly from (2.182) and (2.183) we define $\langle P \rangle$ as the crystal momentum $\bar{P}$, and therefore

$$\frac{d\bar{P}}{dt} = \bar{F}$$

From

$$\hbar\bar{k} = \bar{P}$$

we also have

$$\hbar\frac{d\bar{k}}{dt} = \bar{F} \qquad (6.52c)$$

The effective mass of the electron can now be defined as in (2.184)

$$\frac{1}{m^*} = \frac{1}{\hbar^2} \nabla_k \nabla_k E(k) \qquad (6.52d)$$

6.10 ENERGY BANDS

Examination of the expression (6.52) for the density of states, (6.52b) for the group velocity of a wave packet, and (6.52d) for the effective mass of an electron, indicates that the quantity $\nabla_k E(k)$ is of basic importance in solid state theory. Consequently considerable effort has been devoted to the investigation of $E(k)$ as a function of k for the various solids. Since this problem is one of great complexity we can only present here some results of general interest.

We have already noted some simple cases of energy bands. Thus the free electron in a crystal has an $E(k)$ given by

$$E(k) = \frac{\hbar^2}{2m} [k_x^2 + k_y^2 + k_z^2] \tag{6.52e}$$

In the presence of a periodic potential we have seen that an effective mass may be introduced with components given by

$$\frac{1}{m^*} = \frac{1}{\hbar^2} \nabla_k \nabla_k E(k)$$

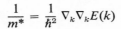

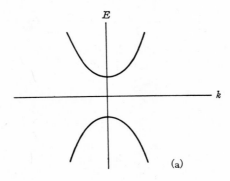

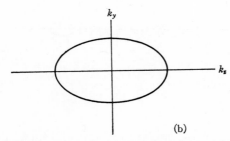

Figure 6.13: Simple energy band with E minimum or maximum at $k = 0$. (a) $E(k)$ vs. (k) and (b) contours of constant E.

Since the components of the tensor m^* may in general be different, we expect that a more widely applicable expression would be

$$E(k) = \frac{\hbar}{2}\left[\frac{k_x^2}{m_1} + \frac{k_y^2}{m_2} + \frac{k_z^2}{m_3}\right] + C \tag{6.53}$$

where m_1, m_2, and m_3 are the effective masses associated with k_x, k_y, and k_z and C is a constant. Energy bands of this simple type are shown in figure 6.13. In this case the minimum or maximum occurs at $k = 0$. However, it is possible

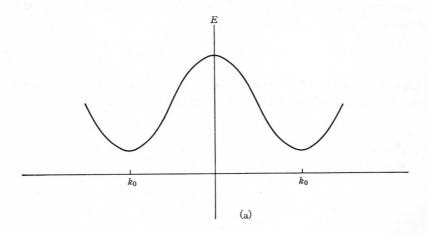

(a)

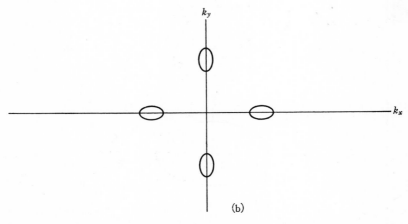

(b)

Figure 6.14: (a) Energy bands corresponding to E minimum at $k = k_0$. (b) Constant energy contours.

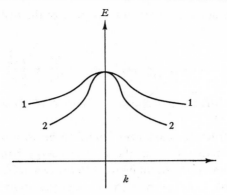

Figure 6.15: Degenerate band structure at $k = 0$.

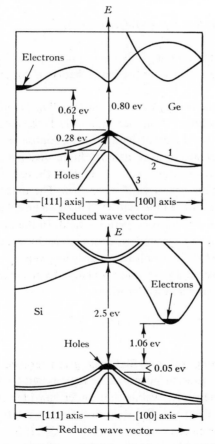

Figure 6.16: Energy bands for Ge and Si (after F. Herman, *Proc. IRE* **43**, 1703, 1955).

for the extremal values to occur in other regions of the Brillouin zone so that, for example,

$$E(k) = \frac{\hbar}{2} \left[\frac{1}{m_1} (k_x^2 - k_0^2) + \frac{k_y^2}{m_2} + \frac{k_z^2}{m_3} \right] \qquad (6.54)$$

This type of band structure is shown in figure 6.14. Degeneracy of $E(k)$ is shown in figure 6.15.

Actual band structures have been found to be very complex combining the various characteristics given above. The energy bands for Ge and Si calculated by Herman is shown in figure 6.16 for two axes. It should be noted that for a given axis, $E(k)$ is symmetrical about the origin.

6.11 BAND THEORY OF CONDUCTION

In order to appreciate more fully the implications of the energy diagrams, it is necessary for us to consider the band theory of conductors in somewhat greater detail.

Let us consider the energy bands of sodium. The isolated atom has eleven electrons with the configuration (see table 3.1) $1s^2 2s^2 2p^6 3s$. These levels are shown on the right-hand side of figure 6.17. Suppose that a collection of N isolated atoms, originally spaced at an infinite distance apart, are brought together. The valency or outer electron ($3s$) feels the effect of the other atoms first and the level splits into a band as shown. The inner electron levels are not split until the atoms are much closer. This is to be expected in view of our discussion of the one-dimensional periodic field. In the present case the inner electrons are more firmly bound to the nucleus by a factor which can be roughly estimated from the result for hydrogen given by (2.137a) and taking into account the screening of the nuclear charge by electrons of equal or lower energy than the one under consideration:

$$E \propto \frac{(Z - S)^2}{n^2}$$

where S is the screening constant. Slater has given detailed rules for evaluating S. However, for our present purposes we may assign to S a value of 0.5 for other electrons of the same level as that under consideration, and a value of unity for the inner electrons. We then find for the relative binding energies of the $1s$, $2s$, and $3s$ electrons the values $10^3 : 150 : 1$. The valency ($3s$) band shows considerable broadening, and at the equilibrium distance r_0 overlaps

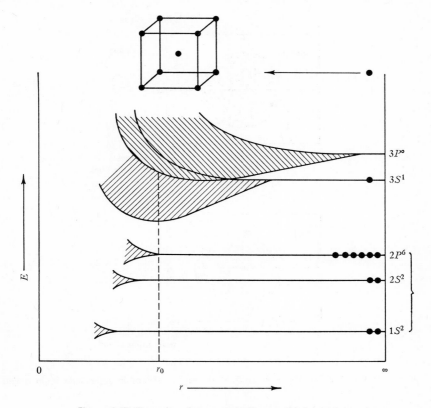

Figure 6.17: Energy vs. interatomic distance (r) for sodium.

with the $3p$ and higher levels. The first Brillouin zone will be populated by the $N\ 3s$ electrons and since the zone can accommodate $2N$ electrons it will be half occupied. Those regions in k-space corresponding to the lowest energy will of course be occupied first. The Fermi level in k-space becomes a constant energy surface, the Fermi surface, which for a free electron is a sphere (6.52e). An illustration of the Fermi surface is shown in figure 6.18.

At equilibrium, states with positive values of k and those with corresponding negative k values are equally occupied. Since we have seen that E is a symmetrical function in k, it follows from (6.52b) that the electron velocity for positive k is oppositely directed to that with negative k. It follows that in order for a net current to flow, the distribution function must be shifted in the presence of a field so that there is a net change in k. The Boltzmann equation already discussed relates the change in distribution function at steady state to the applied field. Figure 6.18 illustrates the essential features

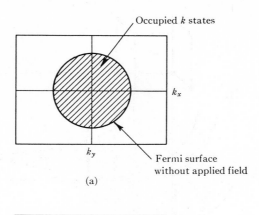

(a)

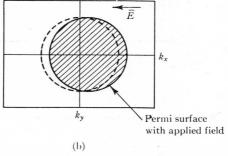

(b)

Figure 6.18: The shift of the Fermi surface, in the first Brillouin zone, with applied field.

of the above discussion. In the absence of a field the distribution is symmetrically situated in the Brillouin zone. Application of a field $\bar{E}$ shifts the distribution of the electrons in k-space so that there is a net increase in k. The change in k is given by (6.52c) so that k changes in the opposite direction of the applied field by an amount $q\bar{E}\,dt/\hbar$ in a time dt. However, the velocity changes in a direction normal to the $E(k)$ surface as is indicated by (6.52b). Similarly the acceleration and effective mass are determined by the geometry of the $E(k)$ surface, and hence depend on $E(k)$ vs. k and the position of the electron in the zone as shown in figure 6.19.

In order to clarify our ideas we consider the specifics of the electron motion in an ideal crystal. Referring to figure 6.20, we consider an electron initially at point 1 in the k-space (figure 6.20a) and a corresponding point in ordinary space shown in figure 6.20b. The direction of the applied field $\bar{E}$ is also indicated in figure 6.20a. Corresponding to the indicated initial position in the Brillouin zone, the electron will have an energy, a group velocity, and effective mass shown as point 1 in figure 6.20c, d, and e respectively. Since

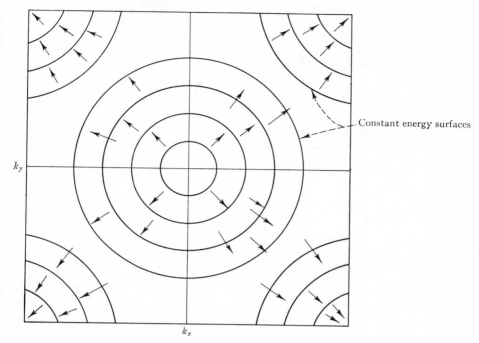

k_y

k_x

Constant energy surfaces

Figure 6.19: The velocity of the electron is normal to the constant energy surfaces.

the group velocity is initially negative, we note that the electron starts to move with the field, rather than against the field as it would classically. As k increases with time, E, $\bar{v}_g$, and m^* change as indicated by the arrows. Thus, the group velocity decreases to zero and then becomes positive. When velocity is maximum we note m^* is infinite and the acceleration is zero. As the electron approaches the zone boundary at point 2, the velocity again decreases to zero. If the energy bands do not overlap so that there is an energy gap at the zone boundary the electron will not be able to leave the first zone and will instead be reflected at (2). This type of reflection, referred to as *Bragg reflection*, should not be confused with scattering due to lattice defects and impurities which will be discussed later. As a consequence of the Bragg reflection, the electron reverses its velocity but the energy is conserved and consequently it can be represented at point (3) in figure 6.20c. In an ideal crystal for which scattering by lattice vibrations, imperfections, and impurities can be neglected, the above processes would be repeated. Thus, reflection would next occur at point (4) on the zone boundary and the electron appears at point 5. In practice, electron scattering by crystal imperfections occurs well before the electron reaches the zone boundary.

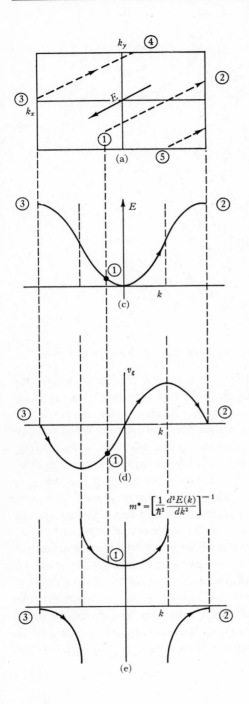

(a)

(c)

(d)

$$m^* = \left[\frac{1}{\hbar^2}\frac{d^2E(k)}{dk^2}\right]^{-1}$$

(e)

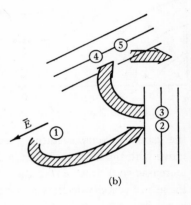

(b)

Figure 6.20: Behavior of an electron in the presence of an applied field.

It is important to note that a net flow of electrons can occur provided that the energy band is not completely filled. In the latter case all of the available states are occupied so that by the Pauli exclusion principle (chapter 3) there cannot be any net change in the distribution of the electrons on applying an electrical field. We see, therefore, *that electrical conduction cannot occur in a completely filled energy band which does not overlap an empty band.*

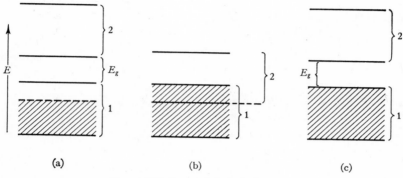

Figure 6.21: Energy band relationships.

Three general types of energy-band relationships may occur and are illustrated in figure 6.21a, b, c. In (a) the band for the outer, or valency, electrons is not filled while in (b) overlap occurs between a filled band and an empty band. In both instances electrical conduction may occur. However, in (c) band (1) is filled and does not overlap an empty band. The energy interval E_g between the two bands is frequently referred to as the energy gap. Substances with the band structure (c) behave as insulators if the energy gap is very large in comparison to the thermal energy of the electrons. Under these circumstances only a negligible number of electrons in band (1) will be excited into band (2). If the gap is sufficiently small so that significant thermal excitation may occur over the ordinary temperature range, then the substance is referred to as an *intrinsic semiconductor*. A list of some semiconductor materials is given in table 6.2.

6.12 *INTRINSIC SEMICONDUCTORS*

We now consider the number of charge carriers available to an intrinsic semiconductor due to thermal ionization of electrons from the topmost filled band—the valency band. A schematic representation of the ionization of Ge or Si is shown in figure 6.22. Since both Ge and Si have four valency electrons

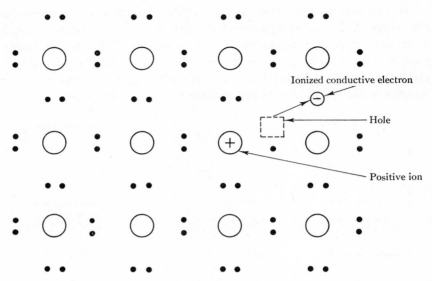

Figure 6.22: Thermal ionization of an intrinsic semiconductor.

these pair-up to form covalent bonds consisting of four pairs of electrons about each atom. If an amount of energy E_g, given in table 6.2, is supplied to a valency electron then thermal ionization can occur resulting in a postive lattice ion and a free conductance electron. In terms of the energy diagram given in figure 6.23, the electron is shown passing from the level at the top

TABLE 6.2

Semiconductors and Energy Gaps (E_g)

SUBSTANCE	E_g (ev)
Si	1.10
Ge	0.68
InSb	0.18
InAs	0.33
InP	1.25
GaAs	1.40
CdS	2.42
PbS	0.34

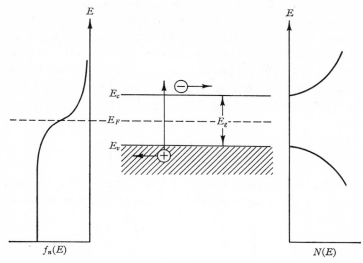

Figure 6.23: Ionization of an intrinsic semiconductor. The Fermi distribution is shown on the left and the density of states on the right.

of the valency band, E_v, to the bottom of the conduction band E_c. The electron in the conductance band, the conductance electron, can now contribute to electrical transport.

As shown in figure 6.22, the ionization of the valency electron leaves a vacancy in the valence band and associated with this vacancy there is a net positive charge. This vacancy is referred to as a hole. Since the valence band is no longer filled we expect, in view of our earlier discussion, that electrical conduction can also occur in the valence band. The mechanism of this conduction is shown in figure 6.24. On applying a field, a valency electron on an

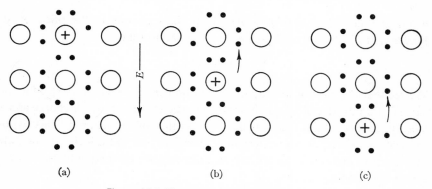

Figure 6.24: The mechanism of hole transport.

atom adjacent to the hole is shifted upward so that the hole now appears one atom below. Repetition of this process results in current flow. Clearly, the transport of valency electrons by this mechanism is equivalent to the transport of a hole in the opposite direction. It is convenient, therefore, to regard the hole as a fictitious positive particle of which the effective mass m_p^* may be assigned by the following considerations. Consider the electron at the top of the filled valency band. According to (6.52b) this electron has a velocity given by

$$\bar{v}_g = \frac{1}{\hbar} \nabla_k E_v(k)$$

where the subscript v refers to the energy level at the top of the valency band. When a field is present the electron undergoes an acceleration given by

$$\frac{d\bar{v}_g}{dt} = \bar{a}_e = -\frac{|e|\bar{E}}{m_e^*} \tag{6.54a}$$

where

$$(m_e^*)^{-1} = \hbar^{-2} \nabla_k \nabla_k E_v(k)$$

Now suppose that this electron is removed and a hole is created. On application of a field, a net current will flow given by

$$I = -e \sum_{-1} \bar{v}_g(k) \tag{6.55}$$

where the sum is taken over all the electrons in the band except the one removed, and the velocity $v_g(k)$ is that of an electron at time t after the field is applied. The expression for the current may also be expressed as

$$I = -e \sum \bar{v}_g(k) + e\bar{v}_g(k)$$

where the sum is now taken over all of the electrons in the filled band. However, for a filled band the current is zero, so that

$$I = e\bar{v}_g(k)$$

We see that the current produced by the absence of a valency electron is the same as that produced by a hypothetical particle with a positive charge and a velocity at any instant which is the same as that of the electron. This hypothetical particle is, of course, the hole. The fact that the velocity of the hole and electron are always equal implies that they are both equally accelerated by an applied field, so that

$$\bar{a}_p = \bar{a}_e \tag{6.56}$$

THERMAL IONIZATION / 199

where $\bar{a}_p$ is the acceleration of the hole. The last equation implies, from (6.54a), that

$$\frac{|e|F}{m_p^*} = -\frac{|e|\bar{E}}{m_e^*}$$

or the effective mass of the hole m_p^* is

$$(m_p^*)^{-1} = -(m_e^*)^{-1} = -\hbar^{-2}\nabla_k\nabla_k E_v(k)$$

6.13 *THERMAL IONIZATION*

We return now to the problem of calculating the number of thermally ionized conductance electrons n. If we assume a spherical conduction band, and on choosing $E(0) = 0$, then

$$E = \frac{\hbar^2}{2m_e^*} [k_x^2 + k_y^2 + k_z^2]$$

or

(6.56a)

$$E = \frac{\hbar^2 k^2}{2m_e^*}$$

and from (6.51) we have for a unit volume of material

$$N_c(k)\, dk = \frac{1}{8\pi^3} \int_{dE} dk_x\, dk_y\, dk_z$$

The integral is taken over the volume in k-space lying between the surfaces E and $E + dE$. This volume is clearly $4\pi k^2\, dk$, so that

$$N_c(E)\, dE = \frac{k^2}{2\pi^2}\cdot dk$$

or from (6.56a)

$$N_c(E)\, dE = 2\pi(2m_e^*)^{3/2}h^{-3}E^{1/2}\, dE$$

If we consider the bottom of the conductance band as $E = 0$, then the total number of conductance electrons is given by

$$n_i = \int_0^\infty f_n(E)N(E)\, dE$$

$$= 2\pi(2m_e^*)^{3/2}h^{-3} \int_0^\infty \frac{E^{1/2}\, dE}{1 + e^{(E-E_F)/kT}}$$

The various functions and the Fermi level are indicated in figure 6.23. In most cases of interest the Fermi level of the intrinsic material lies well in the forbidden gap so that over the range of integration

$$e^{(E - E_F)/kT} \gg 1$$

and we then have

$$n_i = 2\pi(2m_e^*)^{3/2}h^{-3} \int_0^\infty E^{1/2}e^{(E - E_F)/kT}\, dE$$

$$= 2(2m_e^* kT/h^2)^{3/2} \exp E_F/kT$$

hence,

$$n_i = N_c \exp E_F/kT \qquad (6.57)$$

A similar calculation can be carried through for the hole concentration. We assume that the valence band is of the form

$$E = -E_g - \frac{\hbar^2 k^2}{2m_p^*}$$

so that

$$N_v(E)\, dE = 2\pi(2m_p^*)^{3/2}h^{-3}[-(E + E_g)]^{1/2}\, dE$$

The probability $p_p(E)$ that a level is not occupied by an electron and hence occupied by a hole is

$$p_p(E) = 1 - p_n(E) = \frac{1}{1 + e^{-(E - E_F)/kT}} \qquad (6.58)$$

so that the concentration of holes is given by

$$p_i = 2\pi(2m_p^*)^{3/2}h^{-3} \int_{-\infty}^{-E_g} \frac{[-(E + E_g)]^{1/2}\, dE}{1 + e^{-(E - E_F)/kT}}$$

Again we assume that over the range of integration

$$e^{(E_F - E)/kT} \gg 1$$

On introducing the transformation

$$x = -(E_g + E)/kT$$

we find that

$$p_i = 2(2\pi m_p^* kT/h^2)^{3/2} \exp\left[-(E_F + E_g)/kT\right]$$
$$= N_v \exp\left[-(E_F + E_g)/kT\right] \tag{6.59}$$

Since $n_i = p_i$ we have, on equating (6.57) and (6.59),

$$E_F = -\frac{E_g}{2} + \frac{3kT}{4} \ln (m_p^*/m_n^*) \tag{6.60}$$

We see that the Fermi level of an intrinsic semiconductor will lie at the center of the energy gap provided $m_p^* = m_n^*$. This is approximately the case with a number of semiconductors including germanium and silicon.

6.14 SEMICONDUCTORS WITH IMPURITIES

The addition of certain impurities to semiconductors can also provide a source of electrical carriers. Indeed, in a large number of semiconductor applications the carriers are provided by such additions of impurities. As an illustration, the group V elements in the periodic table (P, As, Sb) tend to ionize in Ge and Si as shown

$$D \rightleftharpoons D^+ + n$$

In this way the group V elements donate an electron to the conductance band, as is indicated in figure 6.25, and are appropriately referred to as *donors*. On the other hand the group III elements (B, Ga, In) ionize by trapping an electron from the conductance band with the generation of a hole:

$$A + e \rightarrow A^- + p$$

These elements are referred to as *acceptors*:

Suppose we have an intrinsic semiconductor with the Fermi level at E_{Fi} as indicated in figure 6.25. If a donor which undergoes complete ionization is now added, the Fermi level will rise to a new position E_F, and the equilibrium distribution of electrons is

$$f_n(E) = \frac{1}{1 + e^{(E - E_F)/kT}}$$

The concentration of conductance electrons can be calculated as before and we obtain, assuming $e^{(E - E_F)/kT} \gg 1$

$$n = N_c e^{E_F/kT}$$

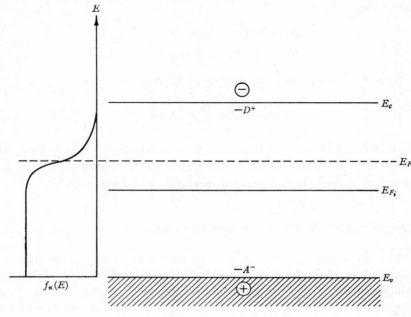

Figure 6.25: Donor (*D*) and acceptor (*A*) levels.

and similarly we find

$$p = N_v e^{-(E_F + E_g)/kT}$$

This result holds provided the Fermi level is about $2kT$ removed from the conductance or valence bands. We also note that

$$np = N_c N_v e^{-E_g/kT} = n_i^2 \tag{6.61}$$

Thus the product of the conductance electron concentration and hole concentration is a constant at a given temperature.

PROBLEM

Show that if n_i and p_i are the intrinsic concentrations of electrons and holes, then

$$n = n_i e^{(E_F - E_{Fi})/kT} \tag{6.62}$$

and also

$$p = p_i e^{-(E_F - E_{Fi})/kT} \tag{6.63}$$

The Fermi level of an impurity semiconductor can be found with the aid of the electroneutrality condition

$$n + (A^-) = p + (D^+) \tag{6.64}$$

where A^- and D^+ are the concentrations of the ionized acceptors and donors. Thus if $A^- = 0$ and $D^+ \gg p_i$, assuming all the donors are ionized, then

$$D^+ = N_c e^{E_F/kT}$$

or

$$E_F = kT \ln \frac{D^+}{N_c}$$

A second situation arises when the donor concentration is in the same order of magnitude as the intrinsic concentration of carriers. We now have

$$n - p = D^+ \tag{6.65}$$

and

$$np = n_i^2 \tag{6.66}$$

so that (6.65) and (6.66) may be simultaneously solved for n and p.

PROBLEM

Assume that both donors and acceptors are present and in the same order of magnitude as n_i. Find p and n.

A third situation arises when the donor or acceptor level lies well within the energy gap so that ionization is not complete. It can be shown that for a singly ionized donor the concentration of un-ionized donor D, is given by

$$D = \frac{N_d}{1 + \frac{1}{2}e^{(E_d - E_F)kT}} \tag{6.67}$$

where E_d is the energy level of the donor and N_d the total donor concentration. It can also be shown that the concentration of ionized acceptors is

$$A^- = \frac{N_a}{1 + 2e^{(E_a - E_F)/kT}} \tag{6.68}$$

and hence the concentration of un-ionized acceptors is

$$A = N_a - A^- = \frac{N_a}{1 + \frac{1}{2}e^{(E_F - E_a)/kT}} \tag{6.69}$$

where E_a is the energy level of the acceptor.

PROBLEMS FOR CHAPTER 6

1. Show that the volume of a unit cell in the reciprocal and direct lattices are reciprocal of each other.

2. Find the equations of the planes bounding the second Brillouin zone for a simple cubic lattice.

3. Derive (6.22).

4. Prove (6.38a) through (6.38d).

5. Show that if $\bar{a}$ is a translation vector, then
a.

$$e^{\bar{a}\cdot\nabla}\psi(\bar{r}) = \psi(\bar{r} + \bar{a})$$

b. If $\psi_k(\bar{r})$ is a Bloch function and $\bar{R}_n$ a lattice vector, then

$$e^{\bar{R}\cdot\nabla}\psi(\bar{r}) = e^{i\bar{k}\cdot\bar{R}_n}\psi_k(\bar{r})$$

6. Let the energy of an electron (or hole) in a solid be given by $E(\bar{k})$, and let $\mathbf{E}(-i\nabla)$ be the operator obtained by replacing $\bar{k}$ by $-i\nabla$. Expand $E(\bar{k})$ and $\mathbf{E}(-i\nabla)$ in the Fourier series

$$E(\bar{k}) = \sum_n E_n e^{i\bar{R}_n\cdot\bar{k}}$$

$$\mathbf{E}(-i\nabla) = \sum_n E_n e^{\bar{R}_n\cdot\nabla}$$

and show by using the results of problem 5 that

$$\mathbf{E}(-i\nabla)\psi_k(\bar{r}) = E(k)\psi_k(\bar{r})$$

Hint:

$$\mathbf{E}(-i\nabla)\psi_k(\bar{r}) = \sum_n E_n e^{\bar{R}_n\cdot\nabla}\psi_k(\bar{r})$$

$$= \sum_n E_n e^{i\bar{k}\cdot\bar{R}_n}\psi_k(\bar{r})$$

$$= E(k)\psi_k(\bar{r})$$

7. Use the above result to show that if

$$\mathbf{H}^{(0)}\psi_k(r) = E(k)\psi_k(r)$$

and

$$(\mathbf{H}^{(0)} + \mathbf{H}^{(1)})\phi(r, t) = i\hbar \frac{\partial \phi}{\partial t}$$

We can write

$$(\mathbf{E}(-i\nabla) + \mathbf{H}^{(1)})\phi(\vec{r}, t) = i\hbar \frac{\partial \phi}{\partial t}$$

Hint:
Let

$$\phi(\vec{r}, t) = \int a(\vec{k}, t)\psi_k(\vec{r}) \, d\vec{k}$$

8. Use the last result to show that if $\mathbf{H}^{(0)}$ is the Hamiltonian operator corresponding to a small periodic potential with eigenvalues $\hbar^2 k^2/2m^*$ (m^* is the effective mass) and $\mathbf{H}^{(1)}$ the operator corresponding to any other forces, then the wave equation is

$$\left(\frac{-\hbar^2}{2m^*}\nabla^2 + \mathbf{H}^{(1)}\right)\phi(\vec{r}, t) = i\hbar \frac{\partial \phi}{\partial t}$$

The last result is just the wave equation for a free particle of mass m^*.

In the present chapter we shall study the consequences of applying electrical, thermal, and magnetic fields to metals and semiconductors. The essential problem is that of solving the Boltzmann equation (4.74) which, in view of (4.75), may be written for the steady state case as

$$\frac{\bar{F}}{\hbar} \cdot \nabla_k f + \bar{v} \cdot \nabla_r f = -\frac{f - f_0}{\tau} \tag{7.1}$$

In the case of electric and magnetic fields

$$\bar{F} = -e\left(\bar{E} + \frac{1}{c}\bar{v} \times \bar{H}\right) \tag{7.2}$$

so that

$$-\frac{e}{\hbar}\left(\bar{E} + \frac{1}{c}\bar{v} \times \bar{H}\right) \cdot \nabla_k f + \bar{v} \cdot \nabla_r f = -\frac{f - f_0}{\tau} \tag{7.3}$$

Once $f(k)$ is known, the electrical current density may be determined from (6.50) but including spin degeneracy, so that

$$\bar{J}_N = \frac{-e}{4\pi^3} \int \bar{v} f \, dk \tag{7.4}$$

where $\bar{v}$ is the velocity of the electron. Similarly the thermal current density $\bar{Q}$ due to the transport of electrons only is given by

$$\bar{Q} = \frac{1}{4\pi^3} \int \bar{v} E f \, dk \tag{7.5}$$

where E is the energy of the electron. In a later section we shall represent the total thermal flux by J_Q.

7.1 ELECTRICAL CONDUCTIVITY

In order to find the electrical conductivity we shall assume that $\bar{H} = 0$ and that the material is homogeneous and at constant temperature so that $\nabla_r f = 0$. For small displacements from equilibrium we place f_0, the equilibrium distribution, into the left-hand side of (7.3) and we find

$$f = f_0 + \frac{e\tau\bar{E}}{\hbar} \cdot \nabla_k f_0 \tag{7.6}$$

or, from (4.79) and (4.81),

$$f = f_0 + e\tau \frac{\partial f_0}{\partial E} \bar{v} \cdot \bar{E}$$

The current density is, from (7.4),

$$\bar{J}_N = -\frac{e^2}{4\pi^3} \int \tau \bar{v}(\bar{v} \cdot \bar{E}) \frac{\partial f_0}{\partial \bar{E}} dk \tag{7.7}$$

where the integral is to be taken over all partially filled bands. Since $\bar{v}(\bar{v} \cdot \bar{E})$ is a vector with components $v_i v_j E_j$ we can write (7.7) as

$$J_{iN} = \sigma_{ij} E_j \qquad i, j = 1, 2, 3 \tag{7.8}$$

where

$$\sigma_{ij} = -\frac{e^2}{4\pi^3} \int \tau v_i v_j \frac{\partial f_0}{\partial E} dk \tag{7.9}$$

Alternatively we may express (7.8) in matrix notation as

$$\begin{pmatrix} J_{1N} \\ J_{2N} \\ J_{3N} \end{pmatrix} = \begin{pmatrix} \sigma_{11} & \sigma_{12} & \sigma_{13} \\ \sigma_{21} & \sigma_{22} & \sigma_{23} \\ \sigma_{31} & \sigma_{32} & \sigma_{33} \end{pmatrix} \begin{pmatrix} E_1 \\ E_2 \\ E_3 \end{pmatrix} \tag{7.10}$$

In order to evaluate the matrix elements σ_{ij} it is convenient to introduce (6.51a) and write

$$\sigma_{ij} = -\frac{e^2}{4\pi^3} \int_S \int_0^{E_m} \tau v_i v_j \frac{\partial f_0}{\partial E} \frac{dE\, dS}{|\nabla_k E|} \tag{7.11}$$

where now the integral is taken over a surface S of constant energy, and E is permitted to range from 0 to E_m, the top of the conductance band. Equation

(7.11) can readily be evaluated with the assumptions that the conductor is isotropic so that $\sigma_{ij} = \sigma$ and that the energy bands are spherical, hence

$$E = \frac{1}{2} m_e v^2 = \frac{\hbar^2}{2m_e^*} k^2 \tag{7.12}$$

where $v_i^2 = 1/3 v^2$ so that

$$\sigma = \frac{-e^2}{12\pi^3} \int_S \int_0^{E_m} \tau v^2 \frac{\partial f_0}{\partial E} \frac{dE \, dS}{|\nabla_k E|} \tag{7.13}$$

$$\sigma = \frac{-e^2}{6\pi^3 m_e^*} \int_S \int_0^{E_m} E\tau \frac{\partial f_0}{\partial E} \cdot \frac{dE \, dS}{|\nabla_k E|} \tag{7.14}$$

Introducing polar coordinates in k-space we have

$$dS = \frac{2m_e^*}{\hbar^2} E \sin\theta \, d\theta \, d\phi \tag{7.15}$$

$$|\nabla_k E|^{-1} = \left(\frac{m_e^*}{2\hbar^2}\right)^{1/2} E^{-1/2} \tag{7.16}$$

hence

$$\sigma = \frac{-e^2}{3\pi^2 m_e^*} \left(\frac{2m_e^*}{\hbar^2}\right)^{3/2} \int_0^{E_m} \tau E^{3/2} \frac{\partial f_0}{\partial E} \cdot dE \tag{7.17}$$

Now from (4.46) we have for the concentration of conductance electrons per unit volume (see problem 2 of this chapter)

$$n = -\frac{1}{3\pi^2} \left(\frac{2m_e^*}{\hbar^2}\right)^{3/2} \int_0^{E_m} E^{3/2} \frac{\partial f_0}{\partial E} \cdot dE \tag{7.18}$$

so that

$$\sigma = \frac{e^2 n}{m_e^*} \langle \tau \rangle \tag{7.18a}$$

where

$$\langle \tau \rangle = \frac{\displaystyle\int_0^{E_m} \tau E^{3/2} \frac{\partial f_0}{\partial E} \cdot dE}{\displaystyle\int_0^{E_m} E^{3/2} \frac{\partial f_0}{\partial E} \, dE} \tag{7.19}$$

In the case of metals or degenerate semiconductors we have seen in section 3.5 that $\partial f_0/\partial E$ is appreciable only in the neighborhood of E_F, the Fermi level, so that

$$\sigma = \frac{e^2 n}{m_e^*}\tau(E_F) \tag{7.20}$$

where $\tau(E_F)$ is the value of the relaxation time at the Fermi surface.

If we consider a nondegenerate semiconductor, then $f_0 \approx e^{-(E-E_F)/kT}$, and the integration extends from the bottom of the conduction band ($E_c = 0$) to infinity so that (7.19) may be written as

$$\langle \tau \rangle = \frac{\displaystyle\int_0^\infty \tau E^{3/2} e^{-E/kT}\, dE}{\displaystyle\int_0^\infty E^{3/2} e^{-E/kT}\, dE} \tag{7.21}$$

We assume that the relaxation time can be represented by an expression of the form

$$\tau = AE^{-s} \tag{7.22}$$

where A and s are constants. On introducing the gamma function

$$\Gamma(y) = \int_0^\infty x^{y-1} e^{-x}\, dx \tag{7.23}$$

we can express (7.21) as

$$\langle \tau \rangle = A(kT)^{-s}\Gamma\left(\frac{5}{2} - s\right)\Big/\Gamma\left(\frac{5}{2}\right) \tag{7.24}$$

7.2 THERMAL CONDUCTION

We now consider the distribution function f when a field $\bar{E}$ directed along x-axis and a temperature gradient dT/dx are both present. Proceeding as before (7.3) may be written

$$f = f_0 + \frac{\tau e}{\hbar}\bar{E}\cdot\nabla_k f_0 - \tau v_x \nabla_r f_0 \tag{7.25}$$

It is convenient to introduce the following

$$\nabla_k f_0 = \frac{\partial f_0}{\partial E} \frac{\partial E}{\partial k_x} = \hbar v_x \frac{\partial f_0}{\partial E} \tag{7.26}$$

$$\nabla_r f_0 = \frac{\partial f_0}{\partial x} = \frac{\partial f_0}{\partial T} \cdot \frac{dT}{dx} \tag{7.27}$$

In (7.26) we have used (6.52b) for the velocity. Now f_0 may be taken as a function of $E' = (E - E_F)/kT$ so that

$$
\begin{aligned}
\frac{\partial f_0}{\partial T} &= \frac{\partial f_0}{\partial E'} \cdot \frac{dE'}{dT} \\
&= \frac{\partial f_0}{\partial E} \frac{\partial E}{\partial E'} \frac{d}{dT} \left(\frac{E - E_F}{kT} \right) \\
&= kT \frac{d}{dT} \left(\frac{E - E_F}{kT} \right) \frac{\partial f_0}{\partial E}
\end{aligned} \tag{7.28}
$$

The Fermi energy E_F is a function of T, so that

$$\frac{\partial f_0}{\partial T} = -\left[T \frac{d}{dT} \left(\frac{E_F}{T} \right) + \frac{E}{T} \right] \frac{\partial f_0}{\partial E} \tag{7.29}$$

and (7.25) may be written on introducing (7.26), (7.27), and (7.29)

$$f = f_0 + \tau v_x \frac{\partial f_0}{\partial E} \left\{ eE_x + \left[T \frac{d}{dT} \left(\frac{E_F}{T} \right) + \frac{E}{T} \right] \frac{dT}{dx} \right\} \tag{7.30}$$

and from (7.4) and (7.5) we have for the current and thermal fluxes

$$J_{Nx} = -\frac{e}{4\pi^3} \int \tau v_x^2 \frac{\partial f_0}{\partial E} \left\{ eE_x + \left[T \frac{d}{dT} \left(\frac{E_F}{T} \right) + \frac{E}{T} \right] \frac{dT}{dx} \right\} dk \tag{7.31}$$

$$Q_x = \frac{1}{4\pi^3} \int \tau v_x^2 E \frac{\partial f_0}{\partial E} \left\{ eE_x + \left[T \frac{d}{dx} \left(\frac{E_F}{T} \right) + \frac{E}{T} \right] \frac{dT}{dx} \right\} dk \tag{7.32}$$

Proceeding as before and introducing the average

$$\langle E^n \tau \rangle = \frac{\int E^{3/2} (E^n \tau) \dfrac{\partial f_0}{\partial E} dE}{\int E^{3/2} \dfrac{\partial f_0}{\partial E} dE} \tag{7.33}$$

it is easy to see that (7.31) and (7.32) may be expressed as

$$J_{Nx} = \frac{ne}{m_e^*}\left[\left\{eE_x + T\frac{d}{dT}\left(\frac{E_F}{T}\right)\frac{dT}{dx}\right\}\langle\tau\rangle + \frac{1}{T}\frac{dT}{dx}\langle E\tau\rangle\right] \qquad (7.34)$$

$$Q_x = -\frac{n}{m_e^*}\left[\left\{eE_x + T\frac{d}{dT}\left(\frac{E_F}{T}\right)\frac{dT}{dx}\right\}\langle E\tau\rangle + \frac{1}{T}\frac{dT}{dx}\langle E^2\tau\rangle\right] \qquad (7.35)$$

These averages can be evaluated as before so that for a metal or degenerate semiconductor $\langle E^n\tau\rangle = E_F^n\tau(E_F)$, the designation $\tau(E_F)$ refers to the quantity evaluated at the Fermi surface. Similarly for a nondegenerate semiconductor we use the form given by (7.33).

In order to calculate the thermal conductivity, we set $J_x = 0$ in (7.34) and use this to eliminate the field E_x from (7.35). The result is

$$Q_x = -\frac{n}{m_e^*T}\left\{\frac{\langle\tau\rangle\langle E^2\tau\rangle - \langle E\tau\rangle^2}{\langle\tau\rangle}\right\}\frac{dT}{dx} \qquad (7.36)$$

It is to be recalled that the heat transport given by (7.36) is due to electrons rather than to lattice vibrations. Consequently, if we represent the thermal conductivity due to electrons by κ_e we have

$$\kappa_e = -\frac{Q_x}{dT/dx} = n\left\{\frac{\langle\tau\rangle\langle E^2\tau\rangle - \langle E\tau\rangle^2}{Tm_e^*\langle\tau\rangle}\right\} \qquad (7.37)$$

In terms of the electrical conductivity given by (7.18a) we can express (7.37) as

$$\kappa_e = L\sigma T \qquad (7.38)$$

where

$$L = \frac{\langle\tau\rangle\langle E^2\tau\rangle - \langle E\tau\rangle^2}{e^2T^2\langle\tau\rangle^2} \qquad (7.39)$$

Equation (7.38) is the well-known *Weidemann–Franz law* expressing the proportionality between thermal and electrical conductivity. The quality L is known as the *Lorentz ratio*.

As might be expected (7.38) holds for metals where a large part of the thermal conductance is due to electrons. However, this is not the case with semiconductors for which the lattice vibrations play an important role in heat transfer.

PROBLEM

a. Show that for a nondegenerate *n*-type semiconductor for which (7.22) holds, that

$$\langle E\tau \rangle = \frac{A(kT)^{1-s}\Gamma(7/2 - s)}{\Gamma(5/2)} \tag{7.39a}$$

$$\langle E^2\tau \rangle = \frac{A(kT)^{2-s}\Gamma(9/2 - s)}{\Gamma(5/2)} \tag{7.39b}$$

b. Using the property of the gamma function

$$\Gamma(t + 1) = t\Gamma(t)$$

show that

$$L = \frac{1}{e^2}\left(\frac{5}{2} - s\right)$$

PROBLEM

a. Show that for a metal or a degenerate semiconductor that $\kappa_e = 0$ if we use the approximations $\langle \tau \rangle \approx \tau(E_F)$; $\langle E\tau \rangle = E_F\tau(E_F)$ etc.

b. Use the better approximation for (7.33) given by the first two terms of (4.96) and show that for a metal the electronic contribution to the thermal conductivity is

$$\kappa_e = \frac{\pi^2 nk^2 T\tau(E_F)}{3m_e^*}$$

In the instance of a *p*-type semiconductor the contribution of the holes to the thermal and electrical conductivity can be similarly found on performing the integrations over the valency band. Representing the hole contributions by the subscript *p* we have

$$\kappa_p = \frac{p}{Tm_p^*\langle \tau_p \rangle}\left(\langle \tau_p \rangle\langle E^2\tau_p \rangle - \langle E\tau_p \rangle^2\right) \tag{7.40}$$

and

$$\sigma_p = \frac{pe^2}{m_p^*}\langle \tau_p \rangle$$

7.3   THERMOELECTRIC EFFECTS

There exists a number of interesting and important interrelationships between electrical and thermal transport in conductors and semiconductors which we shall now discuss. In the way of an introduction, the phenomenological theory will be briefly presented, leaving the details to special treatises in the field of steady state thermodynamics listed in the references. The thermoelectric effects of interest here are shown in table 7.1. Thus, the Seebeck effect refers to the voltage V developed between the junctions of two

TABLE 7.1

Thermoelectric Effects

NAME	ARRANGEMENT	CONDITIONS	EFFECT
Seebeck a.		$T_1 \neq T_2$ $J_N = 0$	Production of voltage, V, between junctions of dissimilar conductors, A and B, under conditions of zero current and a temperature gradient. Thermoelectric power, $$\varepsilon_{AB} = \frac{\partial V}{\partial T_2}$$
Peltier b.		$T_1 = T_2$ $J_N \neq 0$	Evolution or absorption of heat, Q, at the junction of two conductors accompanying the flow of current. Peltier coefficient; $$\pi_{AB} = \frac{J_Q}{eJ_N}$$
Thomson c.		$T_1 \neq T_2$ $J_N \neq 0$	Evolution or absorption of heat, J_Q, in a conductor accompanying flow of current and a temperature gradient. Thomson coefficient; $$\tau_0 = \frac{J_Q}{eJ_N \nabla T}$$

conductors, A and B, when the junctions are at different temperatures and no current is permitted to flow. This effect, as is well known, is utilized in thermo-couples. The effect also underlies thermoelectric generators where n- and p-type semiconductors are employed. The thermoelectric power of a couple is given by

$$\varepsilon_{AB} = \frac{\partial V}{\partial T_2} \tag{7.41}$$

so that the voltage is

$$V = \int_1^2 \varepsilon_{AB} \, dT \tag{7.42}$$

A second well-known effect is the Peltier effect which relates to the absorption of heat at an isothermal junction of two materials when a current flows through the junction. Representing the electron flux by J_n (electrons per unit time per unit area) and the thermal flux by J_Q we define the Peltier coefficient by

$$\pi_{AB} = \frac{J_Q}{eJ_N}$$

The Thomson effect, as indicated in table 7.1, refers to the evolution (or absorption) of heat associated with the flow of current through a material under a temperature gradient. The Thomson coefficient is the heat flux per unit current per unit temperature gradient, i.e.,

$$\tau_0 = \frac{J_Q}{eJ_N \nabla T}$$

Before entering into the more detailed calculations associated with these various effects it is helpful to consider, in qualitative terms, the underlying mechanisms. The Peltier effect, in the case of a metal to n-type semiconductor contact, may be explained by reference to figure 7.1. When the potential is applied, only those electrons with energy greater than E_c can pass into the semiconductor. The metal on the left tends, therefore, to lose those electrons occupying the higher energy states so that heat is absorbed. On the other hand, the junction on the right gains the more energetic electrons and hence heat is evolved. The Seebeck effect in semiconductors, shown in figure 7.2, is readily explained by diffusion of the charge carriers from the hot to the cold end of the material. As a result of this diffusion, an opposing potential is produced as shown.

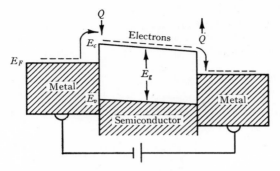

Figure 7.1: Energy band representation of a metal to n-type semiconductor junction in the case of the Peltier effect.

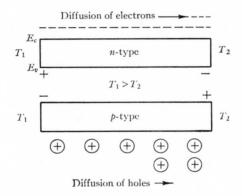

Figure 7.2: Seebeck effect in semiconductors.

7.4 IRREVERSIBLE THERMODYNAMICS

The above thermoelectric effects together with various coupled magnetic effects can be dealt with on the phenomenological level by steady state thermodynamics. We consider a nonequilibrium system in the steady state. If X_k is an extensive parameter (such as energy, or the number of particles), we define the *generalized flux J_k* by

$$J_k = \frac{dX_k}{dt} \tag{7.43}$$

A *current density* $\bar{J}_k$ may be defined as the flux per unit area taken in the direction of flow of X_k. A *generalized force* F_k may be defined in terms of the entropy S of the system

$$F_k = \frac{dS(X_1, X_2, \ldots)}{dX_k} \tag{7.44}$$

For a system not at equilibrium there is a rate of entropy generation, $\dot{S}$, given by

$$\dot{S} = \sum_k \frac{dS}{dX_k} \frac{dX_k}{dt} = \sum_k F_k J_k \tag{7.45}$$

This expression is analogous to that for the rate of mechanical energy change. Thus, if X represents a displacement, the rate of energy change $\dot{E}$ is

$$\dot{E} = \frac{dE}{dX} \cdot \frac{dX}{dt} = \bar{F} \cdot \bar{v}$$

where $\bar{v}$ is the velocity and $\bar{F}$ the force.

We have the fundamental relationship from the first law of thermodynamics

$$dE = dQ - p\,dv + \sum \left(\frac{\partial E}{\partial n_i}\right)_{S,V} dn_i \tag{7.46}$$

or

$$dE = T\,dS - p\,dv + \sum \mu_i\,dn_i \tag{7.47}$$

where μ_i is the electrochemical potential, n_i the number of particles of the ith kind, p the pressure, and v the volume. Equation (7.47) is ordinarily defined for reversible changes since only then can we write

$$dQ = T\,dS \tag{7.48}$$

However, in the theory of steady state thermodynamics, it is postulated that (7.47) holds for the steady state as well. For a constant volume process (7.47) becomes

$$dE = T\,dS + \sum \mu_i\,dn_i \tag{7.49}$$

or in terms of the fluxes

$$J_E = TJ_s + \sum \mu_i J_{N_i} \tag{7.50}$$

PROBLEM

$$T_1 \xleftarrow[\;\;\;\;]{Q} T_2$$

Consider two reservoirs shown above with $T_1 > T_2$. Show that if the heat flux is $dQ/dt = J_Q$, then the rate of entropy generation for the system is

$$\dot{S} = \left(\frac{1}{T_2} - \frac{1}{T_1}\right)J_Q$$

The second postulate of steady state thermodynamics is that the fluxes and forces given by (7.45) are linearly related so that

$$J_i = \sum L_{ik}F_k \qquad (7.51)$$

where L_{ik} is the coupling coefficient. It can be shown that the *Onsager relationship* holds, i.e.,

$$L_{ik} = L_{ki} \qquad (7.51a)$$

More generally, if a magnetic field $\bar{H}$ is present,

$$L_{ik}(\bar{H}) = L_{ki}(-\bar{H})$$

We now apply the above considerations to obtain explicit expressions for the thermoelectric effects. We recall that conservation of any extensive property S requires that

$$\frac{\partial}{\partial t} \iiint s\, dv = \iiint \dot{s}\, dv - \iint_A \bar{J}_s \cdot d\bar{A} \qquad (7.52)$$

where s is the amount of S per unit volume, $\dot{s}$ is the rate at which S is generated per unit time per unit volume, and $\bar{J}_s$ is the current density given by the rate per unit area at which S passes through the surface A bounding the system. From Gauss' theorem and the steady state condition, $\partial/\partial t \iiint s\, dv = 0$, it is easy to show that

$$\nabla \cdot \bar{J}_s = \dot{s} \qquad (7.53)$$

If there are no internal energy or particle sources, then it follows from the above considerations that

$$\nabla \cdot \bar{J}_E = 0 \qquad (7.54)$$

$$\nabla \cdot \bar{J}_N = 0 \qquad (7.55)$$

PROBLEM

Show that if n and p are the concentrations of conductance electrons and holes, and g_n and g_p the rates at which conductance electrons and holes are generated per unit volume, that

$$\frac{\partial n}{\partial t} = g_n + \frac{1}{q} \nabla \cdot \bar{J}_n \qquad (7.56)$$

$$\frac{\partial p}{\partial t} = g_p - \frac{1}{q} \nabla \cdot \bar{J}_p \qquad (7.57)$$

where $\bar{J}_n$ and $\bar{J}_p$ are the current densities for electrons and holes respectively.

Introducing (7.50) into (7.53) we have

$$\dot{s} = \nabla \cdot \left(\frac{J_E}{T} - \frac{\mu}{T} \bar{J}_N \right)$$

and from (7.54) and (7.55) we obtain the important result

$$\dot{s} = \bar{J}_E \cdot \nabla \left(\frac{1}{T} \right) - \bar{J}_N \cdot \nabla \left(\frac{\mu}{T} \right) \qquad (7.58)$$

in the case of a one component system. It should be noted that in (7.58) J_E and J_N are to be taken as the fluxes per unit area. Equations (7.45) and (7.58) permit us to identify the generalized forces so that from (7.51) we have

$$-\bar{J}_N = L_{11} \nabla \left(\frac{\mu}{T} \right) + L_{12} \nabla \left(\frac{1}{T} \right)$$

$$\bar{J}_E = L_{21} \nabla \left(\frac{\mu}{T} \right) + L_{22} \nabla \left(\frac{1}{T} \right)$$

Instead of the energy flux J_E it is convenient to introduce the heat flux J_Q. From (7.48) we have

$$dQ = T \, dS \qquad (7.59)$$

so that

$$\bar{J}_Q = T\bar{J}_s \tag{7.60}$$

and hence from (7.50),

$$\bar{J}_E = \bar{J}_Q + \mu\bar{J}_N \tag{7.61}$$

Introducing the above into (7.58) we find

$$\dot{s} = \bar{J}_Q \cdot \nabla\left(\frac{1}{T}\right) - \frac{\bar{J}_N}{T} \cdot \nabla\mu \tag{7.62}$$

so that

$$-\bar{J}_N = L_{11}\frac{1}{T}\nabla\mu + L_{12}\nabla\frac{1}{T} \tag{7.63}$$

$$\bar{J}_Q = L_{12}\frac{1}{T}\nabla\mu + L_{22}\nabla\frac{1}{T} \tag{7.64}$$

We recall that the Onsager theorem (7.51a) requires that

$$L_{12} = L_{21}$$

The electrochemical potential appearing in the above expressions consists of a part that is dependent on the concentration of the particles, which we consider to be electrons or holes μ_c, and a part which depends on the electrostatic potential μ_e given by $e\phi$, where ϕ is the electrical potential.

$$\mu = \mu_c + e\phi \tag{7.65}$$

For an isothermal and homogeneous system $\nabla\mu_c = 0$ so that $\nabla\mu = e\nabla\phi$.

It is convenient to express the kinetic equations (7.63) and (7.64) in terms of electrical and thermal conductivity. The electrical conductivity σ is defined as the electrical current density $(e\bar{J}_N)$ per unit potential gradient in an isothermal system:

$$\sigma = -e\bar{J}_N \Big/ \frac{1}{e}\nabla\mu \qquad \text{when} \qquad \nabla T = 0$$

so that from (7.63) we have

$$\sigma = \frac{e^2 L_{11}}{T} \tag{7.65a}$$

We define the thermal conductivity as the heat flux per unit temperature gradient when the electrical current is zero:

$$\kappa = \frac{-J_Q}{\nabla T} \qquad J_N = 0 \tag{7.66}$$

The kinetic equations provide the relationship

$$\kappa = \frac{L_{11}L_{22} - L_{12}^2}{T^2 L_{11}} \tag{7.67}$$

The Seebeck effect follows from (7.64) since on taking $J_N = 0$ then

$$\nabla\mu = \frac{L_{12}}{TL_{11}} \nabla T$$

Referring again to table 7.1a we find that

$$\mu_2 - \mu_1 = \int_1^2 \frac{L_{12}^A}{TL_{11}^A} \cdot dT \tag{7.68a}$$

$$\mu_3 - \mu_2 = \int_2^3 \frac{L_{12}^B}{TL_{11}^B} \cdot dT \tag{7.68b}$$

$$\mu_1 - \mu_4 = \int_4^1 \frac{L_{12}^B}{TL_{11}^B} \cdot dT \tag{7.68c}$$

where the superscript designates conductor A or B. Adding (7.68b) and (7.68c) we find that the electrochemical difference across the voltmeter is

$$\mu_3 - \mu_4 = \int_1^2 (\varepsilon_B - \varepsilon_A)\, dT \tag{7.69}$$

where the *absolute thermoelectric power* is given by

$$\varepsilon_A = -\frac{L_{12}^A}{TL_{11}^A} \tag{7.70a}$$

$$\varepsilon_B = -\frac{L_{12}^B}{TL_{11}^B} \tag{7.70b}$$

Since under isothermal conditions the electrochemical potential corresponds to the electrical potential, we have

$$\mu_3 - \mu_4 = e(\phi_3 - \phi_4) = eV \tag{7.71}$$

and therefore

$$V = \frac{1}{e} \int\limits_{1}^{2} (\varepsilon_B - \varepsilon_A)\, dT \qquad (7.72)$$

The thermoelectric power of the couple is then

$$\varepsilon_{AB} = \frac{\partial V}{\partial T} = \varepsilon_B - \varepsilon_A \qquad (7.73)$$

PROBLEM

Introduce (7.65a), (7.67), and (7.73) into (7.63) and (7.64), and show that

$$-\bar{J}_N = \left(\frac{T\sigma}{e^2}\right) \frac{1}{T} \nabla\mu - \left(\frac{T^2\sigma\varepsilon}{e}\right) \nabla\left(\frac{1}{T}\right) \qquad (7.74)$$

$$\bar{J}_Q = -\left(\frac{T^2\sigma\varepsilon}{e}\right) \frac{1}{T} \nabla\mu + (T^3\sigma\varepsilon^2 + T^2\kappa)\nabla\frac{1}{T} \qquad (7.75)$$

where ε is the absolute thermoelectric power. Eliminate $(1/T)\nabla\mu$ and show that

$$\bar{J}_Q = T\varepsilon e\bar{J}_N + T^2\kappa\nabla\frac{1}{T} \qquad (7.76)$$

PROBLEM

On introducing (7.76) into (7.61), eliminating $\nabla\mu$ by means of (7.74), and setting $\nabla\varepsilon = (d\varepsilon/dT)\nabla T$, show that

$$\nabla\cdot\bar{J}_E = \nabla\cdot\left(T^2\kappa\nabla\frac{1}{T}\right) - \frac{e^2}{\sigma}\bar{J}_N^2 + T\frac{d\varepsilon}{dT}\nabla T\cdot(e\bar{J}_N) \qquad (7.77)$$

The last result gives the energy density $\bar{J}_E$ in the presence of a thermal gradient and a current. Clearly the first term on the right represents the heat flux due to the temperature gradient, while the second term is due to the ordinary Joule heating of the conductor. The last term involves both the current and the temperature gradient and represents the Thomson heat Q_T. The Thomson coefficient τ_0 has been defined as the heat evolved per unit current per unit temperature gradient so that, from the last term in (7.77),

$$\tau_0 \equiv \frac{Q_T}{e\bar{J}_N\cdot\nabla T} = T\frac{d\varepsilon}{dT} \qquad (7.78)$$

We now consider the flow of current along a conductor under isothermal conditions. According to (7.76) there is a transport of heat given by

$$\bar{J}_Q = T\varepsilon e \bar{J}_N$$

When two dissimilar conductors, A and B, are joined at a junction, as with the Peltier effect, a heat flux J_Q^A passes into the junction and a flux J_Q^B is carried away from the junction. Since the electrical current must be the same along the conductor, it follows that heat must be evolved from the junction at a rate given by

$$\bar{J}_Q^B - \bar{J}_Q^A = T(\varepsilon_B - \varepsilon_A)(e\bar{J}_N) \tag{7.79}$$

Introducing the Peltier coefficient π_{AB} as the heat that must be supplied to the junction per unit current, we have

$$\pi_{AB} = \frac{J_Q^B - J_Q^A}{eJ_N} = T(\varepsilon_B - \varepsilon_A) \tag{7.80}$$

This last result is known as the *second Kelvin relationship*.

PROBLEM

Derive the *first Kelvin relationship* from (7.80) and (7.78):

$$\frac{d\pi_{AB}}{dT} + (\tau_{0A} - \tau_{0B}) = \varepsilon_B - \varepsilon_A \tag{7.81}$$

7.5 *THERMOMAGNETIC EFFECTS*

A number of interesting effects arise when electrical and thermal currents flow perpendicular to an applied magnetic field as shown in figure 7.3. In the case of two-dimensional flow, equation (7.62) becomes

$$\dot{s} = J_{Qx}\frac{\partial}{\partial x}\left(\frac{1}{T}\right) + J_{Qy}\frac{\partial}{\partial y}\left(\frac{1}{T}\right) - \frac{J_{Nx}}{T}\frac{\partial\mu}{\partial x} - \frac{J_{Ny}}{T}\frac{\partial\mu}{\partial y} \tag{7.82}$$

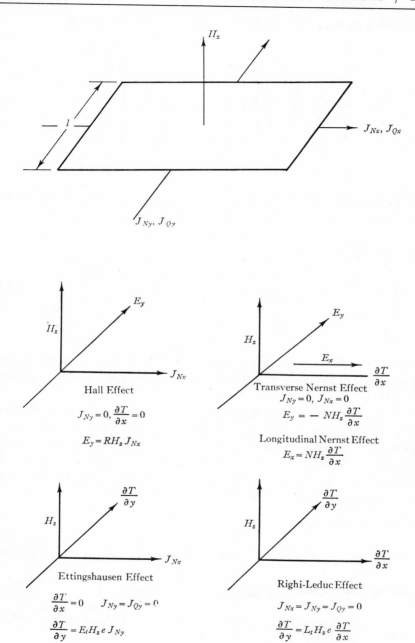

Figure 7.3: Thermoelectric effects in presence of magnetic field.

The steady state equations may be written in matrix notation as

$$
\begin{pmatrix} -J_{Nx} \\ -J_{Ny} \\ J_{Qx} \\ J_{Qy} \end{pmatrix} = \begin{pmatrix} L_{11} & L_{12} & L_{13} & L_{14} \\ L_{21} & L_{22} & L_{23} & L_{24} \\ L_{31} & L_{32} & L_{33} & L_{34} \\ L_{41} & L_{42} & L_{43} & L_{44} \end{pmatrix} \begin{pmatrix} \dfrac{1}{T}\dfrac{\partial \mu}{\partial x} \\ \dfrac{1}{T}\dfrac{\partial \mu}{\partial y} \\ \dfrac{\partial}{\partial x}\dfrac{1}{T} \\ \dfrac{\partial}{\partial y}\dfrac{1}{T} \end{pmatrix}
\tag{7.83}
$$

It can be shown (see Callen in references), by application of the Onsager relationship, that (7.83) gives rise to the more convenient expression

$$
\begin{pmatrix} -\dfrac{1}{e}\dfrac{\partial \mu}{\partial x} \\ -\dfrac{1}{e}\dfrac{\partial \mu}{\partial y} \\ J_{Qx} \\ J_{Qy} \end{pmatrix} = \begin{pmatrix} eL_{11} & eL_{12} & -L_{13} & -L_{14} \\ -L_{12} & eL_{11} & L_{14} & -L_{13} \\ -eTL_{13} & -eTL_{14} & -L_{33} & -L_{34} \\ eTL_{14} & -eTL_{13} & L_{34} & -L_{33} \end{pmatrix} \begin{pmatrix} J_{Nx} \\ J_{Ny} \\ \dfrac{\partial T}{\partial x} \\ \dfrac{\partial T}{\partial y} \end{pmatrix}
\tag{7.84}
$$

where the coefficients L_{ij} appearing in (7.84) are functions of the coefficients appearing in (7.83); we shall not introduce a new notation, however, to mark the distinction.

Various thermomagnetic effects are shown in figure 7.3. The Hall effect refers to the transverse electrical field E_y developed in a material when a current J_{nx} passes. This effect arises because of the well-known Lorentz field $e(\bar{v} \times \overline{H})$, acting normal to the direction of motion of a carrier with velocity $\bar{v}$. It is customary to characterize the Hall effect by the isothermal and adiabatic Hall coefficients:

isothermal Hall coefficient

$$
R_i = \frac{E_y}{eJ_{Nx}H_z} \quad \text{when} \quad \frac{\partial T}{\partial x} = \frac{\partial T}{\partial y} = J_{Ny} = 0
\tag{7.85}
$$

adiabatic Hall coefficient

$$
R_a = \frac{E_y}{eJ_{Nx}H_z} \quad \text{when} \quad \frac{\partial T}{\partial x} = J_{Qy} = J_{Ny} = 0
\tag{7.86}
$$

A tranverse field also arises if, instead of an electrical a thermal flux, J_{Qx} is present. The resulting voltage is referred to as the transverse Nernst effect. As before, we can define a Nernst coefficient for isothermal N_i and adiabatic N_a conditions

$$N_i = -\frac{E_y}{H_z \frac{\partial T}{\partial x}} \qquad J_{Nx} = J_{Ny} = \frac{\partial T}{\partial x} = 0 \qquad (7.87)$$

$$N_a = -\frac{E_y}{H_z \frac{\partial T}{\partial x}} \qquad J_{Nx} = J_{Ny} = J_{Qz} = 0 \qquad . \qquad (7.88)$$

Similarly, we can define coefficients for the longitundinal Nernst voltage shown in figure 7.3. The transverse temperature gradient, which results from an electrical current, and the transverse temperature gradient, resulting from a thermal flux, are also shown in figure 7.3 and are referred to as the Ettingshausen effect and the Righi–Leduc effect, respectively. These effects, as indicated in figure 7.3, are designated by the coefficients E_t and L_t.

On defining the thermoelectric power (ε), isothermal electrical conductivity (σ_i), and isothermal heat conductivity (κ_i) by

$$\varepsilon = \frac{E_x}{\frac{\partial T}{\partial x}} \qquad J_{Nx} = J_{Ny} = \frac{\partial T}{\partial y} = 0 \qquad (7.89)$$

$$\sigma_i = -\frac{eJ_{Nx}}{\frac{1}{e} E_x} \qquad \frac{\partial T}{\partial x} = \frac{\partial T}{\partial y} = J_{Ny} = 0 \qquad (7.90)$$

$$\kappa_i = -\frac{J_{Qx}}{\frac{\partial T}{\partial x}} \qquad J_{Nx} = J_{Ny} = \frac{\partial T}{\partial y} = 0 \qquad (7.91)$$

the steady state equations (7.84) can now be expressed, following Callen, as

$$\begin{pmatrix} -\frac{1}{e}\frac{d\mu}{dx} \\ -\frac{1}{e}\frac{d\mu}{dy} \\ J_{Qx} \\ J_{Qy} \end{pmatrix} = \begin{pmatrix} \sigma^{-1} & H_z R_i & -\varepsilon & -H_z N_i \\ -H_z R_i & \sigma_i^{-1} & N_i H_z & -\varepsilon \\ -T\varepsilon & -H_z T N_i & -\kappa_i & -H_z \kappa_i L_t \\ H_z T N_i & -T\varepsilon & H_z \kappa_i L_t & \kappa_i \end{pmatrix} \begin{pmatrix} eJ_{Nx} \\ eJ_{Ny} \\ \frac{dT}{dx} \\ \frac{dT}{dy} \end{pmatrix}$$

$$(7.92)$$

This last result provides the complete phenomenological expression for the various thermal, magnetic, and electrical interactions in a conductor under the assumption that the generalized fluxes and forces are linearly related.

7.6 *THEORY OF THERMOELECTRIC AND MAGNETIC EFFECTS*

The various coupling coefficients given above can be related to the materials parameters. Thus, on setting $J_x = 0$ in (7.34), we have for the electrical field

$$E_x = -\frac{1}{\langle\tau\rangle e}\left[T\frac{d}{dT}\left(\frac{E_F}{T}\right)\langle\tau\rangle + \frac{1}{T}\langle E\tau\rangle\right]\frac{dT}{dx} \tag{7.93}$$

or it is easy to verify that

$$E_x = T\frac{d}{dT}\left[\frac{\langle E\tau\rangle - E_F\langle\tau\rangle}{eT\langle\tau\rangle}\right]\frac{dT}{dx} \tag{7.94}$$

We recall that the thermoelectric power ε is defined as the change in potential per degree along a material, when one end x' is fixed at a temperature T', and the other end assumes a temperature T

$$\varepsilon = \frac{d}{dT}\int_{x'}^{x} E_x\, dx = \frac{d}{dT}\int_{T'}^{x} E_x\left(\frac{dx}{dT}\right)dT \tag{7.95}$$

On introducing (7.94) into (7.95), we have the desired result

$$\varepsilon = -\frac{\langle E\tau\rangle - E_F\langle\tau\rangle}{eT\langle\tau\rangle} \tag{7.96}$$

The Peltier and Thomson coefficients may be obtained by introducing (7.96) into (7.78) and (7.80).

In the case of a nondegenerate n-type semiconductor the previous values for the averages given by (7.24) and (7.39a) permits us to express (7.96) in the form

$$\varepsilon_n = -\frac{k}{e}\left[\left(\frac{5}{2} - s\right) - \frac{E_F}{kT}\right] \tag{7.97}$$

The Fermi level E_F may be related to the carrier concentration by

$$n = N_c \exp\left[\frac{E_F}{kT}\right] \tag{7.98a}$$

$$p = N_v \exp\left[\frac{-E_F + E_g}{kT}\right] \tag{7.98b}$$

hence

$$\varepsilon_n = -\frac{k}{e}\left[\left(\frac{5}{2} - s\right) + \ln\left(\frac{N_c}{n}\right)\right] \tag{7.99}$$

In the instance of nondegenerate p-type materials similar arguments leads to the result

$$\varepsilon_p = \frac{k}{e}\left[\left(\frac{5}{2} - s'\right) + \ln\frac{N_v}{p}\right] \tag{7.100}$$

where s' is characteristic of the p-type material. It is clear from (7.99) and (7.100) that the thermoelectric power of nondegenerate semiconductors decreases with an increase in carrier concentration. The thermoelectric power of semiconductors may be in the order of 1 mv/°C as compared to 1 μv/°C for metals.

7.7 HALL EFFECT

As we have seen, in the presence of a magnetic field the expression for the total force acting on an electron is

$$\bar{F} = -e[\bar{E} + (\bar{v} \times \bar{B})] \tag{7.101}$$

so that (7.1) becomes, in the homogeneous and isothermal case,

$$f - f_0 = e\tau\hbar^{-1}[\bar{E}\cdot\nabla_k f + (\bar{v} \times \bar{B})\cdot\nabla_k f] \tag{7.102}$$

On setting $f = f_0$ and using

$$\hbar^{-1}\nabla_k f_0 = \bar{v}\frac{\partial f_0}{\partial E} \tag{7.103}$$

and

$$\bar{v}\cdot(\bar{v} \times \bar{B}) = 0 \tag{7.104}$$

we have

$$f = f_0 + e\tau(\bar{E}\cdot\bar{v})\frac{\partial f_0}{\partial E} \tag{7.105}$$

As a second approximation we insert (7.105) into (7.102) and neglect quadratic terms in E. Noting that

$$\hbar^{-1}\nabla_k\frac{\partial f_0}{\partial k} = \bar{v}\frac{\partial^2 f_0}{\partial E^2}$$

it is easy to show that

$$f = f_0 + e\tau(\bar{E}\cdot\bar{v})\frac{\partial f_0}{\partial E} + e^2\tau^2\hbar^{-2}\frac{\partial f_0}{\partial E}(\bar{v}\times\bar{B})\cdot\nabla_k(\bar{E}\cdot\nabla_k E) \quad (7.106)$$

Further simplification is possible in the instance of bands with a scalar effective mass m_e, since we then have

$$\nabla_k(\bar{E}\cdot\nabla_k E) = \frac{\hbar^2\bar{E}}{m_e^*}$$

and hence, (7.106) may be written as

$$f = f_0 + e\tau(\bar{E}\cdot\bar{v})\frac{\partial f_0}{\partial E} + \frac{e^2\tau^2}{m_e^*}\frac{\partial f_0}{\partial E}(\bar{v}\times\bar{B})\cdot\bar{E} \quad (7.107)$$

For the case $\bar{E}_z = \bar{v}_z = 0$, the above may be expressed as

$$f = f_0 + e\tau(E_x v_x + E_y v_y)\frac{\partial f_0}{\partial E} + e\omega_c\tau^2(v_y E_x - v_x E_y)\frac{\partial f_0}{\partial E} \quad (7.108)$$

where

$$\omega_c = \frac{eB}{m_e^*}$$

The expression (7.4) for the current density due to conductance electrons may now be evaluated on recalling that

$$v^2 = \frac{2E}{m_e^*} \quad (7.109)$$

where E is the energy associated with the electron. We have, since terms in $v_x v_y$ vanish on integrating over k,

$$J_{nx} = -\frac{e^2 E_x}{4\pi^3}\int \tau v_x^2 \frac{\partial f_0}{\partial E}\,dk + \frac{e^2\omega_c E_y}{4\pi^3}\int \tau^2 v_x^2 \frac{\partial f_0}{\partial E}\,dk \quad (7.110)$$

$$J_{ny} = -\frac{e^2 E_y}{4\pi^3}\int \tau v_y^2 \frac{\partial f_0}{\partial E}\,dk - \frac{e^2\omega_c E_x}{4\pi^3}\int \tau^2 v_y^2 \frac{\partial f_0}{\partial E}\,dk \quad (7.111)$$

or, on introducing (7.109) and (7.19),

$$J_{nx} = \frac{ne^2}{m_e^*}(\langle\tau\rangle E_x - \omega_c\langle\tau^2\rangle E_y) \quad (7.112)$$

$$J_{ny} = \frac{ne^2}{m_e^*}(\langle\tau\rangle E_y + \omega_c\langle\tau^2\rangle E_x) \quad (7.113)$$

When an electron current is flowing in the x-direction only, and hence $J_{ny} = 0$, then from (7.113) a transverse field E_y is developed, given by

$$E_y = -\frac{\omega_c \langle \tau_n^2 \rangle}{\langle \tau_n \rangle} E_x \qquad (7.114)$$

where τ_n is the relaxation time for electrons. This transverse field gives rise to the Hall effect voltage of magnitude $E_y l$, where l is the width of the sample taken parallel to E_y, as is indicated in figure 7.3. If we assume from (7.112) that

$$J_{nx} \approx \frac{e^2 n \langle \tau_n \rangle}{m_e^*} E_x \qquad (7.115)$$

equation (7.114) can be expressed as

$$E_y = R_H B J_x \qquad (7.116)$$

where R is the *Hall coefficient* given by

$$R_H = -\frac{1}{ne} \frac{\langle \tau_n^2 \rangle}{\langle \tau_n \rangle^2} = -\frac{K_n}{ne}$$

$$K_n = \frac{\langle \tau_n^2 \rangle}{\langle \tau_n \rangle^2} \qquad (7.117)$$

Clearly in the case of a metal or degenerate n-type semiconductor we have

$$\langle \tau_n^2 \rangle = \langle \tau_n \rangle^2 = \tau_n^2(E_F)$$

so that (7.117) reduces to

$$R_H = -\frac{1}{ne} \qquad (7.118)$$

It can be shown by similar arguments that for a p-type semiconductor

$$R_H = \frac{1}{pe} \frac{\langle \tau_p^2 \rangle}{\langle \tau_p \rangle^2} = \frac{K_p}{pe} \qquad (7.119)$$

$$K_p = \frac{\langle \tau_p^2 \rangle}{\langle \tau_p \rangle^2} \qquad (7.120)$$

where τ_p is the hole relaxation time so that the Hall coefficient has the opposite sign to n-type material. It is clear from this that the sign of the Hall voltage provides information as to the carrier type. Again, in the degenerate case (7.119) becomes

$$R_H = \frac{1}{pe}$$

On taking the product of the Hall coefficient with the conductivity we obtain the Hall mobility μ_H, i.e.,

$$\mu_H = -R_H\sigma = K_n\mu_n \tag{7.121}$$

where μ_n is the usual conductivity mobility for the conductive electrons obtained from σ/ne. The Hall and conductivity mobilities will be the same for metals and degenerate semiconductors. However, in the nondegenerate case this will not be so. Thus, in the case $\tau = AE^{-s}$, we have from the properties of the gamma function

$$K_n = \frac{\Gamma(\frac{5}{2} - 2s)\Gamma(\frac{5}{2})}{\{\Gamma(\frac{5}{2} - s)\}^2} \tag{7.122}$$

If $s = \frac{1}{2}$ then

$$K_n = \frac{3\pi}{8}$$

When both carriers contribute significantly to the conductivity the expression for the Hall coefficient is more complicated:

$$R_H = -\frac{1}{e}\frac{K_n b^2 n - K_p p}{(bn + p)^2} \tag{7.123}$$

where

$$b = \frac{\mu_n}{\mu_p}$$

This result may be obtained from the expressions for the x- and y-components of the electron and hole currents. We have on introducing

$$\mu_n = \frac{e\langle \tau_n \rangle}{m_e^*}$$

$$\mu_p = \frac{e\langle \tau_p \rangle}{m_p^*}$$

into the expressions for the electron and hole currents

$$J_{nx} = ne\mu_n[E_x - \mu_n K_n BE_y] \tag{7.124}$$

$$J_{px} = pe\mu_p[E_x + \mu_p K_p BE_y] \tag{7.125}$$

$$J_{ny} = ne\mu_n[E_y + \mu_n K_n BE_x] \tag{7.126}$$

$$J_{py} = pe\mu_p[E_y - \mu_p K_p BE_x] \tag{7.127}$$

Setting $J_{Ny} = J_{ny} + J_{py} = 0$, we find that

$$E_y = -\frac{(n\mu_n^2 K_n - p\mu_p^2 K_p)BE_x}{(n\mu_n + p\mu_p)} \tag{7.128}$$

On neglecting the second term in the right-hand side of (7.124) and (7.125), and eliminating E_x in (7.28), we find the result given by (7.123). If $s = \frac{1}{2}$ applies, we then have

$$R_H = -\frac{3\pi}{8e}\frac{b^2n - p}{(bn + p)^2} \tag{7.129}$$

In the above discussion it was assumed that the effective mass is a scalar quantity. When this assumption does not hold, much more complicated expressions result for the Hall coefficient. The interested student is referred to the more detailed works of Putley and Smith given in the bibliography.

PROBLEMS FOR CHAPTER 7

1. Show that if

$$E(k) = \frac{\hbar k^2}{2m^*}$$

then

$$E = \tfrac{1}{2}m^* v^2$$

Hint: Use $\hbar \bar{v} = \nabla_k E(k)$.

2. Show that (7.18) follows from (4.46).

Hint: Use partial integration and assume $E_m \gg E_F/kT$.

3. Calculate the Peltier and Thomson coefficients from (7.96).

4. The effective mass of a carrier can sometimes be measured by *cyclotron resonance methods*. The material is subject to a static magnetic field $\bar{H}$ and an rf electric field $\bar{E}_x$ normal to $\bar{H}$.

Solve the classical equations of motion, in the case of a scalar effective mass, given by

$$m^*\left(\frac{d\bar{v}}{dt} + \frac{\bar{v}}{\tau}\right) = e\left(\bar{E}_x + \frac{\bar{v} \times \bar{H}}{c}\right) \qquad (\tau = \text{relaxation time})$$

8 / Electromagnetic Interactions

and Lasers

A large number of electronic devices such as photoconductors, photoemitters, masers, and, most recently, lasers depend on the absorption or emission of electromagnetic radiation by bound electrons. In order to develop the theory of electromagnetic interactions we must extend the treatment of perturbation theory given in chapter 2 to the case where the small perturbing term $\bar{H}^{(1)}$ depends explicitly on time. We now seek a solution to the time-dependent wave equation

$$(\mathbf{H}^{(0)} + \mathbf{H}^{(1)})\psi = i\hbar \frac{\partial \psi}{\partial t} \tag{8.1}$$

where $\mathbf{H}^{(0)}$ is independent of time. As before, we begin by assuming that the time-independent equation

$$\mathbf{H}^{(0)}\psi^{(0)} = i\hbar \frac{\partial \psi^0}{\partial t} \tag{8.2}$$

has been solved so that $\psi^{(0)}$ is known. In order to solve (8.1) we expand ψ in terms of $\psi_n^{(0)}$, i.e.,

$$\psi = \sum c_n(t)\psi_n^0(q, t) \tag{8.3}$$

where we recall that $\psi^{(0)}(q, t) = \psi^0(q)e^{-(E/\hbar)it}$. Substituting (8.3) into (8.1) we readily find that

$$\sum [c_n(t)\mathbf{H}^0\psi_n^0 + c_n(t)\mathbf{H}^{(1)}\psi_n^{(0)}] = i\hbar \sum \left[\psi_n^0 \frac{\partial c_n(t)}{\partial t} + c_n(t) \frac{\partial \psi_n^{(0)}}{\partial t}\right] \tag{8.4}$$

However, in view of (8.2), the last result may be written as

$$\sum c_n(t)\mathbf{H}^{(1)}\psi_n^{(0)} = i\hbar \sum \psi_n^{(0)} \frac{dc_n(t)}{dt} \qquad (8.5)$$

In order to obtain the time derivative of c_m, equation (8.5) is multiplied by $\psi_m^{(0)*}$ and the result integrated over the configuration space:

$$\frac{dc_m}{dt} = -\frac{i}{\hbar} \sum_n c_n (m|\mathbf{H}^{(11)}|n)e^{i\omega_{mn}t} \qquad (8.6)$$

where it will be recalled

$$(m|\mathbf{H}^{(1)}|n) = \int \psi_m^{(0)*}(q)\mathbf{H}^{(1)}\psi_n^{(0)}(q)\,d\tau$$

$$\omega_{mn} = \omega_m - \omega_n \qquad (8.7)$$

$$\omega_m = \frac{E_m}{\hbar}$$

Equation (8.6) is the desired result and we see that the time-dependent perturbation theory gives rise to a set of first order differential equations which permit the determination of c_n.

As a simple example of time-dependent perturbation consider a system initially in a state $\psi_1^{(0)}$ and subject to a small perturbation

$$\mathbf{H}^{(1)} = A \cos \omega t$$

Since at $t = 0$, $c_1(0) = 1$, $c_m(0) = 0$, and $m \neq 1$, we may integrate (8.6) on the assumption that the change in c_m is small:

$$c_m(t) = -\frac{i}{\hbar} \int_0^t (m|\mathbf{H}^{(1)}|1)e^{i\omega_{m_1}t}\,dt$$

$$= -\frac{1}{2\hbar}(m|A|1)\left[\frac{\exp[i(\omega_{m_1}-\omega)t]-1}{\omega_{m_1}-\omega} + \frac{\exp[i(\omega_{m_1}+\omega)t]-1}{\omega_{m_1}+\omega}\right] \qquad (8.8)$$

We observe that if the applied field has a frequency

$$\omega \approx |\omega_{m_1}|$$

then one of the denominators in (8.8) becomes very large and there is a large probability that the system will undergo a transition from the state

ψ_1^0 to $\psi_m^{(0)}$. Indeed, if the small term in (8.7) is neglected, it is easy to show that the probability of finding the system in $\psi_m^{(0)}$, at time t, is

$$|c_m(t)|^2 = \frac{t^2(m|A|1)^2}{4\hbar^2} \frac{\sin^2 \frac{\Delta\omega t}{2}}{\left(\frac{\Delta\omega t}{2}\right)^2} \tag{8.9}$$

where

$$\Delta\omega = \omega_{m_1} - \omega$$

This function rises sharply when $\Delta\omega = 0$.

8.1 *CHARGED PARTICLE IN AN* EM *FIELD*

The above discussions will now be extended to an electron in an electromagnetic field. We first require the expression for the Hamiltonian, as explained in chapter 2. This may be derived by recalling the expression for the force acting on an electron of charge e and mass m, moving with a velocity $\bar{v}$, in an electromagnetic field:

$$\bar{F} = -e\left[\bar{E} + \frac{1}{c}(\bar{v} \times \bar{B})\right] \tag{8.10}$$

Expressing the fields in terms of the vector $\bar{A}$, and scalar ϕ, potentials (see appendix III) we have

$$\bar{E} = -\nabla\phi - \frac{1}{c}\frac{\partial\bar{A}}{\partial t}$$
$$\bar{B} = \nabla \times \bar{A} \tag{8.11}$$

These potentials are related to each other through the condition

$$\nabla \cdot \bar{A} + \frac{1}{c}\frac{\partial\phi}{\partial t} = 0 \tag{8.12}$$

Equations (8.11) may be substituted into (8.10) with the result

$$\bar{F} = -e\left\{-\nabla\phi - \frac{1}{c}\left[\frac{\partial\bar{A}}{\partial t} - \bar{v} \times (\nabla \times \bar{A})\right]\right\} \tag{8.13}$$

The last result may be put into a more useful form by expanding the expressions containing the vector potential, thus,

$$v \times \nabla \times \overline{A} = \nabla(v \cdot \overline{A}) - (v \cdot \nabla)\overline{A} \qquad (8.14)$$

$$\frac{d\overline{A}}{dt} = \frac{\partial \overline{A}}{\partial t} + (v \cdot \nabla)\overline{A} \qquad (8.15)$$

On introducing these into (8.13) we have

$$F = -e\left[-\nabla\left(\phi - \frac{1}{c} v \cdot \overline{A} \right) - \frac{1}{c}\frac{d\overline{A}}{dt} \right] \qquad (8.16)$$

It is natural to identify the term in ϕ and $\overline{A}$ with the generalized potential U. Representing the kinetic energy by T, we can now write the Lagrangian L:

$$L \equiv T - U \equiv \left[\frac{m\bar{v}^2}{2} + e\phi - \frac{e}{c} \bar{v} \cdot \overline{A} \right] \qquad (8.17)$$

and, therefore, from the definition of the generalized momentum p, we have

$$\begin{aligned} v_x &= \dot{q}_x \\ p_x &= \frac{\partial L}{\partial \dot{q}_x} = mv_x - \frac{e}{c} A_x \end{aligned} \qquad (8.18)$$

with similar expressions for p_y and p_z. The Hamiltonian may now be obtained from the definition

$$H \equiv \sum_i p_i \dot{q}_i - L$$

hence

$$\begin{aligned} H &= \left(m\bar{v}^2 - \frac{e}{c} \bar{v} \cdot \overline{A} \right) - \left(\frac{m\bar{v}^2}{2} + e\phi - \frac{e}{c} \bar{v} \cdot \overline{A} \right) \\ &= \frac{m\bar{v}^2}{2} - e\phi = \frac{1}{2m}\left(\bar{p} + \frac{e}{c} \overline{A} \right)^2 - e\phi \end{aligned} \qquad (8.19)$$

The Hamiltonian operator is now formed by the usual procedure of placing $\mathbf{p} = -i\hbar\nabla$; we find that

$$\mathbf{H} = \frac{1}{2m}\left(-i\hbar\nabla + \frac{e}{c} \overline{A} \right)^2 - e\phi \qquad (8.20)$$

It should be kept in mind that ϕ is the scalar potential associated with the applied field, and that the system may also have an internal potential V due to electrostatic interactions.

In order to simplify (8.20) we consider the case of a plane wave. It is shown in appendix III that for such a wave $\phi = 0$ and $\nabla \cdot \overline{A} = 0$. It is easy to see therefore that

$$\overline{A} \cdot \nabla - \nabla \cdot \overline{A} = 0$$

so that

$$\overline{A} \cdot \nabla = \nabla \cdot \overline{A} \tag{8.21}$$

Introducing the above simplifications, and also assuming that $e^2/c^2|A|^2$ may be neglected, the Hamiltonian becomes, in the case of a system of particles with internal potential energy V,

$$\begin{aligned}
\mathbf{H} &= -\sum_i \frac{\hbar^2}{2m_i} \nabla_i^2 + V - \sum \frac{ie\hbar}{m_i c} \overline{A}_i \cdot \nabla_i \\
&= \mathbf{H}^{(0)} + \mathbf{H}^{(1)}
\end{aligned} \tag{8.22}$$

on setting

$$\mathbf{H}^{(1)} = \sum \frac{ie\hbar}{m_i c} \overline{A}_i \cdot \nabla_i$$

In (8.22) $\mathbf{H}^{(0)}$ is the Hamiltonian in the absence of a field and $\mathbf{H}^{(1)}$ is the perturbation.

We now evaluate the matrix elements required in (8.6). This may be achieved by means of the following demonstration. We have

$$\mathbf{H}^{(0)}\psi_m^{(0)} = E_m \psi_m^{(0)}$$

$$\mathbf{H}^{(0)*}\psi_n^{(0)*} = E_n \psi_n^{(0)*}$$

from which it can readily be shown that

$$\int (\psi_n^{0*} \bar{r}_i \mathbf{H}^{(0)} \psi_m^{(0)} - \psi_m^{(0)} \bar{r}_i \mathbf{H}^{(0)*} \psi_n^{(0)*}) \, d\tau = (E_m - E_n) \int \psi_n^{(0)*} \bar{r}_i \psi_m^{(0)} \, d\tau \tag{8.23}$$

where $\bar{r}_i$ is the position vector of the corresponding particle. Since $\mathbf{H}^{(0)}$ is Hermitian, (8.23) can be written as

$$\int \psi_n^{(0)*}(\mathbf{H}^{(0)}\bar{r}_i - \bar{r}_i \mathbf{H}^{(0)})\psi_m^{(0)} \, d\tau = (E_n - E_m) \int \psi_n^{(0)*} \bar{r}_i \psi_m^{(0)} \, d\tau$$

Recalling that

$$\mathbf{H}^{(0)} = -\frac{\hbar^2}{2m} \sum \nabla_i^2 + V$$

we see that since $\bar{r}_i$ and V commute, and also $\bar{r}_i$ and ∇_j^2, if $i \neq j$, that

$$-\frac{\hbar^2}{2m} \int \psi_n^{(0)*} (\nabla_i^2 \bar{r}_i - \bar{r}_i \nabla_i^2) \psi_m^{(0)} \, d\tau = (E_n - E_m) \int \psi_n^{(0)*} \bar{r}_i \psi_m^{(0)} \, d\tau$$

Introducing the identity

$$\nabla^2 (\bar{r}\psi) = \bar{r}\nabla^2\psi + 2\nabla\psi$$

we have finally

$$\int \psi_n^{(0)*} \nabla_i \psi_m^{(0)} \, d\tau = -\frac{m}{\hbar^2} (E_n - E_m) \int \psi_n^{(0)*} \bar{r}_i \psi_m^{(0)} \, d\tau \qquad (8.24)$$

In the case of a molecule, the wavelength of light is large in comparison to the dimensions of the system and we can assume that $\overline{A}$ is constant in space. Using the last result, (8.6) may be written as

$$\frac{dc_m}{dt} = -\frac{1}{c\hbar^2} \overline{A} \cdot \sum_n c_n (E_m - E_n) e^{-(E_m - E_n)it/\hbar t} \overline{D}_{mn} \qquad (8.25)$$

where D_{mn} is the dipole moment matrix element given by

$$\overline{D}_{mn} = \int \psi_m^{(0)*} \sum_i e\bar{r}_i \psi_n^{(0)} \, d\tau \qquad (8.26)$$

In order to integrate (8.25) we assume, as before, that at $t = 0$ the system is initially in state $\psi_n^{(0)}$ so that $c_n = 1$ and all other c_n is zero. We consider the probability of finding the system in state $\psi_m^{(0)}$ when it is perturbed by an electromagnetic field. If the field has a frequency ν, we can write for the vector potential

$$\overline{A} = \overline{A}_0 \cos 2\pi\nu t = \frac{\overline{A}_0}{2} (e^{2\pi\nu ti} + e^{-2\pi\nu ti}) \qquad (8.27)$$

Introducing (8.27) into (8.25), we have

$$\frac{dc_m}{dt} = -\frac{1}{2c\hbar^2} \overline{A}_0 \cdot \overline{D}_{mn} (E_m - E_n) [e^{(E_m - E_n + h\nu)/\hbar \cdot it} + e^{(E_m - E_n - h\nu)/\hbar \cdot it}] \quad (8.28)$$

Integrating (8.28) and choosing the constant of integration such that $c_m = 0$ when $t = 0$, we find that

$$c_m = \frac{i}{2c\hbar^2} \, \bar{A}_0 \cdot \bar{D}_{mn}(E_m - E_n)\left[\frac{e^{(E_m - E_n + h\nu)/\hbar \cdot it}}{E_m - E_n + h\nu} + \frac{e^{(E_m - E_n - h\nu)/\hbar \cdot it}}{E_m - E_n - h\nu}\right]$$

Absorption will take place if a transition occurs with $E_m > E_n$, while emission corresponds to the case $E_n > E_m$. The coefficient c_m will be large in the instance of absorption if the frequency of the field is such that $h\nu_{nm} = E_m - E_n$, the well-known quantum condition for absorption. As before, we may determine the probability that the system is in state ψ_m by neglecting the small term and evaluating $|c_m|^2$:

$$|c_m|^2 = \frac{t^2}{4c^2\hbar^2} \, |\bar{A}_0|^2 |\bar{D}_{mn}|^2 (E_m - E_n)^2 \sin^2 \frac{\{E_m - E_n - h\nu/2\hbar \cdot t\}^2}{\{E_m - E_n - h\nu/2\hbar \cdot t\}^2} \quad (8.29)$$

In practice the perturbing field will have a range of frequencies about ν_{nm} so that (8.25) must be integrated over ν_{nm}. Since (8.25) falls off rapidly for frequencies removed from ν_{nm} it is acceptable to integrate over the frequency range $\pm \infty$ and to consider $\bar{A}_0$ as a constant. The result is

$$|c_m|^2 = \frac{\pi^2 \nu_{mn}^2}{c^2\hbar^2} \, |\bar{A}_0|^2 |\bar{D}_{mn}|^2 t \quad (8.30)$$

This last result can also be expressed in terms of the radiation density at ν_{nm}, $\rho(\nu_{nm})$, by introducing the well-known result from electromagnetic theory

$$|A_0|^2 = \frac{2c^2}{3\pi\nu_{mn}^2} \, \rho(\nu_{nm})$$

so that

$$|c_m|^2 = \frac{2\pi}{3\hbar^2} \, |\bar{D}_{mn}|^2 \rho(\nu_{nm}) t \quad (8.31)$$

It is also convenient to consider the probability that a transition will occur from state n to m in a unit time. This probability is designated by B_{nm} and is referred to as the Einstein transition probability for induced absorption. Similarly a transition probability B_{mn} may be defined for emission. It follows from (8.30) that the transition probabilities for induced absorption and emission are given by

$$B_{mn} = B_{nm} = \frac{|c_m|^2}{\rho(\nu_{nm}) t} = \frac{2\pi}{3\hbar^2} \, |\bar{D}_{nm}|^2 \quad (8.32)$$

8.2 SPONTANEOUS AND INDUCED TRANSITIONS

It is well known that a system of electrons may emit radiation even in the absence of an inducing electromagnetic field so that the above theory must be incomplete. In order to take into account spontaneous emission, it is necessary to quantize the electromagnetic field and to consider the field and the electrons as one system. Details of this procedure are given in the books by Heitler, and by Mott and Sneddon.

The required coefficients for spontaneous emission, A_{mn}, were obtained by Einstein using equilibrium considerations. Though this procedure is much simpler than that of field quantatization it is of course not as satisfactory from the theoretical point of view. However, because of its simplicity, we shall follow Einstein's procedure here. We consider a system of molecules at thermal and radiative equilibrium at a temperature T. We are interested in the transition between two states with energies E_m and E_n. The ratio of the number of molecules in the two states is given by Boltzmann statistics, see (4.19), as

$$\frac{N_m}{N_n} = \frac{g_m e^{-E_m/kT}}{g_n e^{-E_n/kT}} = \frac{g_m}{g_n} e^{-h\nu_{nm}/kT} \tag{8.33}$$

Since the system is in radiative equilibrium the rate of emission and absorption at ν_{nm} must be equal. If A_{mn} is the transition probability for spontaneous emission and B_{mn} for induced emission, then the number of systems making the transition from m to n per unit time is simply

$$N_m[A_{mn} + B_{mn}\rho(\nu_{mn})] \tag{8.34}$$

while the number of systems making the reverse transition is

$$N_n B_{nm}\rho(\nu_{nm}) \tag{8.35}$$

Equating (8.34) and (8.35) and using (8.33) there results, on solving for the radiation density,

$$\rho(\nu_{nm}) = \frac{\dfrac{g_m}{g_n} A_{mn} e^{-h\nu_{nm}/kT}}{B_{nm} - \dfrac{g_m}{g_n} B_{mn} e^{-h\nu_{nm}/kT}} \tag{8.36}$$

The above may be written as

$$\rho(\nu_{nm}) = \frac{\dfrac{A_{mn}}{B_{mn}}}{\dfrac{g_n B_{nm}}{g_m B_{mn}} e^{h\nu/kT} - 1} \tag{8.37}$$

On comparing (8.37) with the well-known Planck's law given by

$$\rho(\nu_{nm}) = \frac{8\pi h \nu_{nm}^3}{c^3} \cdot \frac{1}{e^{h\nu_{nm}/kT} - 1} \tag{8.38}$$

we see that

$$A_{mn} = \frac{8\pi h \nu_{nm}^3}{c^3} B_{mn} \tag{8.39}$$

and

$$g_n B_{nm} = g_m B_{mn} \tag{8.40}$$

Introducing (8.32) for B_{mn} we have

$$A_{mn} = \frac{32\pi^3 \nu_{nm}^3}{3c^3 \hbar} |D_{mn}|^2$$

It is interesting to note that the spontaneous emission coefficient increases with the cube of the frequency. Since spontaneous emission constitutes noise from the view point of laser devices (discussed below), it is clear that devices operated at optical frequencies will be considerably noisier than those operated at microwave frequencies.

8.3 SELECTION RULES

With certain transitions the dipole moment matrix element D_{mn} always vanishes so that these transitions and the corresponding changes in the quantum numbers are forbidden. The rules indicating the allowed charges in the quantum numbers are referred to as selection rules. General selection rules for electrons in a central field may be derived by noting that $\bar{r}$ occurring in the dipole matrix element corresponds to a vector operator, as was discussed in chapter 2. Consequently, equation (2.232) applies here with the general vector operator **A**, now to be identified with the vector operator **r**, where

$$\mathbf{r} = x\bar{\imath} + y\bar{\jmath} + z\bar{k} \tag{8.41}$$

On introducing (8.41) into (2.232) and expanding the resulting expression, we find

$$[\mathbf{J}_x, x] = 0 \qquad [\mathbf{J}_y, x] = -iz\hbar \qquad [\mathbf{J}_z, x] = iy\hbar$$

$$[\mathbf{J}_x, y] = iz\hbar \qquad [\mathbf{J}_y, y] = 0 \qquad [\mathbf{J}_z, y] = -ix\hbar \qquad (8.42)$$

$$[\mathbf{J}_x, z] = -iy\hbar \qquad [\mathbf{J}_y, z] = ix\hbar \qquad [\mathbf{J}_z, z] = 0$$

In order to obtain the desired matrix elements we make use of the Hermitian properties of $\mathbf{J}_z$ and the above commutator relationships to show, for an eigenfunction with eigenvalues j and m, that

$$(j'm'|\mathbf{J}_z z - z\mathbf{J}_z|jm) = \hbar(m' - m)(j'm'|z|jm) \equiv 0 \qquad (8.43)$$

The first equality is readily obtained on recalling the adjoint relationship $(\mathbf{J}_z z)^\dagger = z\mathbf{J}_z$, while the second equality follows from the commutator relationship. It is clear that the dipole matrix element vanishes unless

$$m' - m = \Delta m = 0$$

Similarly, it can be readily shown, using $[\mathbf{J}_z, x]$ and $[\mathbf{J}_z, y]$, that

$$(j'm'|x + iy|jm) = (m' - m)(j'm'|x + iy|jm) \qquad (8.44)$$

$$(j'm'|x - iy|jm) = -(m' - m)(j'm'|x - iy|jm) \qquad (8.45)$$

These dipole elements vanish (see problem 1) unless $\Delta m = 1$ for the element (8.44), and $\Delta m = -1$ for the other element. Since

$$x = \frac{r_+ + r_-}{2} \qquad r_+ = x + iy \qquad (8.46)$$

$$y = \frac{r_+ + r_-}{2i} \qquad r_- = x - iy \qquad (8.47)$$

it is clear that the dipole matrix element vanishes unless transition occurs between states for which

$$\Delta m = 0, \pm 1 \qquad (8.48)$$

It is also easy to show that the selection rule for the spin s is

$$\Delta s = 0 \qquad (8.49)$$

since the two spin functions are orthogonal.

Other selection rules may be established from the commutator relationships given above. However, since a good deal of tedious algebra is involved, we shall merely state the result

$$\Delta l = \pm 1$$

$$\Delta j = 0, \pm 1$$

with the transition $s = 0$ to $j = 0$ forbidden. The interested reader will find the details in Condon and Shortley.

PROBLEM

The dipole matrix element of the one-dimensional harmonic oscillator is

$$(m'|ex|m) = e \int \psi_{m'} x \psi_m \, dx$$

The wave function has been shown to be of the form

$$\psi_m(y) = A_m e^{-\xi^2/2} H_m(\xi)$$

where H_m is the Hermite polynomial. Use the recursion relationship

$$x H_m = m H_{m-1} + \tfrac{1}{2} H_{m+1}$$

to show that the matrix element vanishes unless

$$m' = m \pm 1$$

8.4 LINE WIDTH

We have seen that an uncertainty relationship exists between energy and time given by

$$\Delta t \, \Delta E \approx \hbar$$

This relationship implies that the energy state occupied by a system can be measured precisely only if the system occupies the state for an infinite time. If the system is unstable with a lifetime α then there will be an uncertainty in the energy state given by

$$\Delta E \approx \frac{\hbar}{\alpha} \qquad (8.50)$$

It follows that there will be a corresponding spread in the frequency of the emitted light since the energy and frequency ν are related by

$$E = h\nu$$

The uncertainty implies that a perturbed system cannot be regarded as occupying a discrete state with energy E_0, but rather the energy of the system is distributed about E_0. The width of the distribution should be expected to increase with a decrease in lifetime. In order to find the energy distribution we consider a state ψ initially, with energy E_0, and decaying with a rate constant $\beta = 1/\alpha$, so that

$$\psi(t) = \psi_0 e^{-\beta t/2} e^{-iE_0 t/\hbar} \tag{8.51}$$

The probability of finding the system with energy E_0 decreases exponentially:

$$|\psi(t)|^2 = |\psi_0|^2 e^{-\beta t} \tag{8.52}$$

The distribution (8.51) can also be represented by a Fourier integral over the energy domain

$$\psi(t) = \int_{-\infty}^{\infty} f(E) e^{-Eti/\hbar} \, dE \tag{8.53}$$

By the inverse property we have, therefore, the representation in the energy domain

$$f(E) = \frac{1}{2\pi} \int_{0}^{+\infty} \psi(t) e^{Eti/\hbar} \, dt \tag{8.54}$$

so that

$$|f(E)|^2 = |\psi_0|^2 \left(\frac{\hbar}{2\pi}\right)^2 \frac{1}{(E - E_0)^2 + \dfrac{\Gamma^2}{4}} \tag{8.55}$$

where

$$\Gamma = \hbar\beta$$

This last result is represented graphically in figure 8.1. It is apparent that the distribution has a maximum at E_0 and falls to half the maximum at $E = E_0 \pm \Gamma/2$ so that Γ is the effective width of the band. Because of this broadening effect the emitted frequency must also be distributed over a band. The

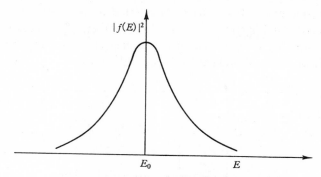

Figure 8.1: The energy distribution of a state.

intensity vs. frequency curve will have a shape similar to that shown in figure 8.1. Indeed, if we assume that probability per unit frequency interval, for radiation of frequency ν is given by an expression of the form (8.55), then

$$g(\nu) = \frac{A}{(\nu - \nu_0)^2 + \left(\dfrac{\Gamma}{2}\right)^2} \tag{8.56}$$

where the constant A is determined by the normalization requirement

$$A \int_{-\infty}^{+\infty} g(\nu)\, d\nu = 1$$

and hence

$$A = \frac{\Gamma}{2\pi}$$

Equation (8.56) now becomes

$$g(\nu) = \frac{\Gamma}{2\pi} \frac{1}{(\nu - \nu_0)^2 + \left(\dfrac{\Gamma}{2}\right)^2} \tag{8.57}$$

so that for $\nu = \nu_0$,

$$g(\nu_0) = \frac{2}{\pi\Gamma} \tag{8.57a}$$

8.5 STIMULATED EMISSION AMPLIFIERS

Within recent years devices have been developed capable of amplifying electromagnetic waves by means of induced (stimulated) emission. Devices operating at microwave frequencies are referred to as masers, an acronyme for microwave amplification by stimulated emission of radiation, while devices operating at infrared or optical frequencies are referred to as lasers (light amplification by stimulated emission radiation).

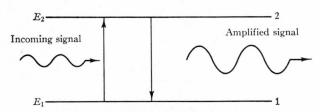

Figure 8.2: Energy diagram for the two level maser. The system has N_2 molecules in state E_2 and N_1 in state E_0. The emitted frequency is, assuming discrete states, $h\nu_0 = E_2 - E_1$.

The essential conditions which must be satisfied in order to achieve gain by stimulated emission can readily be derived. In the following we consider the case of a device which operates between only two energy levels, as indicated in figure 8.2. We consider the net emission of radiation on illuminating the material, when both induced emission and absorption occurs, but we neglect spontaneous emission. In the case of monochromatic illumination at frequency ν_0 and intensity $\rho(\nu_0)$, we may write by means of the Dirac delta function

$$\rho(\nu) = \rho(\nu_0)\delta(\nu - \nu_0) \tag{8.58}$$

where, by definition,

$$\delta(\nu - \nu_0) = 0 \qquad \text{for} \qquad \nu \neq \nu_0$$

and for an arbitrary function $f(\nu)$,

$$\int_{-\nu}^{\nu} f(\nu)\delta(\nu - \nu_0)\, d\nu = f(\nu_0) \tag{8.59}$$

The net rate of induced energy emission in a frequency interval $d\nu$ centered about ν is given by

$$h\nu g(\nu)\rho(\nu)[B_{21}N_2 - B_{12}N_1]\, d\nu$$

or, from (8.33),

$$h\nu B_{21}g(\nu)\rho(\nu)\left[N_2 - N_1\frac{g_2}{g_1}\right] d\nu \tag{8.60}$$

where $g(\nu)$ is given by (8.57).

On introducing (8.58) and integrating, we have for the rate of induced energy emission,

$$\frac{d\rho(\nu_0)}{dt} = h\nu_0 B_{21} g(\nu_0)\rho(\nu_0)[N_2 - N_1 g_2/g_1] \tag{8.61}$$

If losses occur due to photon absorption by impurities, or the escape of photons from the system, then an additional term must be included. Representing the lifetime of the photon by τ_p we write

$$\frac{d\rho}{dt} = h\nu_0 B_{21} g(\nu_0)\left(N_2 - N_1 \frac{g_2}{g_1}\right)\rho(\nu_0) - \frac{\rho(\nu_0)}{\tau_p} \tag{8.62}$$

The photon lifetime τ_p may be identified with the Q, or quality factor, of the system by means of

$$\tau_p = \frac{Q}{2\pi\nu_0} \tag{8.63}$$

On integrating (8.62) we obtain the expression for the radiation density

$$\rho(\nu_0) = \rho_0 \exp\left[h\nu_0 B_{21} g(\nu_0)\left(N_2 - N_1 \frac{g_2}{g_2}\right) - \frac{1}{\tau_p}\right]t \tag{8.64}$$

Clearly this corresponds to a growing signal provided the exponent is positive so that

$$\left(N_2 - N_1 \frac{g_2}{g_1}\right) > \frac{\pi\Gamma}{2\tau_p h\nu_0 B_{21}} \tag{8.65}$$

where we have introduced (8.57a) for $g(\nu_0)$. Equation (8.65) may also be expressed as

$$\left(N_2 - N_1 \frac{g_2}{g_1}\right) = \frac{\tau_s}{\tau_p}\frac{4\pi^2\Gamma\nu_0^2}{c^3} \tag{8.66}$$

On introducing

$$B_{21} = \frac{c^3 A_{21}}{8\pi h\nu_0^3}$$

and

$$A_{21} \equiv \frac{1}{\tau_s}$$

Some of the conditions favoring gain are apparent from the above results:

a. The term $N_1(g_2/g_1)$ should be made small by selecting the terminal level far enough above the ground state.

b. The line width for emission Γ should be narrow.

c. The lifetime of the upper state should be large in comparison to the terminal state, and the transition should be radiative, i.e., the excited state should not be depopulated by predominately nonradiative mechanisms.

d. The medium should have low scattering losses and should have as little absorption as possible due to mechanisms other than the transition between the two operating levels.

e. The system should be designed so as to minimize energy losses.

8.6 *OPERATING MASERS AND LASERS*

We now consider some typical stimulated emission amplifiers and several techniques that have been used to realize conditions for gain. The first maser to operate was the ammonia gas device of Gordon, Zeiger, and Townes described in 1954. This device was operated in the microwave region at

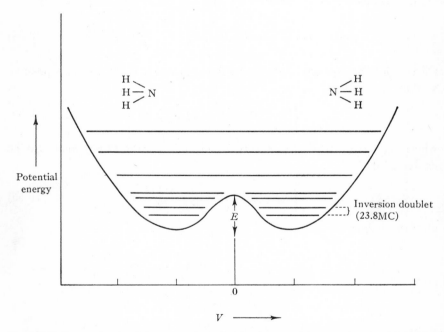

Figure 8.3: Energy levels of the ammonia molecule. A potential energy barrier E separates the two positions of the nitrogen relative to the plane of the hydrogen atoms. Tunneling of the nitrogen results in the splitting of the vibrational level into the indicated inversion doublet.

24 KMC and utilized the transition between the two levels of the lowest inversion doublet. The ammonia molecule consists of three hydrogen atoms lying in a plane, while the nitrogen may occupy a position above or below this plane. A potential energy barrier having a maximum in the plane of the hydrogen atoms serves to hinder the motion of the nitrogen, as shown in figure 8.3. The nitrogen vibrates in a direction normal to the hydrogen plane. The nitrogen can, however, tunnel through the barrier—this results in the splitting of the vibrational energy levels into closely spaced doublets. The doublet levels are almost equally populated. In order to achieve maser action, it is first necessary to prepare a system of NH_3 molecules enriched in the

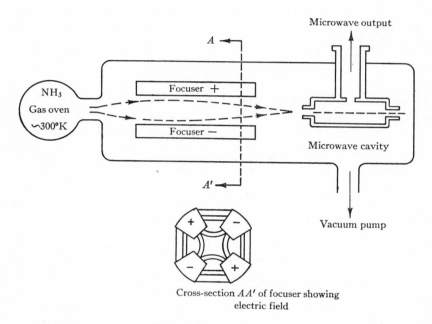

Cross-section AA' of focuser showing electric field

Figure 8.4: Hydrogen maser.

upper level of the doublet. This was achieved by the device shown in figure 8.4, which utilizes an electric field gradient to focus the higher energy molecules toward the center of the field, while the force on the lower energy molecules serves to divert them away from the center. The higher energy molecules are thus concentrated in the microwave cavity which is tuned to the desired frequency. A signal at 24 KMC which is sent into the cavity will induce emission at 24 KMC resulting, as indicated above, in an exponential build up of the signal with consequent oscillation.

Solid state masers utilizing the splitting of atomic levels in a magnetic field have also been operated. The basic theory has been described in chapter 3 where it was shown that in the presence of a field magnitude H, the levels are shifted according to the relationship (3.144)

$$\Delta E = -\mu_0 H g M_J \qquad (8.67)$$

where

$$M_J = -j, -j + 1, \ldots, +j$$

Thus the gadolinium ion Gd^{+3} is characterized by a $4f^7$ configuration, that is, the ion has seven electrons in the $4f$ shell. Spectroscopic studies indicate a $^8S_{7/2}$ ground term, using the notation explained in chapter 2. Since $J = 7/2$ in a magnetic field, there will be eight states with M_J given by

$$-7/2, \ -5/2-, \ 3/2, \ -1/2, \ 1/2, \ 1/3, \ 5/2, \ 7/2$$

In a field of 2850 oersted, the level separation of $(-5/2)$ $(-3/2)$ is 9 KMS, and $(-5/2) \rightarrow (-1/2)$ is 17.5 KMS. In the solid state maser studied by Scovil, Feher, and Seidel these three levels were used in the compound consisting of 0.5% of Gd^{+3} in lanthanum ethyl sulphate. The latter is paramagnetically inert and serves as a diluent. The general principles of the three

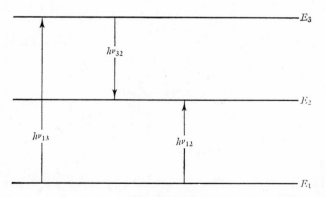

Figure 8.5: Three level maser.

level maser is shown in figure 8.5. It is desired to achieve gain at the frequency $\nu_{32} = (E_3 - E_2)/h$. In order to satisfy the condition given by (8.65), the upper state E_3 is populated by introducing a frequency ν_{13} so that the transition $1 \rightarrow 3$ occurs. If the rate at which E_3 is populated exceeds the rate of spontaneous emission for the transition $3 \rightarrow 2$, then eventually a condition may be realized where $N_3 > N_2$. The population of E_3 is then said to be *inverted* with respect to E_2. This inverted distribution is clearly quite different from the equilibrium distribution for which

$$\frac{N_3}{N_2} = \frac{e^{-E_3/kT}}{e^{-E_2/kT}} = e^{-(E_3 - E_2)/kT} < 1$$

since $E_3 > E_2$. It should also be pointed out that in order to obtain inversion the rate of transition from $3 \to 2$ must be less than that from $2 \to 1$. When N_3 is sufficiently greater than N_2, a point is reached when the introduction of a signal at frequency ν_{32} results in gain, since the stimulated emission from $3 \to 2$ exceeds the reverse absorption processes and other losses. A reflection

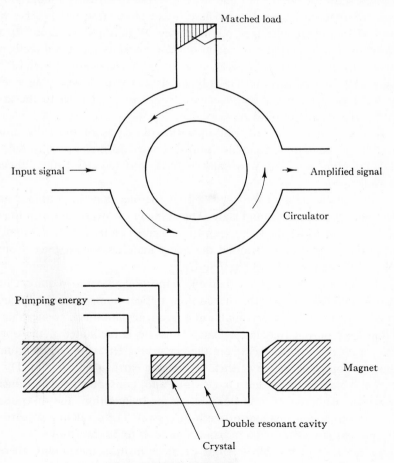

Figure 8.6: Reflection cavity maser.

cavity maser using a doubly tuned cavity for both the signal and pumping frequencies is shown schematically in figure 8.6. A ferrite circulator is used to separate input and output signals.

We turn now to stimulated emission amplifiers which operate in the infrared and optical regions—the laser. Electron transitions are involved here with considerably larger separations between the energy levels. The first laser was reported by Maiman in 1960 and utilized ruby as the active material. From the chemical point of view ruby consists of a few hundredths of a percent of Cr^{+3} ions in Al_2O_3. The energy transitions of the Cr^{+3} ion is shown schematically in figure 8.7, while the physical arrangement is shown in figure 8.8. The ruby is pumped by means of the high intensity illumination from the flash tube to the $^4F_1$ and $^4F_2$ levels (the spectroscopic notation used here is the Racah designation). These broad absorption bands serve to enhance the pumping efficiency of the device. Within a short time (10^{-8} sec) the energy is transferred by a radiationless (energy loss occurs directly to the lattice) transition to the relatively long lived or metastable state (10^{-3} sec) designated as ^2E. The latter actually consists of two closely lying levels, as shown. Laser action ordinarily occurs from the lower level to the ground state at the R_1 line of 6943 Å.

In order to achieve efficient operation the ends of the ruby must be carefully polished flat. One end is silver coated to make it fully reflective, while the other end is only partially coated to provide about 10 to 20 percent transmission.

One disadvantage of the ruby laser is the fact that the terminal state is the highly populated ground state. This difficulty is overcome with the four-level lasers for which the lasing transition occurs to a terminal state somewhat above the ground state. Among the many materials investigated from this point of view are U^{+3} and Sm^{+2} in CaF_2.

It is obvious from (8.65) that one important material requirement is a narrow emission line width. In addition, optical pumping is facilitated if a broad absorption band is available at a frequency not much greater than that of the laser output frequency. Sharp emission is facilitated if the optically active electrons are shielded from the perturbing effects of the environment. Thus, the optically active $4f$ shell of the rare earths (Nd, Pr, Sm, Dy, etc.) are well shielded by $5s$ and $6p$ electrons and, consequently, the transitions associated with the $4f$ electrons are sharp. In addition, the $4f$ transitions are very nearly independent of the host crystal. The divalent rare earth ions also possess strong absorption bands due to $4f$ to $5d$ transitions.

In the case of the $3d$ electrons of the transition metal ions, there is a dependency of the spectra on the host material since the $3d$ electrons are not

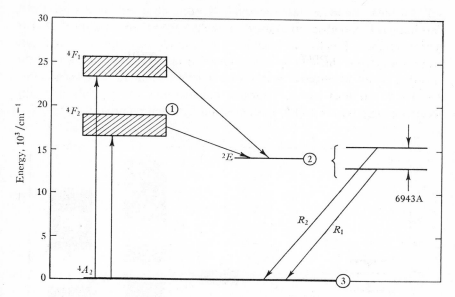

Figure 8.7: Energy-level diagram for chromium ruby.

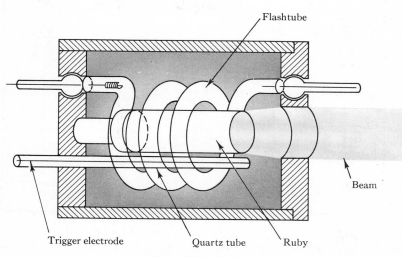

Figure 8.8: Ruby laser.

well shielded. To date, laser action has been observed only with Cr^{+3}. This ion has broad absorption bands in the 0.5–0.6 micron and the 0.32–0.44 micron regions. Finally, we mention the actinide elements with optically active $5f$ electrons shielded by $6s$ and $6p$ electrons. However, in this case, the shielding is not as effective as the rare earths so that the spectra is more sensitive to the host lattice. Thorium and uranium are the only naturally occurring long lived isotopes. Lasing action has been reported with U^{+3}.

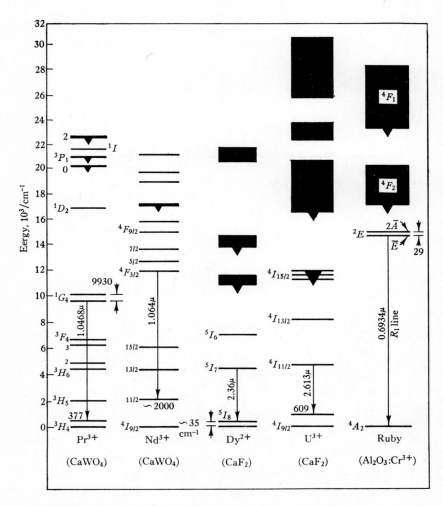

Figure 8.9: Energy-level diagrams of $CaWO_4$: Pr^{3+}, $CaWO_4$: Nd^{3+}, CaF_2 : Dy^{2+}, CaF_2 : U^{3+} and Al_2O_3 : Cr^{3+}. The dark triangles indicate useful adsorption bands or levels. [*After A. Yariv and J. P. Gordon, Proc. IEEE,* **51**, 14 (1963).]

It is to be noted that such properties as the thermal conductivity, heat capacity, and the temperature at which nonradiative transitions become significant, and hence the fluorescence is quenched, are also of considerable significance since the heat generated in the laser must not result in a greatly decreased quantum efficiency for radiative emission. Energy level diagrams of a number of ions are given in figure 8.9.

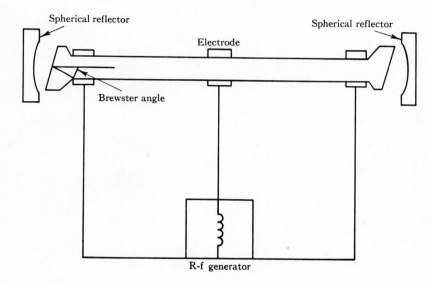

Figure 8.10: Diagram of the Helium-neon laser with external confocal spherical reflectors.

We conclude this section with a discussion of the helium-neon gas laser. Helium, with a small amount of neon, is placed in a glass tube and is excited by an electrical discharge, as shown in figure 8.10. Spherical reflectors are employed to confine the photon energy while the ends of the tube are terminated at the Brewster angle to avoid unwanted reflections. The energy transitions are indicated in figure 8.11. Helium is excited by the electrical discharge to the metastable 2^3S state. This is a triplet state, so that a direct radiative transition from the ground state is forbidden [see (8.49)], but the helium atoms can arrive at this state by collisions. Energy transfer to the neon atoms occurs by a collision process which excites the neon to the $2S$ state. Radiative transitions at 11,522 Å from the neon $2S$ state to the $2P$ state occurs with a lifetime of 0.1 μsĕc while the $2P$ state decays at a much faster rate to the $1S$ state. The $2S$–$2P$ neon transition is thus of interest for the lasing transition.

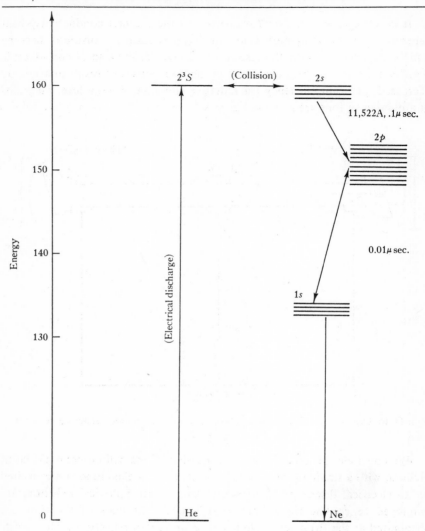

Figure 8.11: Energy-level scheme of the He-Ne laser.

PROBLEM

Depopulation of an excited level will occur because of spontaneous emission. Show that the minimum pumping power (per unit volume) P, which must be supplied to a crystal of volume V in order to maintain N_2 given by (8.46), is expressed by

$$P = \frac{N_2}{V\tau_s}$$

where

$$P = \frac{1}{hc} \int \lambda f(\lambda) I(\lambda) \alpha(\lambda) \, d\lambda$$

$I(\lambda)$ is the energy incident on a unit area of the crystal per unit time per unit wavelength and is given by Beer's law

$$I = I_0 e^{-\alpha(\lambda)x}$$

$f(\lambda)$ is the fraction of the absorbed energy utilized in exciting the atom to the required energy state; c is the velocity of light in the crystal; h is Planck's constant; and τ_s is the rate for spontaneous emission.

Most recently laser action has been demonstrated at the *pn*-junction of diodes made from degenerate gallium arsenide. The effect occurs in the presence of a large forward current (8500 amp/cm²). Similar results have also been reported with other III–V compounds. Strong radiative transitions with these semiconductors occur due to the downward transition of injected electrons which combines with the holes of the *p*-region. The wavelength of the emitted light (8420 Å) is determined by the width of the energy gap, since the transition occurs between the bottom of the conductance band and the top of the valence band. Laser action is possible because absorption of the emitted photons cannot occur by interband transition since the electron levels just below the energy gap on the *p*-side of the degenerate material are empty. Similarly, the levels just above the gap are filled in the case of the degenerate *n*-material. Thus, because of the degeneracy, optical absorption due to interband transitions can only occur at a frequency greater than the energy gap. Losses, however, can occur by other mechanisms, such as scattering and free carrier absorption. We shall return to semiconductor lasers in the last section of this chapter.

8.7 COHERENT LIGHT

The most important property of optical output of the laser is that the light is highly monochromatic and *coherent*, that is, any two points on the wave front have a fixed phase relationship so that the difference in phase between the two points is constant. This characteristic of laser light is to be contrasted with an ordinary light source for which the phase relationships in time and space are random. This high coherency is the consequence of induced emission because the emitted photon has the same phase and direction as that of the photon inducing the emission. Of course a certain amount of spontaneous emission also occurs so that the coherent output is contaminated by random, or "noisy," photons.

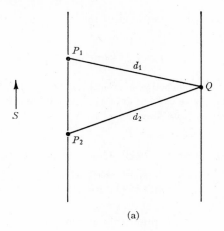

(a)

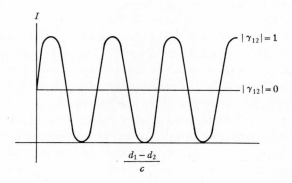

(b)

Figure 8.12: Intensity distribution of the interference pattern at Q.

The concept of coherence will now be put on a quantitative basis. Consider an extended source S, shown in figure 8.12a, and the pin holes P_1 and P_2 which pass two rays of light which add at point Q. The amplitude $V(t)$, at Q at a time t, may be taken as the superposition of the two amplitudes $V_1(t - t_1)$ and $V_2(t - t_2)$ at P_1 and P_2 respectively, where t_1 and t_2 are the times required for the light to travel from P_1 and P_2 to Q. Hence if c is the velocity of the light then,

$$d_1 = \frac{t_1}{c} \quad \text{and} \quad d_2 = \frac{t_2}{c}$$

and

$$V(t) = K_1 V_1(t - t_1) + K_2 V_2(t - t_2) \qquad (8.68)$$

where K_1 and K_2 are phase factors. Since we are not usually interested in the instantaneous values of the intensity of illumination, we shall calculate the time average intensity I, at Q. Suppose the system is turned on for a time t, of duration

$$-T \leqslant t \leqslant T$$

and, consequently, the amplitude at Q is given by

$$V_T(t) = V(t) \qquad |t| \leqslant T$$

$$V_T(t) = 0 \qquad |t| > T$$

We now define the time average intensity at Q as

$$I(Q) = \lim_{T \to \infty} \frac{1}{2T} \int_{-T}^{+T} V_T(t) V_T^*(t) \, dt \equiv \langle V(t) V^*(t) \rangle \qquad (8.69)$$

where the asterisks designate the complex conjugate. On introducing (8.68) into (8.69), we find

$$I(Q) = |K_1|^2 I_1 + |K_2|^2 I_2 + 2|K_1| \, |K_2| \Gamma_{12}^{(r)}(t_1, t_2) \qquad (8.70)$$

since K_1 and K_2 are complex, and where we have introduced $\Gamma_{12}^{(r)}(t_1, t_2)$ as the real part of

$$\begin{aligned} \Gamma_{12}(t_1, t_2) &= \lim_{T \to \infty} \frac{1}{2T} \int_{-T}^{+T} V_{1T}(t_1) V_{2T}^*(t_2) \, dt \\ &= \langle V_{1T}(t_1) V_{2T}^*(t_2) \rangle \end{aligned} \qquad (8.71)$$

The quantity defined by (8.71) is referred to as the cross-correlation or *mutual coherence function* of the light. Clearly for light with a random time distribution of phase, Γ_{12} vanishes, and the light is said to be *incoherent*.

It is convenient to rewrite (8.70) by introducing the normalized form of the coherence function

$$\gamma_{12}^{(r)} = \frac{\Gamma_{12}^{(r)}}{\sqrt{I_1} \, \sqrt{I_2}} \qquad (8.72)$$

and also

$$I_1' = |K_1|^2 I_1$$

$$I_2' = |K_2|^2 I_2$$

Assuming a stationary time distribution for the field, the origin for the time may be shifted in each average thus

$$\langle V_2(t - t_2) V_2^*(t - t_2) \rangle = \langle V_2(t) V_2^*(t) \rangle = I_2$$

so that we can write

$$I(Q) = I_1' + I_2' + 2\sqrt{I_1' I_2'}\, \gamma_{12}^{(r)}\!\left(\frac{d_1 - d_2}{c}\right) \tag{8.73}$$

where we have also introduced the distances d_1 and d_2. By means of the Schwarz inequality it is easy to show that

$$|\Gamma_{12}|^2 \leqslant |I_1|\,|I_2| \tag{8.74}$$

hence

$$\frac{|\Gamma_{12}|}{\sqrt{I_1}\,\sqrt{I_2}} \leqslant 1 \tag{8.75}$$

In the extreme case of incoherent light $\gamma_{12}^{(r)} = 0$ and it is clear from (8.73) that it is not possible to have interference since I_1' and I_2' cannot cancel and indeed, in this case, $I(Q)$ remains constant on passing from point to point on the screen. However, in the case of partially coherent light from a nearly monochromatic source, the intensity of the light on the screen will vary sinusoidally with $\gamma_{12}^{(r)}(d_1/c - d_2/c)$ resulting in a series of fringes. The maximum and minimum intensities will be given by

$$I_{\max} = I_1' + I_2' + 2\sqrt{I_1' I_2'}\,|\gamma_{12}^{(r)}|$$
$$I_{\min} = I_1' + I_2' - 2\sqrt{I_1' I_2'}\,|\gamma_{12}^{(r)}| \tag{8.76}$$

The *visibility ratio* of the fringes is defined by

$$V(a) = \frac{I_{\max} - I_{\min}}{I_{\max} + I_{\min}} = \frac{2\sqrt{I_1' I_2'}}{I_1' + I_2'}\,|\gamma_{12}^{(r)}| \tag{8.77}$$

so that the visibility ratio equals the coherence of the source when $I_1' = I_2'$. The two extreme cases are shown in figure 8.12b. Thus, on passing from an incoherent to a coherent source, the image at Q changes from an inform and diffuse pattern to sharp series of fringes. Indeed a more intensive analysis indicates that highly coherent light can be focused into an extremely well collimated beam, and also that such light can be focused into a very small spot. The higher directivity of the collimated beams from lasers, as well as the very broad bandwidths that are obtainable at optical frequencies, have aroused considerable interest in various communications applications. In addition, the fact that laser beams can be focused into an area of about one square micron (10^{-8} cm²) makes possible a variety of applications requiring very high energy concentrations. Thus, 10 milliwatts from a gaseous laser can provide a power density of 10^6 watts/cm², while a 100 megawatt pulsed output from a ruby laser gives a density of 10^{16} watts/cm². With such high power densities any known material can be readily vaporized.

8.8 LIGHT ABSORPTION IN SEMICONDUCTORS

It is interesting at this point to consider light absorption in semiconductors due to optical transitions between energy bands. In particular we shall obtain the selection rules regulating such transitions. We recall from the first order theory that a transition may occur between two states provided the matrix elements given by (8.7) do not vanish. The required elements are of the form

$$H_{n'n} = (n' | \mathbf{H}^{(1)} | n) \tag{8.78}$$

where, from (8.22),

$$\mathbf{H}^{(1)} = \frac{ie\hbar}{mc} \overline{A} \cdot \nabla \tag{8.79}$$

and the vector potential is given by (72A) in the appendix

$$\overline{A} = \tfrac{1}{2} A \bar{a} [e^{i(\overline{K} \cdot \bar{r} - \omega t)} + e^{-i(\overline{K} \cdot \bar{r} - \omega t)}] \tag{8.80}$$

where $\overline{K}$ is the propagation vector of the photon. The wave functions will be taken to be the Bloch functions (6.31) for the electron in the valence and conduction bands

$$\psi_v = \frac{1}{\sqrt{N}} \mu(k', \bar{r}) e^{i\bar{k}' \cdot \bar{r}} \tag{8.81a}$$

$$\psi_c = \frac{1}{\sqrt{N}} \mu(k'', \bar{r}) e^{i\bar{k}'' \cdot \bar{r}} \tag{8.81b}$$

where the normalization is now expressed in terms of the number N of unit cells in the crystal, and where k' refers to the valence band, and k'' to the conduction band. Inserting the first term of the vector potential (8.80) and (8.81) into the matrix element (8.78), we obtain

$$H_{k'k''} = \frac{e\hbar Ai}{2Nmc} \int \mu^*(k', r)[\bar{a} \cdot \nabla \mu(k'', \bar{r}) + ik'' \cdot \bar{a}\mu(k'', \bar{r})]e^{i(\bar{k}'' + \bar{K} - \bar{k}') \cdot \bar{r}} d\tau \quad (8.82)$$

where the integration is over the whole volume of crystal. Since the functions $\mu(k', \bar{r})$ and $\mu(k'', \bar{r})$ are periodic with the lattice, (8.82) may be written in the same form as (6.42), i.e.,

$$H_{k'k''} = \sum_n e^{i(\bar{k}'' + \bar{K} - \bar{k}') \cdot \bar{R}_n} \int_{\text{cell}} \phi \, d\tau$$

where the integration is now over the volume of a single cell and R_n is a translation of a vector associated with the nth cell. By means of the arguments already given in chapter 6, the exponential sum will vanish unless

$$\bar{k}'' + \bar{K} - \bar{k}' = \bar{K}_m \quad (8.83)$$

where

$$\bar{K}_m = m_1 \bar{b}_1 + m_2 \bar{b}_2 + m_3 \bar{b}_3 \quad (8.83a)$$

Here $\bar{b}$ is the vector of the reciprocal lattice, while m is a positive or negative integer or zero. Since the photon wavelength is several orders of magnitude greater than the lattice spacing, it follows that $|K| \ll |k|$ and, therefore, we expect that k' will not differ much from k''. Hence, (8.83) may be written as

$$\bar{k}'' + \bar{K} - \bar{k}' = 0 \quad (8.84)$$

or

$$\bar{k}' - \bar{k}'' = \bar{K}$$

This result is the conservation condition on the crystal momentum since, on multiplying by $\hbar$, we have

$$\bar{p}' - \bar{p}'' = \bar{p}_p \quad (8.85)$$

where $\bar{p}''$ and $\bar{p}'$ are the crystal momentum of the electron, and $\bar{p}_p$ the momentum of the photon. Since $|K|$ is small, (8.84) can be approximated as

$$\bar{k}' \approx \bar{k}'' \quad (8.86)$$

This last result implies that the optical transition between bands may be represented by a nearly vertical line on the $E(k)$ vs. k diagram as indicated in figure 8.13.

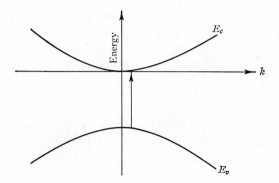

Figure 8.13: Vertical transition between bands.

8.9 INDIRECT TRANSITIONS

With a number of semiconductors, such as Ge or Si, the maximum in the valence band and the minimum in the conduction band do not coincide at $k = 0$ but, rather, the extrema correspond to different k. The situation is shown in figure 8.14. With this kind of band structure there exists the possibility of *indirect* transitions between bands, namely, transitions for which $\Delta k \neq 0$. A detailed treatment of optical transition which takes into account

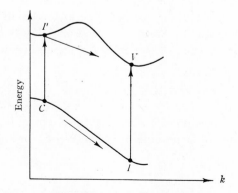

Figure 8.14: Indirect transitions.

interactions with the lattice shows that momentum is conserved, but now the appropriate expression is

$$\bar{k}_i - \bar{k}_f = \bar{K}_p \pm \bar{K}_s \tag{8.87}$$

where the electron wave vectors for the initial and final states are designated by $\bar{k}_i$ and $\bar{k}_f$ respectively, while $\bar{K}_p$ and $\bar{K}_s$ are the wave vectors for the photon and phonon. Energy conservation also applies so that if ω_p and ω_s are the frequencies associated with the photon and phonon, we have

$$E(\bar{k}_i) - E(\bar{k}_f) = \hbar\omega_p \pm \hbar\omega_s \tag{8.88}$$

Under certain conditions the conservation of energy may be relaxed. Thus, if the system is excited into a very short lived intermediate state then, because of the uncertainty principle, conservation may be violated. Such short lived states are called virtual states.

Two indirect transition processes are shown in figure 8.14 for the transition from C to V. Thus, the system may absorb a photon and the electron may be excited to I'. Subsequent emission of a phonon will bring the electron to the state indicated by V. Alternatively, the electron may initially emit a phonon so that it passes to state I, and then photon absorption may occur to state V. Of course, analogous processes may occur accompanied by phonon absorption.

8.10 *QUASI–FERMI LEVELS AND SEMICONDUCTOR LASERS*

In this section we shall consider in somewhat greater detail the principles underlying the operation of the semiconductor laser. It is necessary at the outset to extend the earlier discussion of the Fermi level to the nonequilibrium situation. As pointed out by Shockley, the probability that a conductance state $E_c(k_i)$ is occupied when the system is not at equilibrium is given by

$$f_c = \frac{1}{1 + e^{(E_c(k_i) - F_n)/kT}} \tag{8.89}$$

where F_n is defined as the quasi–Fermi level for electrons in the conductance band. Similarly, we may define a quasi–Fermi level F_p for holes in the valence band by

$$f_{pv} = \frac{1}{1 + e^{-[E_v(k_j) - F_p]/kT}} \tag{8.90}$$

so that the probability of finding an electron at $E_v(k_j)$ is

$$f_{nv} = 1 - f_{pv} = \frac{1}{1 + e^{[E_v(k_j) - F_p]/kT}} \qquad (8.91)$$

At equilibrium

$$F_n = F_p = E_F$$

These expressions will now be used to calculate the rate of induced radiative transitions between a state $E_c(k_i)$ in the conductance band, and $E_v(k_j)$ in the valence band. The rate of absorption is governed by the Einstein coefficient, B_{vc}, for an induced transition to occur from the valence to conduction band as well as the number of electrons at $E_v(k_j)$ and holes at $E_c(k_i)$, i.e.,

$$N_a = B_{vc} N_v(E) N_c(E) \rho(\nu) f_{nv}(1 - f_c) \cdot (\Delta E)^2 \qquad (8.92)$$

in a region ΔE about E_c and E_v, where $N_v(E)$ and $N_c(E)$ are density of state functions associated with the valence and conductance bands, and $\rho(\nu_{cv})$ is the radiation density at the frequency

$$\nu = \frac{E_c(k_i) - E_v(k_j)}{h}$$

In the case of emission, we similarly find

$$N_e = B_{cv} N_v(E) N_c(E) \rho(\nu) f_c(1 - f_{nv}) \Delta E^2 \qquad (8.93)$$

The conduction for net gain by stimulated emission (i.e., laser action) is

$$N_e > N_a \qquad (8.94)$$

so that from (8.92) and (8.93)

$$f_c(1 - f_{nv}) > f_{nv}(1 - f_c) \qquad (8.95)$$

or

$$\begin{aligned} F_n - F_p &> E_c(k_i) - E_v(k_j) \\ F_n - F_p &> h\nu \end{aligned} \qquad (8.96)$$

This last condition implies that the semiconductors are degenerate in the case of a direct transition as is shown in figure 8.15. As is indicated, interband absorption occurs at a higher frequency ν_a than emission so that gain can be realized. The required degeneracy can be realized by high doping levels and large forward current densities at *pn*-junctions. In the case of indirect transitions, which occur for example with Ge or Si, condition (8.96) also applies even though phonon absorption or emission occurs concomitant with the absorption of the photon.

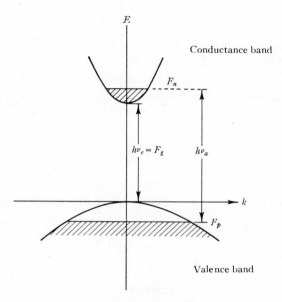

Figure 8.15: Band structure of degenerate semiconductor showing absorption (ν_a) and emission (ν_e) frequencies for a direct transition.

PROBLEMS FOR CHAPTER 8

1. Prove equations (8.43) through (8.45).

Hint: Show

$$[\mathbf{J}_z, \bar{r}_+] = \bar{r}_+$$

$$- [\mathbf{J}_z, \bar{r}_-] = \bar{r}_-$$

and hence, show

$$(j'm'|\mathbf{J}_z\bar{r}_+ - \bar{r}_+\mathbf{J}_z|jm) = (j'm'|\bar{r}_+|jm) = (m' - m)(j'm'|\bar{r}_+|jm)$$

with analogous results for r_-.

2. Discuss the advantages of a four-level laser with the terminal state above the ground state:

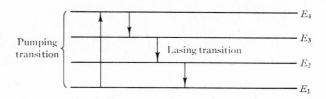

3. Prove (8.74) by means of the Schwarz inequality.

4. In the case of phonon-electron interactions, an electron of wave number k' will be scattered into another state k'' by a phonon of wave number $\bar{K}_s$ and frequency ω_s provided that

$$k'' - k' = \bar{K}_m \pm \bar{K}_s$$

where $\bar{K}_m$ is given by (8.83a). In addition, conservation of energy requires

$$E(k'') - E(k') = \hbar\omega_s$$

Assume a small angle of scattering θ, and that the phonon energy can be neglected with respect to that of the electrons. Take

$$E(k) = \frac{\hbar k^2}{2m^*}$$

and show that

$$\sin\frac{\theta}{2} = \frac{|\bar{K}_s|}{2|k'|}$$

Hint: Consider the vector diagram:

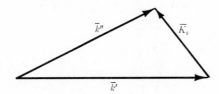

APPENDIX I / *Elements of*

Classical Mechanics

GENERALIZED COORDINATES

Consider a dynamical system consisting of N particles. If the particles are not constrained, then the system is specified by $3N$ independent coordinates. However, if k constraints exist of the form,

$$f_i(\bar{r}_1, \bar{r}_2, \ldots, \bar{r}_N, t) = 0 \qquad i = 1, 2, \ldots, k \tag{1A}$$

Where $\bar{r}_i$ is the position vector of the ith particle, then the constraints are said to be *holonomic* and the system is now specified by $3N\text{-}k$ independent coordinates. The system is now said to have $3N\text{-}k$ degrees of freedom. Any set of $3N\text{-}k$ independent quantities which completely specify the system in the dynamical sense are referred to as *generalized coordinates* and will be designated by $q_1, q_2, \ldots, q_{3N-k}$. It is clear that generalized coordinates need not have the dimensions of distance since, for example, angular displacements are used in the cylindrical and spherical coordinate systems.

DYNAMICAL LAWS

Classical mechanics is usually derived from Newton's laws

$$\sum_i \dot{\bar{p}}_i = \sum_i \bar{F}_i \tag{2A}$$

where $\bar{p}_i$ is the momentum of the ith particle, and $\bar{F}_i$ is the total force acting on the ith particle and consists of forces due to the constraints $\bar{F}_{ic}$ and applied forces $\bar{F}_{ia}$:

$$\bar{F}_i = \bar{F}_{ia} + \bar{F}_{ic} \tag{3A}$$

Newton's law (2A) may also be written as

$$\sum (\bar{F}_i - \dot{\bar{p}}_i) = 0 \tag{4A}$$

If we regard $-\dot{\bar{p}}_i$ as an inertial force, then (4A) may be considered to be a generalization of the laws of statics stating that the system is in formal equilibrium with the conventional forces and the inertial forces.

Let $\delta \bar{r}_i$ be an infinitesimal change in $\bar{r}_i$ consistent with the constraints, so that from (4A) we have

$$\sum_i (\bar{F}_i - \dot{\bar{p}}_i) \cdot \delta \bar{r}_i = 0 \tag{5A}$$

In the case of constraints arising from the internal forces of a rigid body, friction-free surfaces, or inextensible rods, we must have

$$\sum_i \bar{F}_{ic} \cdot \delta \bar{r}_i = 0 \tag{6A}$$

so that (5A) becomes

$$\sum (F_{ia} - \dot{\bar{p}}_i) \cdot \delta \bar{r}_i = 0 \tag{7A}$$

This last result is also referred to as D'Alembert's principle.

We now derive Lagrange's equations from (5A) by introducing the generalized coordinates by means of the relationships

$$\bar{r}_i = \bar{r}_i(q_1, \ldots, q_n, t) \tag{8A}$$

so that

$$\delta \bar{r}_i = \sum_{k=1}^{n} \frac{\partial \bar{r}_i}{\partial q_k} \delta q_k \tag{9A}$$

On introducing (9A) into (5A) we obtain

$$\sum_k Q_k \delta q_k - \sum_i \dot{\bar{p}}_i \cdot \delta \bar{r}_i = 0 \tag{10A}$$

Where Q_k is the generalized force given by

$$Q_k \equiv \sum_i \bar{F}_i \cdot \frac{\partial \bar{r}_i}{\partial q_k} \tag{11A}$$

We next transform the second term on the left-hand side of (10A) by writing

$$\sum_i \dot{\bar{p}}_i \cdot \delta \bar{r}_i = \sum_{i,k} m_i \ddot{\bar{r}}_i \cdot \frac{\delta \bar{r}_i}{\partial q_k} \delta q_k$$

Now it is easily seen that

$$\sum_i m_i \ddot{\vec{r}}_i \cdot \frac{\partial \vec{r}_i}{\partial q_k} = \sum_i \frac{d}{dt}\left(m\dot{\vec{r}}_i \cdot \frac{\partial \vec{r}_i}{dq_k}\right) - \sum_i m_i \dot{\vec{r}}_i \cdot \frac{d}{dt}\frac{\partial \vec{r}_i}{\partial q_k} \qquad (12A)$$

and since

$$\frac{\partial \vec{r}_i}{\partial q_k} = \frac{\partial \dot{\vec{r}}_i}{\partial \dot{q}_k} = \frac{\partial \vec{v}_i}{\partial \dot{q}_k} \qquad (13A)$$

we have

$$\sum_i m_i \ddot{\vec{r}}_i \cdot \frac{\partial \vec{r}_i}{\partial q_k} = \frac{d}{dt}\frac{\partial}{\partial \dot{q}_k}\sum_i \frac{1}{2}m_i v_i^2 - \frac{\partial}{\partial q_k}\sum_i \frac{1}{2}m_i v_i^2 \qquad (14A)$$

On substituting (14A) into (12A), we see that (10A) may be written as

$$\sum_k \left\{\frac{d}{dt}\left(\frac{\partial T}{\partial \dot{q}_j}\right) - \frac{\partial T}{\partial q_j} - Q_j\right\}\delta q_k = 0 \qquad (15A)$$

$$T = \frac{1}{2}\sum_i m_i v_i^2$$

Since q_j is independent, it follows that for each coordinate

$$\frac{d}{dt}\left(\frac{\partial T}{\partial \dot{q}_k}\right) - \frac{\partial T}{\partial q_k} - Q_k = 0 \qquad j = 1, 2, \ldots, n \qquad (16A)$$

This last result is one form of the Lagrangian equations of motion. In the case of a conservative force field, the forces may be expressed in terms of the gradient of a potential function $V(r)$, which depends on the position co-ordinates, but not on the velocity, so that for the ith particle

$$\vec{F}_i = -\nabla_i V(r)$$

and

$$Q_k = -\sum_i \nabla_i V \cdot \frac{\partial \vec{r}_i}{\partial q_k} = -\frac{\partial V}{\partial q_k} \qquad (17A)$$

On introducing (17A) into (16A), we have

$$\frac{d}{dt}\frac{\partial(T-V)}{\partial \dot{q}_k} - \frac{\partial(T-V)}{\partial q_k} = 0 \qquad (18A)$$

It is customary to define the Lagrangian L by

$$L = T - V$$

so that (18A) may be written

$$\frac{d}{dt}\left(\frac{\partial L}{\partial \dot{q}_k}\right) - \frac{\partial L}{\partial q_k} = 0 \tag{19A}$$

HAMILTONIAN EQUATIONS OF MOTION

Corresponding to each generalized coordinate we may define a *generalized momentum* p_k given by

$$p_k = \frac{\partial L}{\partial \dot{q}_k} \tag{20A}$$

where p_k is said to be *canonically conjugate* to q_k. Introducing (20A) into (19A), we readily find that

$$\dot{p}_k = \frac{\partial L}{\partial q_k} \tag{21A}$$

If L is now expressed as a function of q_k and $\dot{q}_k$, then we define the *Hamiltonian* of the system by

$$H = \sum_k p_k \dot{q}_k - L(q, \dot{q}, t) \tag{22A}$$

An increment in H may be expressed in two forms. Thus, from (22A), we have

$$dH = \sum_k \left[p_k\, d\dot{q}_k + \dot{q}_k\, dp_k - \frac{\partial L}{\partial q_k}\, dq_k - \frac{\partial L}{\partial \dot{q}_k}\, d\dot{q}_k \right] - \frac{\partial L}{\partial t}\, dt$$

but, from (20A) and (21A), we have

$$dH = \sum_k \left[\dot{q}_k\, dp_k - \dot{p}_k\, dq_k \right] - \frac{\partial L}{\partial t}\, dt \tag{23A}$$

Regarding H as a function of p, q, and t, we can also express an increment in H as

$$dH = \sum_k \left[\frac{\partial A}{\partial p_k}\, dp_k + \frac{\partial H}{\partial q_k}\, dq_k \right] + \frac{\partial H}{\partial t}\, dt \tag{24A}$$

On comparing (23A) and (24A), we have

$$\dot{q}_k = \frac{\partial H}{\partial p_k}$$

$$\dot{p}_k = -\frac{\partial H}{\partial q_k} \qquad\qquad (25A)$$

$$\frac{\partial H}{\partial t} = -\frac{\partial L}{\partial t}$$

The first two sets of equations are called Hamilton's equations of motion. Finally, for a conservative system it is not difficult to show, for example by introducing cartesian coordinates, that

$$H = T + V$$

PROBLEM

Let μ and v be two functions of the generalized coordinates and momenta, then the Poisson's bracket is defined by

$$\{\mu, v\} = \sum_i \left(\frac{\partial \mu}{\partial q_i} \frac{\partial v}{\partial p_i} - \frac{\partial \mu}{\partial p_i} \frac{\partial v}{\partial q_i} \right)$$

If the function $A(p, q)$ represents a dynamical property of the system, show that

$$\frac{dA}{dt} = \{A, H\} \qquad\qquad (25.1A)$$

where H is the Hamiltonian.

APPENDIX *II* / *Theory of Small Oscillations*

The theory of small oscillations will now be developed by means of Lagrange's equations given by (19A). We first require the expression for the potential energy of a system of N particles which undergoes a small displacement about the equilibrium position. A Taylor series expansion of the potential function $V(q_1, \ldots, q_n)$ about the equilibrium position gives

$$V = V(0) + \sum_i \left(\frac{\partial V}{\partial q_i}\right)_0 q_i + \frac{1}{2} \sum_{i,j} \left(\frac{\partial^2 V}{\partial q_i \, \partial q_j}\right)_0 q_i q_j + \cdots \qquad (26A)$$

where $V(0)$ is the potential at the equilibrium position and the derivatives are evaluated at the equilibrium position. Since V is a minimum at equilibrium we have

$$\left.\frac{\partial V}{\partial q_i}\right)_0 = 0 \qquad (27A)$$

and on choosing $V(0) = 0$, we see that (26A) may be written as

$$V = \frac{1}{2} \sum_{i,j} \frac{\partial V}{\partial q_i \, \partial q_j} q_i q_j \equiv \frac{1}{2} \sum_{i,j} k_{ij} q_i q_j \qquad (28A)$$

We note that $k_{ij} = k_{ji}$ so that the corresponding matrix is symmetric.

The kinetic energy is given by

$$T = \frac{1}{2} \sum_k m_k(\dot{x}_k^2 + \dot{y}_k^2 + \dot{z}_k^2) \qquad (29A)$$

the sum is taken over all of the masses.

On introducing the generalized coordinates and noting that

$$\dot{x}_k = \sum_j \frac{\partial x_k}{\partial q_j} \dot{q}_j \tag{30A}$$

we find the result

$$T = \frac{1}{2} \sum_{i,j} m_{,j} \dot{q}_i \dot{q}_j \tag{31A}$$

where

$$m_{ij} = \sum_k m_k \left(\frac{\partial x_k}{\partial q_i} \frac{\partial x_k}{\partial q_j} + \frac{\partial y_k}{\partial q_i} \frac{\partial y_k}{\partial q_j} + \frac{\partial z_k}{\partial q_i} \frac{\partial z_k}{\partial q_j} \right) \tag{32A}$$

We again note that $m_{ij} = m_{ji}$. Expressions (28A) and (31A) may be written in matrix notation as

$$\begin{aligned} V &= \tfrac{1}{2} \bar{q}^T \bar{K} \bar{q} \\ T &= \tfrac{1}{2} \dot{\bar{q}}^T \bar{M} \dot{\bar{q}} \end{aligned} \tag{33A}$$

where q is a column matrix of q_i, while $\bar{K}$ and $\bar{M}$ are the $n \times n$ matrices of the elements k_{ij} and m_{ij}, respectively. The matrix $\bar{q}^T$ represents the transpose of q obtained by converting a column to a row, or vice versa.

It is desirable for most purposes to diagonalize $\bar{K}$ and $\bar{M}$. Since T is a positive definite, i.e.,

$$\bar{q}^T \bar{M} \bar{q} > 0 \qquad \text{if} \quad \bar{q} \neq 0 \tag{34A}$$

it is possible to find a $n \times n$ transformation matrix $\bar{R}$ which will simultaneously diagonalize $\bar{K}$ and $\bar{M}$ so that

$$\begin{aligned} \bar{R}^T \bar{M} \bar{R} &= \bar{I} \\ \bar{R}^T \bar{K} \bar{R} &= \bar{D} \end{aligned} \tag{35A}$$

where $\bar{I}$ is the unit matrix (δ_{ij}) and $\bar{D}$ is the matrix ($\lambda_i^{-1} \delta_{ij}$). The matrix $\bar{R}$ has as its columns the vectors $\bar{R}_i$ which satisfy the equation

$$\bar{M} \bar{R}_i = \lambda_i \bar{K} \bar{R}_i \tag{36A}$$

where λ_i is the solution to the secular equation

$$|\bar{M} - \lambda \bar{K}| = 0$$

This result is proven in all works on matrix algebra and therefore need not be derived here. Let us now introduce a new set of coordinates Q_i, the normal coordinates, by means of the matrix expression

$$\bar{q} = \bar{R}\bar{Q} \tag{37A}$$

where $\bar{Q}$ is a column matrix of the Q_i, then

$$T = \frac{1}{2}(\bar{R}\dot{\bar{Q}})^T \bar{M}(\bar{R}\dot{\bar{Q}}) = \frac{1}{2}\dot{\bar{Q}}^T(\bar{R}^T\bar{M}\bar{R})\dot{\bar{Q}} = \frac{1}{2}\sum_i \dot{Q}_i^2 \tag{38A}$$

and similarly

$$V = \frac{1}{2}(\bar{R}\bar{Q})^T \bar{K}(\bar{R}\bar{Q}) = \frac{1}{2}\sum \frac{Q_i^2}{\lambda_i} \tag{39A}$$

The Lagrangian equations are now

$$\frac{d}{dt}\left(\frac{\partial L}{\partial \dot{Q}_i}\right) - \frac{\partial L}{\partial Q_i} = 0 \tag{40A}$$

hence

$$\ddot{Q}_i - \omega_i^2 Q_i = 0 \tag{41A}$$

where ω_i is the frequency of the normal mode

$$\omega_i^2 \equiv \frac{1}{\lambda_i} \tag{42A}$$

Equation (41A) has the solution

$$Q_i = A_i \cos \omega_i t + B_i \sin \omega_i t \tag{43A}$$

If we introduce the diagonal matrices

$$\bar{C} = (\cos \omega_i t \delta_{ij})$$

$$\bar{S} = (\sin \omega_i t \delta_{ij})$$

then the solutions (43A) may be expressed as

$$\bar{Q} = \bar{C}\bar{A} + \bar{S}\bar{B} \tag{44A}$$

where $\bar{A}$ and $\bar{B}$ are column matrices for the arbitrary constants. Using (37A), we may invert the above so that

$$\bar{q} = \bar{R}\bar{Q} = \bar{R}\bar{C}\bar{A} + \bar{R}\bar{S}\bar{B} \tag{45A}$$

Suppose that the initial conditions are given as

$$\bar{q} = \bar{q}_0 \quad \text{and} \quad \dot{\bar{q}} = \bar{v}_0 \quad \text{at} \quad t = 0$$

We also have at $t = 0$

$$\bar{C} = \bar{I} \quad \text{and} \quad \bar{S} = \bar{0}$$

$$\dot{\bar{C}} = 0 \quad \text{and} \quad \dot{\bar{S}} = \bar{\omega} = (\omega_i \delta_{ij})$$

where I is the unit matrix and $\bar{0}$ the null matrix so that

$$\begin{aligned} \bar{q}_0 &= \bar{R}\bar{A} &\quad \text{hence} \quad \bar{A} &= R^{-1}\bar{q}_0 \\ \bar{v}_0 &= \bar{R}\bar{\omega}\bar{B} &\quad \text{hence} \quad B &= \bar{\omega}^{-1}R^{-1}\bar{v}_0 \end{aligned} \tag{46A}$$

The final solution is, therefore,

$$\bar{q} = \bar{R}\bar{C}\bar{R}^{-1}\bar{q}_0 + \bar{R}\bar{S}\bar{\omega}^{-1}\bar{R}^{-1}\bar{v}_0 \tag{47A}$$

APPENDIX *III* / *Elements of*

Electromagnetic Theory

MAXWELL'S EQUATIONS

The solution of problems in electromagnetism generally require finding the electrical ($\bar{E}$) and magnetic fields ($\bar{H}$) which satisfy Maxwell's equations given below in mks units

$$\nabla \times \bar{H} = \dot{\bar{D}} + \bar{J} \qquad (48A)$$

$$\nabla \times \bar{E} = -\dot{\bar{B}} \qquad (49A)$$

$$\nabla \cdot \bar{D} = \rho \qquad (50A)$$

$$\nabla \cdot \bar{B} = 0 \qquad (51A)$$

where e is the charge density and

$$\bar{D} = \varepsilon \bar{E}$$

$$\bar{B} = \mu \bar{H}$$

$$\bar{J} = \sigma \bar{E}$$

where ε, μ, and σ are the dielectric constant, magnetic permeability, and electrical conductivity, respectively. The polarization $\bar{P}$ and magnetization $\bar{M}$ are also frequently used

$$\bar{P} = \bar{D} - \varepsilon_0 \bar{E}$$

$$\bar{M} = \frac{\bar{B}}{\mu_0} - H$$

278

where ε_0 and μ_0 are the values of s and μ in a vacuum. In atomic work Gaussian units are frequently used, and Maxwell's equations are

$$\nabla \times \bar{H} = \frac{1}{c}\dot{\bar{D}} + 4\pi\bar{J}$$

$$\nabla \times \bar{E} = -\frac{1}{c}\dot{\bar{B}}$$

$$\nabla \cdot \bar{D} = 4\pi\rho$$

$$\nabla \cdot \bar{B} = 0$$

where c is the velocity of light.

The electrical field is related to the electrostatic, or scalar, potential ϕ by

$$\bar{E} = -\nabla\phi \qquad (52A)$$

The electrostatic potential is determined by the charge distribution. In the case of a discrete distribution of charge, the electrostatic potential at a specified point is given by

$$\phi = \frac{1}{4\pi\varepsilon}\sum\frac{q_i}{r_i} \qquad (53A)$$

where q_i is the magnitude of the charge and $\bar{r}_i$ the distance of the charge to the point. In the case of a continuous distribution, the sum goes over to an integral so that

$$\phi = \frac{1}{4\pi\varepsilon}\int\frac{\rho\,dV}{r} \qquad (54A)$$

VECTOR POTENTIAL

The solution to the field equation is often facilitated by introducing a vector potential $\bar{A}$, which is related to the magnetic field by

$$\bar{B} = \nabla \times \bar{A} \qquad (55A)$$

From (49A) we have

$$\nabla \times \bar{E} = -\nabla \times \dot{\bar{A}} \qquad (56A)$$

hence

$$\nabla \times (\bar{E} + \dot{\bar{A}}) = 0 \tag{57A}$$

Clearly, (57A) is satisfied by choosing

$$\bar{E} = -\dot{\bar{A}} - \nabla\phi \tag{58A}$$

where ϕ is an arbitrary scalar potential. It is important to note that the vector potential is not uniquely defined by (55A), since if we add the gradient of any scalar function to the vector potential the resulting magnetic field is unchanged, thus if

$$\bar{A} = \bar{A}' + \nabla f \tag{59A}$$

then

$$\bar{B} = \nabla \times \bar{A} = \nabla \times \bar{A}'$$

However, in order that the transformation (59A) does not effect $\bar{E}$, it is necessary to transform the scalar potential by means of the relationship

$$\phi = \phi' - \frac{\partial f}{\partial t} \tag{60A}$$

so that

$$\bar{E} = -\dot{\bar{A}} - \nabla\phi = -\dot{\bar{A}}' - \nabla\phi'$$

We see, therefore, that the combined transformations given by (59A) and (60A) leave the physical situation unchanged. This transformation is referred to as the *gauge transformation*.

The wave equation for the vector and scalar potentials will now be derived. On substituting the above expressions for the potentials into (48A), we obtain

$$\nabla \times \nabla \times \bar{A} + \mu\varepsilon\left[\frac{\partial^2 \bar{A}}{\partial t^2} + \nabla\frac{\partial\phi}{\partial t}\right] = \mu\bar{J} \tag{61A}$$

This result may be transformed by means of the vector identity

$$\nabla \times \nabla \times \bar{A} = \nabla(\nabla \cdot A) - \nabla^2\bar{A}$$

so that we obtain the result

$$-\nabla^2\bar{A} + \mu\varepsilon\frac{\partial^2 \bar{A}}{\partial t^2} + \nabla\left(\nabla \cdot \bar{A} + \mu\varepsilon\frac{\partial\phi}{\partial t}\right) = \mu\bar{J} \tag{62A}$$

We now seek to simplify the above by introducing a gauge transformation such that

$$\nabla \cdot \overline{A}' + \mu\varepsilon \frac{\partial \phi'}{\partial t} = 0 \qquad (63A)$$

This relationship, referred to as the *Lorentz condition*, places a condition on the arbitrary function f, since on carrying out the gauge transformation (59A) and (60A), we have

$$\nabla \cdot \overline{A} + \mu\varepsilon \frac{\partial \phi}{\partial t} = \nabla \cdot \overline{A}' + \mu\varepsilon \frac{\partial \phi'}{\partial t} + \nabla^2 f - \mu\varepsilon \frac{\partial^2 f}{\partial^2 t} \qquad (64A)$$

so that the Lorentz condition (63A) requires that f satisfies

$$\nabla^2 f - \mu\varepsilon \frac{\partial f}{\partial t} = \nabla \cdot \overline{A} + \mu\varepsilon \frac{\partial \phi}{\partial t} \qquad (65A)$$

It is customary to assume that the Lorentz condition is satisfied and to omit the primes. The wave equations for the potentials may now be written as

$$\nabla^2 \overline{A} - \mu\varepsilon \frac{\partial^2 \overline{A}}{\partial t^2} = -\mu \overline{J} \qquad (66A)$$

and from (63A), we have on differentiating with respect to time,

$$\nabla \cdot \dot{\overline{A}} + \mu\varepsilon \frac{\partial^2 \phi}{\partial t^2} = 0 \qquad (67A)$$

but, from (58A) and (50A),

$$\nabla \cdot E = \frac{\rho}{\varepsilon} = -\nabla \cdot \dot{\overline{A}} - \nabla^2 \phi$$

so that

$$\nabla^2 \phi - \mu\varepsilon \frac{\partial^2 \phi}{\partial t^2} = -\frac{\rho}{\varepsilon} \qquad (68A)$$

Equations (66A) and (68A) are the required wave equations.

As an example of a solution to (66A) in the case $\overline{J} = 0$, we select the gauge such that $\phi = 0$, so that according to (63A)

$$\nabla \cdot \overline{A} = 0 \qquad (69A)$$

In the case of a plane wave, the wave equation has a solution given by

$$\bar{A} = \bar{A}_0 e^{i(\bar{K}\cdot\bar{r} - \omega t)} \tag{70A}$$

where $\bar{A}_0$ is a constant polarization vector and $\bar{K}$ the vector wave number. In view of (69A), we have

$$\bar{A}_0 \cdot \bar{K} = 0 \tag{71A}$$

so that $\bar{A}_0$ is normal to the direction of propagation. It is usually convenient to work with the real part of the vector potential so that

$$\bar{A} = \tfrac{1}{2}A_0\bar{a}[e^{i(\bar{K}\cdot\bar{r} - \omega t)} + e^{-i(\bar{K}\cdot\bar{r} - \omega t)}] \tag{72A}$$

where $\bar{a}$ is a unit polarization vector.

ENERGY FLUX

Consider an electromagnetic field in the presence of matter characterized by the parameters ε, μ, and σ defined above. From Maxwell's equations, we have

$$E\cdot\nabla \times \bar{H} = \varepsilon\bar{E}\cdot\dot{E} + \sigma\bar{E}^2 = \frac{\partial}{\partial t}\left(\frac{\varepsilon\bar{E}^2}{2}\right) + \sigma E^2 \tag{73A}$$

$$H\cdot\nabla \times E = -\mu\bar{H}\cdot\dot{H} = -\frac{\partial}{\partial t}\left(\frac{\mu\bar{H}^2}{2}\right) \tag{74A}$$

Subtracting (73A) from (74A), and using the identity

$$\nabla\cdot(\bar{E} \times \bar{H}) = H\cdot\nabla \times E - E\cdot\nabla \times \bar{H}$$

we find that

$$\nabla\cdot(\bar{E} \times \bar{H}) = -\frac{\partial}{\partial t}\left[\frac{\varepsilon\bar{E}^2}{2} + \frac{\mu\bar{H}^2}{2}\right] - \sigma\bar{E}^2 \tag{75A}$$

The vector $\bar{E} \times \bar{H}$ is referred to as the *Poynting* vector and has the dimensions of power per unit area (watts/meter^2 in mks units) and can easily be shown to lie in the direction of propagation of the field. It is reasonable to interpret the surface integral

$$\int \bar{E} \times \bar{H}\cdot d\bar{\sigma} \tag{76A}$$

as the rate at which energy leaves the material bounded by the surface, that is, (76A) is the power flow through the surface. Application of the divergence theorem to (75A) leads us to the following identifications

$$\frac{\varepsilon E^2}{2}$$ is the energy density stored in the electrical field (77A)

$$\frac{\mu \overline{H}^2}{2}$$ is the corresponding magnetic energy density (78A)

$$\sigma \overline{E}^2$$ is the power loss per unit volume due to current flow, i.e., ohmic losses. (79A)

The variation in a dynamical quantity $A(p, q)$ can be represented by

$$\delta A = \sum_i \frac{\partial A}{\partial q_i} \, dq_i + \sum_i \frac{\partial A}{\partial p_i} \, dp_i \qquad (80A)$$

A generating function $G(p, q)$ is now defined by

$$\delta q_i = \varepsilon \frac{\partial G}{\partial p_i} \qquad (81A)$$

$$\delta p_i = -\varepsilon \frac{\partial G}{\partial q_i} \qquad (82A)$$

where ε is an infinitesimal. It is easy to see that

$$\delta A = \varepsilon \{A, G\} \qquad (83A)$$

using Poisson's brackets. Quantatization of the last result leads to the transformation

$$\delta \mathbf{A} = \frac{\varepsilon}{i\hbar} [\mathbf{A}, \mathbf{G}] = \frac{\varepsilon i}{\hbar} [\mathbf{G}, \mathbf{A}] \qquad (84A)$$

As an example of (84A) we consider the case when $\mathbf{G} = \mathbf{J}_z$, and $\mathbf{A} = r$, so that for a small angle of rotation

$$\delta x = \frac{\varepsilon i}{\hbar} [\mathbf{J}_z, x] = -\varepsilon y$$

$$\delta y = \frac{\varepsilon i}{\hbar} [\mathbf{J}_z, y] = \varepsilon x \qquad (85A)$$

$$\delta z = 0$$

It is easy to see that this result corresponds to an infinitesimal rotation about the z-axis.

Finally, it is easy to show that

$$\mathbf{A}(\varepsilon) = \mathbf{A} + \delta\mathbf{A} = \left(1 + \frac{i\varepsilon}{\hbar}\,\mathbf{G}\right)\mathbf{A}\left(1 - \frac{i\varepsilon}{\hbar}\,\mathbf{G}\right) \qquad (86A)$$

If this transformation is repeated n times

$$A(n\varepsilon) = \left(1 + \frac{i\varepsilon\,\mathbf{G}}{\hbar}\right)^{n}\mathbf{A}\left(1 - \frac{i\varepsilon\,\mathbf{G}}{\hbar}\right)^{n} \qquad (87A)$$

On going to the limit $n \to \infty$ and $\varepsilon \to 0$ such that $n\varepsilon \to a$ then

$$\mathbf{A}(a) = e^{ia\mathbf{G}/\hbar}\mathbf{A}e^{-ia\mathbf{G}/\hbar} \qquad (88A)$$

so that a unitary transformation corresponds to a finite change.

References

QUANTUM MECHANICS

1. Messiah, A., *Quantum Mechanics*, 2 vols., New York: Wiley, 1962. SEE VOLUME 1 IN PARTICULAR.
2. Merzbacher, E., *Quantum Mechanics*, New York: Wiley, 1961, chapt 8.
3. Powell, J. L. and Crasemann, B., *Quantum Mechanics*, Mass: Addison-Wesley, 1961.
4. Dicke, R. H. and Wittke, J. P., *Quantum Mechanics*, Mass: Addison-Wesley, 1960.

The above books proved to be of particular value in preparing the material on quantum mechanics and the related mathematical background. The reader should also consult the following.

5. Morse, P. M. and Feshback, H., *Methods of Theoretical Physics*, 2 vols., New York: McGraw-Hill, 1953, volume 1, chapters 1 and 2.
6. Condon, E. V. and Shortley, G. H. *The Theory of Atomic Spectra*, New York: Cambridge U.P., 1935. THIS IS THE CLASSIC WORK ON THE SUBJECT.
7. Slater, J. C., *The Quantum Theory of Atomic Structure*, 2 vols., New York: McGraw-Hill, 1960.

SOLID STATE THEORY AND ELECTRON EMISSION

8. Smith, R. A., *Wave Mechanics of Crystalline Solids*, New York: Wiley, 1961.
9. Smith, R. A., *Semiconductors*, New York: Cambridge University Press, 1959.
10. Raimes, S., *The Wave Mechanics of Electrons in Metals*, New York: Interscience, 1961.
11. (a) Kittel, C., *Introduction to Solid State Physics*, 2nd ed., New York: Wiley, 1956.
    (b) ———, *Quantum Theory of Solids*, New York: Wiley, 1963.

12. Dekker, A., *Solid State Physics*, Englewood Cliffs, N.J.: Prentice-Hall, 1957.
13. Wilson, A. H., *The Theory of Metals*, 2nd ed., New York: Cambridge University Press, 1954.
14. Ziman, J. M., *Electrons and Phonons*, New York: Oxford University Press, 1960.

The last two references are somewhat more advanced than the others but with a little additional work (13) and (14) should be readable.

THERMODYNAMICS AND STATISTICAL MECHANICS

15. Callen, H. B., *Thermodynamics*, New York: Wiley, 1962.
16. Wilson, A. H., *Thermodynamics and Statistical Mechanics*, New York: Cambridge University Press, 1957.

LASERS AND MASERS

17. Singer, J. R., *Masers*, New York: Wiley, 1959.
18. Troup, G., *Masers*, New York: Wiley, 1959.
19. Lengyel, B., *Lasers*, New York: Wiley, 1962.
20. Vulysteke, A. A., *Elements of Maser Theory*, Princeton, N.J.: Van Nostrand, 1960.
21. Fox, J. (Ed.), *Optical Masers*, New York: Polytechnic Press, 1963.
22. See also the Proceedings IEEE, vol. 51, No. 1 (1963). This issue is devoted to Quantum Mechanics.

ELECTRONIC DEVICE APPLICATION

23. Levine, S. N., *Principles of Solid State Microelectronics*, New York: Holt, Rinehart & Winston, 1963.
24. Levine, S. N. (ed.), *New Techniques For Energy Conversion*, New York: Dover, 1961.
25. Levine, S. N. and Kurzrock, R. (eds.), *Semiconductor Microwave Electronics*, New York: Dover, 1964.
26. Levine, S. N., *Readings In Thin Film and Microelectronics*, New York: Holt, Rinehart and Winston, 1964.
27. Chang, S. S. L., *Energy Conversion*, Englewood Cliffs, N.J.: Prentice-Hall, 1963.
28. Nanavati, R. P., *An Introduction to Semiconductor Electronics*, New York: McGraw-Hill, 1963.
29. Valdes, L. B., *The Physical Theory of Transistors*, New York: McGraw-Hill, 1961.
30. Putley, E. H., *The Hall Effect and Related Phenomena*, London: Butterworths, 1960.

Index

289